Doctors and their Careers:

A new generation

Isobel Allen

POLICY STUDIES INSTITUTE
London

1000350557

The publishing imprint of the independent
POLICY STUDIES INSTITUTE
100 Park Village East, London NW1 3SR
Telephone: 0171-387 2171   Fax: 0171-388 0914

ISBN 0 85374 660 5

PSI Research Report 792

A CIP catalogue record of this book is available from the British Library.

1 2 3 4 5 6 7 8 9

PSI publications are available from
BEBC Distribution Ltd
P O Box 1496, Poole, Dorset, BH12 3YD

Books will normally be despatched within 24 hours. Cheques should be made payable to BEBC Distribution Ltd.

Credit card and telephone/fax orders may be placed on the following freephone numbers:

FREEPHONE: 0800 262260
FREEFAX: 0800 262266

Booktrade representation (UK & Eire):
Broadcast Books
24 De Montfort Road, London SW16 1LW
Telephone: 081-677 5129

PSI subscriptions are available from PSI's subscription agent
Carfax Publishing Company Ltd
P O Box 25, Abingdon, Oxford OX14 3UE

Laserset by Policy Studies Institute
Printed in Great Britain by BPC Books and Journals Ltd, Exeter

DOCTORS AND THEIR CAREERS
A NEW GENERATION

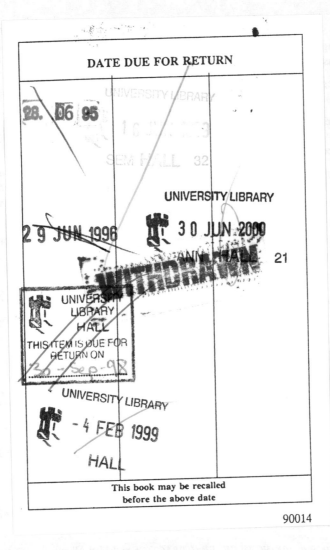

The Policy Studies Institute (PSI) is Britain's leading independent research organisation undertaking studies of economic, industrial and social policy, and the workings of political institutions.

PSI is a registered charity, run on a non-profit basis, and is not associated with any political party, pressure group or commercial interest.

PSI attaches great importance to covering a wide range of subject areas with its multi-disciplinary approach. The Institute's researchers are organised in groups which currently cover the following programmes:

Crime, Justice and Youth Studies – Employment and Society – Ethnic Equality and Diversity – European Industrial Development – Family Finances – Information and Citizenship – Information and Cultural Studies – Social Care and Health Studies – Work, Benefits and Social Participation

This publication arises from the Health and Social Care Studies group and is one of over 30 publications made available by the Institute each year.

Information about the work of PSI, and a catalogue of available books can be obtained from:

Marketing Department, PSI
100 Park Village East, London NW1 3SR

Acknowledgements

This study of doctors who qualified in 1986 was initiated and funded by the Department of Health as part of a follow-up study to *Doctors and their Careers* which was published in 1988. Many members of staff at the Department of Health helped at various stages of the research, and the author is grateful to colleagues in the Medical Education, Training and Staffing Division, the Research and Development Division and the NHS Women's Unit for their advice and support.

Staff at the General Medical Council played a vital part in the sampling and tracing of doctors, and particular thanks are due to Carol Stone for her help and interest in all our research on doctors' careers.

The author has benefited from considerable help and support over the years from many members of the medical profession in our series of studies of doctors' careers. Special thanks go to Dr Beulah Bewley, Dr Ruth Gilbert, Dr Ilfra Goldberg, Dr Tony Isaacs and Dr Elizabeth Shore.

The study was designed and directed by Isobel Allen, who wrote the report. Deborah Charnock was closely involved throughout the preparatory and fieldwork stages of the study and carried out a number of interviews as well as constructing the coding frame. Many thanks are due to her and to the interviewers on this research who are listed below. Their perseverance in tracing and interviewing the doctors all over the country resulted in the very high response rate we achieved.

Karen MacKinnon was responsible for the computing and preparation of tables and gave indispensable help on the computer analysis of the data. Mary Haydon and Helen Kinnings were responsible for the coding and selection of material from most of the questionnaires, and additional coding and analysis were carried out by Paul Stanaway and Adam Berthoud. Karin Erskine prepared the text for publication.

Finally, our greatest debt is to the 229 doctors whom we interviewed for this study. The report is based mainly on their accounts of their careers. We are grateful for the time they gave us and the clarity with which they expressed themselves. The author has tried to reflect their views faithfully.

The interviewers were: Isobel Bowler, Olivia W. Brown, Sheila Chetham, Lilian Cockerill, Beverley Davies, Jenny Green, Mary Haydon, Debra Hogg, Hilary Gellman, Sally Hunt, Jenny Jacoby, Jenny Leask, Diana Leat, Jean Mackay, Jane Malone, Frances Richards, Liz Mills, Bernice Roberts, Joanna Gordon Smart, Helen Thompson, Sally Walker, Doreen Winning.

Contents

Tables

1   Introduction

This report is one of two parallel studies carried out to follow up the findings of *Doctors and their Careers* (Allen, 1988) which was a study initiated and funded by the Department of Health to look at the factors affecting the activity and participation rates of women doctors. *Doctors and their Careers* had four main aims:

(i)   to collect more information on possible changes or trends in the activity or participation rates of women doctors;

(ii) to identify the main obstacles which prevent women from participating as fully as they would like in medicine;

(iii) to examine the usefulness and relevance of careers advice in medicine at all stages from school to postgraduate training and beyond;

(iv) to assess the extent to which women doctors have found their aspirations limited more by the demands of the medical career system rather than by their own ambitions.

The fieldwork for *Doctors and their Careers* was conducted in the spring of 1986. We had selected random samples of equal numbers of men and women who had qualified from British medical schools in 1966, 1976 and 1981. They were aged around 43, 33 and 28 at time that we carried out personal interviews with them, and had post-qualification experience of approximately 20, 10 and 5 years respectively. These were thought to be ages and stages in careers of particular interest. The aim was to achieve personal interviews with 100 men and 100 women from each year of qualifiers. We achieved a better response rate than expected and in the event we interviewed 640 doctors living and working in all parts of Great Britain.

Doctors and their Careers, with its companion 'popular' summary, *Any Room at the Top?*, was published in 1988 and attracted a lot of attention, both within medicine and among the general public. It generated considerable debate, and both the Department of Health and the British Medical Association set up working parties to consider its recommendations resulting in influential publications – *Women Doctors and their Careers: Report of the Joint Working Party* (Department of Health, 1991) and *Report of the Council Working Party on Career Progress of Women Doctors* (BMA, 1989).

The follow-up studies
The follow-up studies were carried out in the late summer and autumn of 1991, five years after the last study. They were designed to update the last study by contacting the 1976 and 1981 qualifiers interviewed last time and by adding a new cohort of doctors who qualified in 1986, five years after the 1981 cohort and ten years after the 1976 cohort.

The follow-up studies had four main aims which built on the work of *Doctors and their Careers*:
(i)   to examine what had happened in the past five years to the 1976 and 1981 medical qualifiers interviewed for *Doctors and their Careers*, both in their careers and their personal circumstances;
(ii) to compare the experience, views and characteristics of a sample of 1986 medical qualifiers with their counterparts from previous cohorts;
(iii) to examine the extent to which opportunities for women doctors were seen to have changed since 1986 and to look at perceptions of constraints on the careers of women doctors;
(iv) to examine in detail the question of part-time or less than full-time training and career posts in medicine.

Background to the research
The point of departure for the last study was the fact that women would account for around half of those entering medical schools by the early 1990s. It was recognised that it was essential to assess the main influences on their careers as part of future medical manpower planning. The proportion of women among entrants to medical school had been rising steadily since 1970. All through the 1960s the proportion hovered around 25 per cent, but as Table 1.01 shows, it increased from 28 per cent in 1970 to 35 per cent in 1975 to 41 per cent in 1980 and 46 per cent in 1985. By 1990, women accounted for 49 per cent of those entering medical school and in 1992 the proportion was 52 per cent.

There is clearly a time lag before the results of these changes are seen in medical staffing, but Table 1.01 shows the different contexts in which the four cohorts we have studied were working. In the 1966 cohort, the women accounted for 25 per cent, in the 1976 cohort for 31 per cent, and in the 1981 cohort for 35 per cent of the qualifiers. Among the 1986 cohort, whose careers we examine in this report, women accounted for 43 per cent of qualifiers. As the table shows, the proportion of women qualifiers had risen to 47 per cent by 1993 and it is clear that women will account for 50 per cent of those entering the medical profession in the mid 1990s.

There has been an enormous change in the composition of the medical workforce among the younger generation, and this report indicates that this fact has not been fully recognised by many people both within and outside the profession. The implications of these changes will be discussed in Chapters 16 and 17, but it is important to bear these facts in mind throughout the reading of this report.

Table 1.01   Medical students admitted to pre-clinical courses and numbers obtaining first registrable qualifications in Great Britain

Academic year	Number admitted to pre-clinical courses				Number obtaining first registrable qualifications			
	Total (100%)	Male	Female	(%)	Total	Male	Female	(%)
1965-66	2478	1937	541	(21.8)	1939	1458	481	(24.8)
1970-71	2878	2066	812	(28.2)	2190	1704	486	(22.2)
1975-76	3468	2249	1219	(35.1)	2749	1895	854	(31.1)
1980-81	3857	2292	1565	(40.6)	3433	2215	1218	(35.5)
1985-86	3938	2134	1804	(45.8)	3483	1985	1498	(43.0)
1986-87	3967	2170	1797	(45.3)	3430	1896	1534	(44.7)
1987-88	3957	2152	1805	(45.6)	3595	1967	1628	(45.3)
1988-89	4015	2148	1867	(46.5)	3376	1863	1513	(44.8)
1989-90	4053	2119	1934	(47.7)	3584	1981	1603	(44.7)
1990-91	4153	2127	2026	(48.8)	3445	1867	1578	(45.8)
1991-92	4151	2095	2058	(49.6)	3502	1896	1606	(45.9)
1992-93	4270	2033	2237	(52.4)	3494	1848	1646	(47.1)

Source: University Grants Committee and the Higher Education Funding Councils for England, Scotland and Wales

At the time of the fieldwork for the last study in 1986, some 13 per cent of all consultants in medical specialties and 20 per cent of GP principals were women. By 1991 these proportions had risen to nearly 16 per cent of consultants and 25 per cent of GP principals, and latest figures for 1993 show an increase to 17 per cent of consultants and 26 per cent of GP principals.

We noted in the last report that these proportions included doctors of all ages and that the proportion of women consultants and senior registrars had been creeping up among those appointed in recent years. This trend has, of course, continued, as would be expected from the steadily increasing proportions of women among medical qualifiers. Nevertheless, the progress towards parity remains slow and in certain specialties, such as surgery, women are still a tiny minority at the most senior grades, although there is some evidence of increasing numbers at junior levels. More details are given later in this chapter.

Design of the study and methods

We used different methods for the two parallel studies. We followed up the 1976 and 1981 qualifiers by sending postal questionnaires to all those whom we had interviewed for the last study. We selected a new cohort of 1986 qualifiers from the lists held by the General Medical Council of all students gaining their first registrable qualification from medical schools in Great Britain in that year in exactly the same way that we had sampled the cohorts from 1966, 1976 and 1981.

We had decided with the Department of Health to drop the 1966 qualifiers from the follow-up studies. It was agreed that the costs involved in following them up might not justify their inclusion in relation to the amount of new material which would be generated.

Details of the sampling methods are given in the Appendix to this report and in the parallel report of the 1976 and 1981 follow-up study. It is, however, of interest that of the 414 qualifiers from 1976 and 1981 whom we interviewed last time, we succeeded in achieving an overall response rate of 77 per cent, with 73 per cent of the men and 80 per cent of the women completing the long questionnaire we sent them. The response from the 1976 qualifiers was rather higher than that of the 1981 qualifiers, but we felt that this excellent response rate was an indication of the interest that had been aroused in these doctors in the study we had carried out five years earlier. There were certainly many indications that they felt a sense of 'ownership' of the original study which was reflected in their willingness to respond in such numbers – and in such detail – to a postal questionnaire.

This report is concerned with the study of the new cohort of 1986 qualifiers. We drew a final sample of 143 men and 143 women in the same way as last time, stratified by sex and medical school, having gone through the various procedures described in the Appendix to remove from the final sampling frame those who were on the Overseas Register and those who had died. This sample was designed to give us 100 interviews with men and 100 with women, assuming a 70 per cent response rate.

In the event, 7 per cent of the sample were found to be overseas at the time of the fieldwork and therefore unavailable for interview. Of the remaining 265 doctors, 229 were interviewed (86 per cent of the available sample and 80 per cent of the total sample) – including 124 women (91 per cent of the available sample and 87 per cent of the total female sample) and 105 men (82 per cent of the available sample and 73 per cent of the total male sample). Only 12 doctors refused to be interviewed and 24 could not be traced, although it appeared likely that some of these were abroad.

It is clear that the present study achieved a very high response rate among the 1986 qualifiers, much of which must be attributed to the dedication of PSI interviewers and staff who followed up the letters of invitation to the doctors with personal contact. As we found last time, young doctors in postgraduate training posts move around a great deal, and, in spite of the enormous help given to us by staff at the General Medical Council, we were unable to trace some of them. It is not possible to make general assumptions about the present employment status of the 24 doctors who could not be traced after their last known address. Only 1 per cent of the respondents in this survey were working outside medicine. We consider it very unlikely that the non-respondents did not respond because they had left medicine. Indeed, it is more likely that most, if not all, were still working in medicine but were untraceable because of their frequent geographical mobility or because they were abroad.

We should add some comments on the sample here. Among the 229 doctors interviewed there were marginally more women than would be expected from a true cross section of all qualifiers from 1986, although the imbalance was considerably less in 1986, when women represented almost 50 per cent of qualifiers, than in 1966, when they represented only 25 per cent of qualifiers. Nevertheless, some caution should be exercised in generalising from the results of this survey to all members of the cohorts. However, within each group, the doctors interviewed form an unbiased and representative sample.

The majority of comments in the text refer to comparisons between the samples of 1986 men and women qualifiers or between the samples of men and women qualifiers from the various cohorts studied. In other words, the comparisons are usually between the separate samples of qualifiers and we rarely draw comparisons between the total responses from cohorts, although we present these in the tables for illustrative purposes. The report draws attention to differences only where the probability was less than 5 per cent that they could have arisen by chance. However, there were many instances where significant differences were not perhaps as important as trends or cumulative evidence or strong associations. We have tried to highlight these in the text. It should be stressed that this type of analysis entails close knowledge of the completed questionnaires and the interlocking use of quantitative and qualitative data.

In addition, we must describe how the tables in this report have been compiled. One of our main aims was to compare the 1986 men and women qualifiers with the 1981 men and women qualifiers interviewed for the last study. They were at much the same stage of their careers approximately five years after qualification and four years after registration and were much the same average age of 28. The only slight difference was that the 1986 qualifiers were interviewed on average six months later in their careers than the 1981 qualifiers had been.

We decided that to present the comparative material in an easily digestible form we would compile tables which showed the data collected in this study from the 1986 qualifiers side by side with the data collected in the last study from the 1981 qualifiers. In some cases, where the data were historical and particularly pertinent, for example, giving 'A' level results, we also used data collected from the 1976 qualifiers in the last study. We should stress that all the material presented about 1966, 1976 and 1981 qualifiers in this study relates only to the last study, except on the rare occasions where we explicitly refer to the follow-up study of 1976 and 1981 qualifiers conducted in parallel to this study. None of the tables in this report uses any results from the 1976 and 1981 follow-up study.

The interviews with 1986 qualifiers were carried out by a team of experienced interviewers, most of whom had worked on the previous study of *Doctors and their Careers*. The questionnaire was based closely on the questionnaire used in the previous study, and, indeed, most of the questions were identical. Further areas of investigation were requested by the Department of Health and the new questions were developed in close collaboration with staff from the Department. A very small number of questions which were no longer relevant were dropped from the new questionnaire. The questionnaire was fully structured, in that the exact wording of each question was specified and the questions were asked in a predetermined sequence. A fairly high proportion of questions allowed for an open-ended response and the interviewers were expected to record the answers verbatim.

Data analysis
The questionnaires were analysed using the predetermined codes on the questionnaires, as well as coding frames developed from detailed textual analysis of the 'open-ended' questions. Verbatim quotes were extracted from the questionnaires and selected for inclusion in a rigorous manner in proportion to the numbers making such comments.

The medical career structure
The research we have carried out has shown the fairly rapid change in the proportion of women entering the medical profession, rising from around a quarter of medical qualifiers in 1970 to around half of all qualifiers by the mid-1990s. And yet the medical career structure has changed very little in that time. We observed in the last study that the career structure was perceived to be inflexible and that there was thought to be an unnecessarily rigid adherence to linking age to grade. It was thought that there was little or no recognition of the need to allow for more flexible career paths for women who represented increasing proportions of the medical workforce. But women were not the only doctors to find that the medical career structure imposed constraints on their careers. Indeed, one of the main findings of the last report was the need to look more closely at the demands from men as well as women for changes in the medical career structure and the organisation of medical careers.

The career structure in medicine is a complex area, and we described it in some detail in the first chapter of the last report (Allen, 1988), building on the clear outline given in the Social Services Committee's 1981 report (HMSO, 1981). Although we do not feel it necessary to repeat the details given in that chapter, we summarise the main structure so that the non-medical reader is familiar with the broad categories of grades of doctors within the National Health Service:

(i) postgraduate training grades (junior doctors) – pre-registration house officers, senior house officers, registrars, senior registrars and trainee general practitioners;

(ii) non-training grades subject to consultant clinical direction – clinical assistants, hospital practitioners, staff grade doctors and associate specialists;

(iii) autonomous career grades – principals in general practice, hospital consultants and community physicians.

In addition to these three broad grades, there are doctors working in community health: senior community medical officers, community medical officers and other medical officers. Much of their work is done on a part-time or sessional basis. It is debatable whether these doctors can be said to be strictly clinically autonomous, since there are no formal training programmes for doctors who enter the community health service, so that they cannot be regarded as 'trained' in an independent specialty. There are also doctors working in medicine or in medically-related occupations outside the NHS, for example in industry, government departments, the armed services etc.

The staff grade was introduced in 1988 as one of the results of the consultation following *Hospital Medical Staffing: Achieving a Balance* (DHSS, 1986; DHSS, 1987). It is a non-training intermediate-level service grade designed for doctors who do not wish or are unable to train for consultant grade (Department of Health, HC(88)90, 1988) and is discussed in more detail in Chapter 12 of this report.

Women doctors in the career structure
This section is designed to give a brief account of the changes over the years in the proportions of women in the various grades of hospital medicine and general practice and the proportion of women consultants in the hospital specialties. It provides the backcloth against which this report should be read and reinforces the underlying theme of this research of a changing workforce with changing needs and demands which cannot be easily met within the traditional medical career structure.

Table 1.02 shows the steady increase in the proportion of women in each of the grades in hospital medicine. The proportion of women medical staff in hospital medicine has increased from 23 per cent in 1983 to 29 per cent in 1993 overall. There has been an increase in the proportion of women consultants from 12 per cent to 17 per cent. However, it is unlikely that the goal set in *Women in the NHS: an Implementation Guide to Opportunity 2000* (NHSME, 1992) of increasing the percentage of women consultants to 20 per cent by 1994 will be met.

It can be seen that, although women accounted for 47 per cent of pre-registration house officers by 1993, they accounted for 38 per cent of senior house officers (SHOs), 28 per cent of registrars and 30 per cent of senior registrars. The proportions of women are creeping up but hospital medicine remains a less attractive option for women doctors than general practice, for a variety of reasons which will be explored in this report.

One of the reasons for the relatively low representation of women within the consultant grade is clearly demonstrated in Table 1.03 which shows the proportion of women consultants by specialty group. Women accounted for 30 per cent of consultants in paediatrics, 28 per cent of consultant psychiatrists and 26 per cent of consultant pathologists by 1993. But they still only accounted for 4 per cent of consultants in surgery, and an even lower proportion of consultants in general surgery. The proportion had risen from 2 per cent in 1983, but it is still

Table 1.02   Female hospital medical staff by grade: numbers and percentage of total in England at 30 September of each year

	1983	1988	1991	1992	1993
All grades	9,640	11,780	13,720	14,110	14,840
% of all staff	23%	26%	27%	28%	29%
Consultant	1,560	2,080	2,540	2,690	2,840
% of all staff	12%	14%	16%	17%	17%
Associate specialist	420	330	330	320	340
% of all staff	44%	41%	38%	36%	35%
Staff grade*	..	..	150	200	310
% of all staff			31%	27%	28%
Senior Registrar	720	870	1,090	1,130	1,200
% of all staff	23%	27%	29%	30%	30%
Registrar	1,290	1,460	1,500	1,570	1,780
% of all staff	22%	24%	24%	25%	28%
Senior House Officer	2,730	3,610	4,210	4,410	4,610
% of all staff	28%	36%	37%	38%	38%
House Officer	1,070	1,270	1,410	1,390	1,440
% of all staff	38%	44%	46%	46%	47%
Hospital practitioner	60	70	80	70	70
% of all staff	7%	8%	9%	9%	10%
Clinical assistant	1,780	2,100	2,400	2,330	2,260
% of all staff	27%	29%	32%	33%	33%

*   new grade from 1989

Source: *Statistical Bulletin 1994/10: Hospital, Public Health Medicine and Community Health Service Medical and Dental Staff in England 1983 to 1993* (Department of Health, 1994)

Table 1.03   Female hospital medical consultants by specialty group: number and percentage of all consultants in England 30 September of each year

	1983	1988	1991	1992	1993
All specialties	1,560	2,080	2,540	2,690	2,840
% of all consultants	12%	14%	16%	17%	17%
General medicine group	210	300	390	450	450
% of all consultants	7%	9%	11%	12%	12%
Paediatrics	90	150	230	240	280
% of all paediatrics	17%	23%	28%	28%	30%
Accident and emergency	10	20	20	20	30
% of all consultants	9%	11%	10%	10%	11%
Surgical group	60	80	110	120	130
% of all consultants	2%	3%	3%	4%	4%
Obstetrics and gynaecology	80	80	100	120	130
% of all consultants	11%	11%	13%	14%	15%
Anaesthetics	330	390	450	460	490
% of all consultants	19%	20%	21%	21%	21%
Radiology group	130	210	270	280	290
% of all consultants	16%	20%	22%	23%	23%
Clinical oncology	40	40	40	40	50
% of all consultants	18%	18%	19%	19%	20%
Pathology group	250	330	400	400	410
% of all consultants	17%	22%	25%	25%	26%
Psychiatry group	370	470	530	560	590
% of all consultants	21%	25%	26%	27%	28%

Source: *Statistical Bulletin 1994/10: Hospital, Public Health Medicine and Community Health Service Medical and Dental Staff in England 1983 to 1993* (Department of Health, 1994)

Table 1.04   **Female general practitioners in England and Wales as a proportion of practitioners by grade in October of each year**

	1983	1988	1991	1992	1993
All practitioners (total)	26,962	29,196	29,696	30,020	30,310
% female	19%	23%	27%	28%	29%
Unrestricted principals					
(total)	24,719	26,921	27,333	27,644	27,991
% female	17%	22%	25%	26%	26%
Restricted principals (total)	188	161	139	140	149
% female	39%	37%	37%	41%	41%
Assistants (total)	286	264	447	490	517
% female	58%	62%	60%	59%	59%
Trainees (total)	1,769	1,850	1,777	1,746	1,653
% female	37%	45%	48%	48%	53%

Source: *Statistical Bulletin 1994/4: Statistics for General Medical Practitioners in England and Wales, 1983-1993* (Department of Health, 1994)

clear that women in surgery have a very long way to go. However, there are other specialties where women have made slow progress even though it might be thought that there would be a demand for women consultants. For example, women only accounted for 12 per cent of consultants in general medicine and 15 per cent of consultants in obstetrics and gynaecology in 1993.

There is encouraging evidence for women in their representation in the senior registrar grade, with 52 per cent in paediatrics, 44 per cent in psychiatry and 37 per cent in pathology (Department of Health, 1994). The proportion in obstetrics and gynaecology was above average at 35 per cent. However, women only represented 8 per cent of senior registrars in the surgical specialties, reinforcing the observation that women's progress in the senior ranks of surgery continues to be very slow.

However, as Table 1.04 shows, women have made rather greater progress in general practice. The proportion of women GP principals increased from 17 per cent in 1983 to 22 per cent in 1988 to 26 per cent in 1993. But it is among GP trainees that the most marked increase in the proportion of women has been found – from 37 per cent in 1983 to 45 per cent in 1988 to 53 per cent in 1993. Over half the doctors entering general practice are now women and there can be little doubt that this has major implications for the future organisation of general practice.

The context of this research

Since the publication of *Doctors and their Careers* in 1988 there have been a number of working parties and reports, both from the Department of Health and other representative bodies, which have considered many aspects of the medical career structure and have made recommendations which are designed to have far-reaching consequences. A number of these have been published since the fieldwork for this study took place. It is to be hoped that their consequences will alleviate some of the undoubted pressure under which the doctors in this study found themselves.

Among those which directly address some of the most important issues raised in this report are *Junior Doctors: the New Deal* (Department of Health, 1991); *Planning the Medical Workforce. Medical Manpower Standing Advisory Committee: First Report* (the Campbell Report), (Department of Health 1992); *Flexible Training: Report of the Joint Working Party* (NHSME, 1993); *Hospital Doctors: Training for the Future* (the Calman Report), (Department of Health, 1993). Others are referred to in the course of this report, but it should be stressed that we have kept our references to other literature at a minimum in this report. Our main aim was to produce empirical data to aid policy makers rather than to write a treatise only of interest to academics.

Structure and presentation of the report

The report follows much the same structure adopted in *Doctors and their Careers*. Chapter 2 outlines in detail the main characteristics of the doctors interviewed in terms of their working status and personal circumstances and gives an essential framework to the ensuing chapters which present and analyse the views and experience of the doctors on a variety of questions about their careers and views and experience.

Chapter 16 brings together much of the material presented in the report and is a discussion of the main findings, placed in the context of the continuing debate about the best way of organising the medical career structure so that both men and women doctors can make the best use of their talents and so that the country may benefit from their contribution. Chapter 17 brings together the policy implications of the main findings and puts forward specific recommendations. There is a detailed summary at the end of the book.

Much of the detail given in Chapter 2 is often given in an Appendix and some readers may wish to move straight to Chapter 3 and return to Chapter 2 for reference. Others may wish to start at Chapter 16 and read the discussion of findings, implications for policy makers and the summary before returning to the rest of the book. It is to be hoped that readers will not be daunted by the complexity of some of the material presented in this report but will listen to the voices of the young doctors who speak for themselves. Their messages may not be comfortable but all those concerned with the future of the medical profession in this country should hear what they have to say.

2 Who were the doctors?

The follow-up study was designed in exactly the same way as the previous study with the objective of achieving 200 interviews with 1986 medical qualifiers – 100 men and 100 women. In the event, we interviewed 229 qualifiers from 1986 – 105 men and 124 women. Further details on sampling and response rates are given in the Appendix, but it should be noted that the response from 1986 male qualifiers was higher than that of the 1981 men and the response of the 1986 female qualifiers was considerably higher than that of the 1981 women. The main reason for non-response was the fact that the doctor was overseas at the time of interviewing.

Medical school

The doctors were sampled in such a way as to give male and female qualifiers from each medical school an equal chance of selection, given the requirement for an equal sample size of men and women, and Table 2.01 shows the even spread of respondents among the medical schools, repeating the findings from the last study. There was some evidence of a more even distribution of women qualifiers. For example, Scottish medical schools had accounted for 25 per cent of the 1966 women qualifiers but the proportion had declined to 16 per cent of the 1986 women, while London medical schools had accounted for 41 per cent of the 1966 women but for 29 per cent of the 1986 women. The proportions of doctors from Oxford and Cambridge who had done their clinical training at a London medical school had also declined considerably over the 20 years. Two doctors – one male and one female – had conjoint only as their primary medical qualification in the United Kingdom.

Age

The 1986 qualifiers were very similar in age to the 1981 qualifiers at the time that we had interviewed them five years earlier, as Table 2.02 shows. Both men and women were slightly older on average than the 1981 qualifiers had been, but this is mainly accounted for by the fact that we interviewed a few months later in 1991 than we had in 1986. In both cohorts the men were a little older than the women on average, mainly because over 10 per cent of both the 1981 and 1986 men qualifiers were over 30, compared with well under 10 per cent of the women from both years.

Table 2.01   Where doctors qualified

column percentages

	Male			Female		
	1976	1981	1986	1976	1981	1986
Aberdeen	2	3	2	4	6	2
Birmingham	8	7	5	7	3	2
Bristol	6	1	3	8	6	5
Cambridge	10	5	3	5	2	5
Dundee	2	5	5	5	3	3
Edinburgh	9	5	5	5	3	6
Glasgow	4	4	3	8	5	5
Leeds	3	3	5	4	6	4
Leicester	0	2	2	0	2	2
Liverpool	4	4	3	6	4	3
London	29	36	39	30	36	29
Manchester	5	9	4	6	5	8
Newcastle	5	0	2	4	4	5
Nottingham	1	2	2	0	3	3
Oxford	3	2	6	2	2	6
Sheffield	5	2	4	6	3	5
Southampton	2	4	6	2	5	3
Wales	4	7	3	2	3	2
Conjoint only	2	0	1	0	0	1
London medical schools						
St. Thomas's	5	4	6	5	1	5
Westminster	1	4	0	3	4	3
St. George's	2	1	3	2	3	4
London Hospital	6	5	3	2	4	0
Royal Free	5	4	5	2	2	3
St. Bartholomew's	8	6	3	2	3	2
Charing Cross	2	5	2	1	4	3
Guy's	5	4	9	2	2	3
UCH	3	2	7	4	6	7
Middlesex	4	4	2	0	3	1
St. Mary's	0	3	2	3	2	2
King's College Hospital	1	1	2	6	2	4
Base: all qualifiers	*(105)*	*(101)*	*(105)*	*(105)*	*(103)*	*(124)*

Table 2.02   Age of doctors

column percentages

	Total		Male		Female	
	1981	1986	1981	1986	1981	1986
26-30	91	90	87	88	95	92
31-35	6	9	9	11	4	6
36-40	2	1	4	1	1	1
41-45	0	*	0	0	0	1
Mean age	*28.4*	*29.0*	*28.7*	*29.2*	*28.1*	*28.8*
Base: all qualifiers	*(204)*	*(229)*	*(101)*	*(105)*	*(103)*	*(124)*

Marital status

It was rather surprising to find that the proportion of women who were single was considerably lower among the 1986 women than among the 1981 women. Table 2.03 shows that just over one third of the 1986 women were single, compared with nearly half the 1981 women. The proportions of single men remained at just under one third for both the 1981 and 1986 cohorts. Nearly two-thirds of the men from the 1981 cohort were married or living as married, compared with 55 per cent of the women from that year. On the other hand, 70 per cent of the 1986 men were married or living as married, compared with 63 per cent of the 1986 women.

Table 2.03   Marital status

column percentages

	Total		Male		Female	
	1981	1986	1981	1986	1981	1986
Single	39	32	32	30	46	35
Married	54	59	64	63	45	56
Living as married	5	7	1	7	10	7
Widowed	0	0	0	0	0	0
Divorced/separated	1	*	3	1	0	0
Base: all qualifiers	*(204)*	*(229)*	*(101)*	*(105)*	*(103)*	*(124)*

We had noted the relatively high proportion of 1966 women qualifiers who were divorced, and there have been concerns about increasing divorce rates among doctors. In the last study we were unable to establish the true incidence of divorce since we did not ask whether doctors had remarried after a divorce.

Table 2.04   Stage in medical career at which (first) married.

column percentages

	Male			Female		
	1976	1981	1986	1976	1981	1986
Before entry to medical school	3	1	3	0	2	0
During medical school course	23	22	7	27	22	11
Within one year of qualification (pre-reg year)	15	21	15	16	17	20
1 -2 years after qualification	25	25	23	18	28	21
3 - 5 years after qualification	26	31	43	28	30	37
6 - 10 years after qualification	8	0	0	10	0	0
Not stated	0	0	9	0	0	11
Base: ever married qualifiers	*(96)*	*(68)*	*(74)*	*(88)*	*(46)*	*(81)*

We therefore asked doctors in this study whether they had ever been divorced and found that 1 per cent of both men and women said that they had. These doctors were mainly in their late twenties so that it would perhaps have been surprising if there had been higher divorce rates. In addition, the majority of them had not been married for very long, as Table 2.03 indicates.

One of the most striking features of Table 2.04 is the extent to which marriage has increasingly been postponed among the medical qualifiers, even among those who were married at the time of the interview. The table compares the 1976, 1981 and 1986 cohorts. It can be seen that the 1986 qualifiers, both men and women, were considerably less likely than their 1981 counterparts to have got married at medical school, and that they were more likely to have postponed marriage until 3-5 years after qualification.

The 1976 qualifiers were rather different in that they were interviewed some ten years after qualification, which accounts both for a higher proportion of marriages and for some later marriages. However, if those are discounted, it can be seen that five years after qualification, a considerably higher proportion of both men and women from the 1976 cohort would have been married during the medical school course than among either of the succeeding cohorts.

To a large extent, the behaviour of the successive cohorts of doctors reflects the trend towards later marriage in society as a whole, but there are a number of important factors which should be considered, such as the question of whether the demands of medical postgraduate training are particularly inimical to married

Table 2.05   Social class/occupation of husbands/partners of women doctors

column percentages

	Female 1976	1981	1986
Professional I	70	83	60
Intermediate II	24	10	34
Skilled non-manual IIIN	0	2	0
Skilled manual IIIM	0	2	1
Semi-skilled IV and unskilled V	0	0	1
Other[1]	3	2	4
Working in medicine (doctors)	44	57	43
Working outside medicine	55	41	54
Not working	1	2	4
GP	21	14	10
Hospital doctor	18	39	30
Other doctor	3	4	3
Base: all women qualifiers with husbands/partners for whom occupation given	*(84)*	*(56)*	*(80)*

1. Student, armed forces, house husband, retired.

life and the question of whether later marriage leads to even later age at having a first baby.

Whom did the doctors marry? We were interested in the occupation of husbands, wives or partners with whom the doctors were living, and were particularly interested to establish whether these young qualifiers were continuing the tradition of drawing their spouses from a relatively narrow social band and type of occupation.

Table 2.05 looks at the social class and occupation of the husbands or partners of women doctors and compares the 1986 qualifiers with those of 1976 and 1981. It can be seen that there had been a marked shift from 1981 to 1986 in the proportion of women married to men in Social Class I occupations, from 83 per cent of the 1981 women to 60 per cent of the 1986 women. It must be remembered that higher numbers of 1986 women were married or living as married, but the pattern is quite clear. As the table indicates, the main reason for this appears to be the considerably lower proportion of 1986 women who were married to doctors – a drop from 57 per cent of the 1981 married women to 43 per cent of their 1986 counterparts. Over one third of the 1986 women were married to men in Social Class II occupations, compared with some 10 per cent of 1981 women.

Successive surveys of women doctors have shown that around half of all married women doctors are married to other doctors. Among these more recent qualifiers it looks as though some reversal of the trend is setting in. It is not possible to establish the reasons for this, but it may be that young women doctors are recognising the many problems attached to medical marriages in which the demands of the medical career system are compounded when both partners wish to follow a satisfying career. However, nearly one third of the married women doctors were married to hospital doctors, 10 per cent to GPs and 3 per cent to other doctors. The high proportion married to hospital doctors might be expected, given the age and stage of career of these young women. The overwhelming majority of husbands were working full-time.

Table 2.06   Social class/occupation of wives/partners of men doctors

column percentages

	1976	Male 1981	1986
Professional I	22	24	27
Intermediate II	19	47	49
Skilled non-manual IIIN	5	6	4
Skilled manual IIIM	1	0	0
Semi-skilled IV and Unskilled V	1	0	0
Housewife	52	21	19
Other[1]	0	2	1
Medically qualified	21	29	24
Currently working doctors	16	23	21
Currently working as nurses	7	24	27
Currently working as paramedics[2]	2	12	4
Base: all men qualifiers with wives/partners	*(91)*	*(66)*	*(70)*

1. Student, unemployed
2. Including physio/occupational therapists etc.

Table 2.06 shows that the social class and occupation of the wives and partners of male doctors were very similar among the 1981 and 1986 qualifiers, with around a quarter in both cohorts in Social Class I occupations, nearly half in Social Class II occupations and around one fifth being described as housewives. The proportion of housewives was much lower among these cohorts than among the 1976 men, and, even allowing for the fact that these men were some five years older than the two later cohorts at the time of interviewing, with the related increased likelihood of young families, nevertheless there appears to be a trend for the younger cohorts to be more likely to have working wives. Well over two-thirds of the working wives were working full-time, while the rest were working part-time. Over 60 per cent of wives or partners with children were working either full or part-time, with the result that less than 40 per cent of those with children were housewives.

The study confirmed the trend away from the traditional picture of doctors' wives being available at home to answer the telephone. There is a clear picture among these young doctors of dual career families, and the implications of this, both for the careers of the male doctors as well as their wives, must be recognised in the increasing complaints among young doctors of both sexes about the constraints imposed by what they see as the rigidity and demands of the medical career system.

The proportion of medically qualified wives was 21 per cent among the 1976 cohort, 29 per cent of the 1981 cohort and 24 per cent of the 1986 cohort, but the proportion of these women who were working was similar for all three cohorts. On the other hand, around a quarter of the wives of the two later cohorts were currently working as nurses, compared with less than 10 per cent of the wives of 1976 men. It is interesting that half of the non-working wives of the 1986 men had previously worked as nurses, reflecting the findings of the last study.

Children

The last study highlighted some differences between men and women doctors in the extent to which they had children. These differences were more marked in the 1966 cohort, among whom 91 per cent of the men but 79 per cent of the women had children of their own. Among the 1976 cohort, the relative proportions were 69 per cent of the men and 62 per cent of the women. As Table 2.07 shows, the differences between men and women in both the 1981 and 1986 cohorts were not as marked, with rather more than 20 per cent of the men in both cohorts having children, compared with around 20 per cent of the women in both cohorts having children or being pregnant at the time of the interview.

Table 2.07   Whether doctors had children

column percentages

	Total		Male		Female	
	1981	1986	1981	1986	1981	1986
Has children of own	18	20	23	22	14	18
Has adopted/stepchildren	0	1	0	1	0	1
Pregnant now (no other children)	3	1	0	0	6	2
Has no children	79	78	77	77	81	79
Base: all qualifiers	*(204)*	*(229)*	*(101)*	*(105)*	*(103)*	*(124)*

It is important, however, to reinforce the finding of the last study that only one fifth of these young women doctors in their late twenties had children. Although the average age at first birth has been getting later in general over the last decade, it is still perhaps a matter of concern that 80 per cent of these women doctors had no children and were not pregnant. Many of them were clearly delaying the birth of their first child for career reasons, and there can be little doubt that some might experience problems in achieving pregnancy in their thirties.

Table 2.08   Number of children of doctors with children of own

column percentages

	Total		Male		Female	
	1981	1986	1981	1986	1981	1986
One	70	71	65	48	79	95
Two	27	22	35	39	14	5
Three	0	4	0	9	0	0
Four	0	2	0	4	0	0
n.a.	3	0	0	0	7	0
Mean no. of children of own	*1.3*	*1.4*	*1.3*	*1.7*	*1.2*	*1.0*
Base: all qualifiers with children of own	*(37)*	*(45)*	*(23)*	*(23)*	*(14)*	*(22)*
Mean no. of children of own of all doctors (inc. those with no children)	*0.2*	*0.3*	*0.3*	*0.4*	*0.1*	*0.2*
Base: all qualifiers	*(204)*	*(229)*	*(101)*	*(105)*	*(103)*	*(124)*

Table 2.08 shows clearly that women doctors with children from both the 1981 and 1986 cohorts were much less likely than their male counterparts to have more than one child. It was not surprising that the vast majority of children of both men and women doctors were under the age of five, and, indeed, all but one of the children of the 1986 women were under the age of three.

Given the high level of working among the women doctors and the wives of men doctors it was surprising that less than half of the men and just over half the women said that they had help with child care. The level of child care among the 1986 women doctors with children was lower than that found among the 1981 women with children, while among the men the reverse was true. The numbers were, of course, small, so that it is difficult to read too much into the figures.

The most common form of child care was a childminder, used by around half of 1986 men and women who had help with child care. Nannies were used by

Table 2.09   Whether doctors had help with childcare

column percentages

| | Total | | Male | | Female | |
	1981	1986	1981	1986	1981	1986
Yes	43	51	26	48	71	55
No	54	49	74	52	21	45
School hols/varies	3	0	0	0	7	0
Base: all qualifiers						
with children	*(37)*	*(45)*	*(23)*	*(23)*	*(14)*	*(22)*

only one of the 22 women with children and two of the 23 men. This was in sharp contrast to the findings of the previous study where a much higher proportion of doctors had nannies, and indeed a quarter of the women doctors with children of all ages employed nannies. Around one third of the 1986 women who used child care used a day nursery and one in ten was helped by a relative. There was a broad spread in the intensity of child care, but on average men doctors used nearly 16 hours of child care a week compared with 30 hours used by women doctors.

The relative lack of child care used by working mothers in this survey, whether doctors or not, underlines the later findings of career constraints imposed by lack of child care facilities. It is clearly a general problem, but nevertheless,

Table 2.10   Stage in medical career when first child born

column percentages

| | Total | | Male | | Female | |
	1981	1986	1981	1986	1981	1986
Before entry to medical school	0	2	0	4	0	0
During medical school course	3	4	4	9	0	0
Within 1 year of qualification	11	0	9	0	14	0
1-2 years after qualification	30	16	39	26	14	5
3-5 years after qualification	56	76	48	57	71	95
n.a.	0	2	0	4	0	0
Base: all qualifiers						
with children of own	*(37)*	*(45)*	*(23)*	*(23)*	*(14)*	*(22)*

Table 2.11   Age when first child born

column percentages

	Total		Male		Female	
	1981	1986	1981	1986	1981	1986
21-23	3	4	0	8	7	0
24-26	27	22	26	25	29	18
27-29	51	60	48	51	57	68
30-32	11	13	17	13	0	14
33-35	3	0	4	0	0	0
Over 35	3	0	0	0	7	0
n.a.	3	2	0	4	0	0
Mean age	*26.7*	*27.2*	*26.6*	*27.0*	*26.8*	*27.5*
Base: all qualifiers						
with children of own	*(37)*	*(45)*	*(23)*	*(23)*	*(14)*	*(22)*

it was of great importance to the young women interviewed both in the present study and the last one. There must be speculation on whether the high cost of live-in child care made this an unlikely option for these young doctors, most of whom were still in training posts or had only just achieved GP principal status.

We have already seen that the 1986 cohort had tended to get married later than their 1981 counterparts. Those who had had children had certainly had their first child at a later stage, but Tables 2.10 and 2.11 which show the age and stage of career at which the doctors had had their first child should be treated with some caution, since the numbers are small and some of the difference could be accounted for by the few months relative difference in interviewing of the two cohorts.

However, the tables do show that both cohorts of women were less likely than the men to have had their first child before they had been qualified for at least three years. Nearly three-quarters of the 1981 women with children and all but one of the 1986 women with children had waited until at least three years after qualification before embarking on motherhood, compared with less than half the 1981 men but rather more than half the 1986 men. The average age at first birth, however, was not strikingly different between the men and women, perhaps reflecting the fact that the women were rather younger on average than the men at qualification.

It remains to be seen what happens to the remainder of the doctors in these two cohorts. The figures for the 1981 cohort are available in the accompanying follow-up report. There can be no doubt that many of the 1981 and 1986 women delaying the birth of their first child were not necessarily certain that they had made the right decision, either in career or in personal terms.

Ethnic origin

In the last study we did not make any enquiry about the ethnic origin of the doctors we interviewed. Our study was restricted to qualifiers of UK medical schools and many of the problems surrounding doctors from minority ethnic groups appeared at the time to be related as much to the question of the country of qualification of doctors as to their ethnic origin as such. A PSI report had been published on *Overseas Doctors in the National Health Service* (Smith, 1980).

Since the last study, however, there has been greater interest in questions surrounding equal opportunities for doctors from minority ethnic groups, not least the question of whether doctors from minority ethnic groups who were born and educated in this country experienced any discrimination. We therefore asked the doctors in this follow-up study which ethnic group they considered themselves to be a member of.

Overall 91 per cent of the 1986 qualifiers (90 per cent of the men and 93 per cent of the women) said that they were of white ethnic origin; less than 1 per cent of the qualifiers (one man and no women) were of Black-Caribbean origin; 3 per cent of the qualifiers (8 per cent of the men and no women) were of Indian ethnic origin; 1 per cent of the qualifiers (2 per cent of the women and no men) were of Pakistani origin; 2 per cent of the qualifiers (3 per cent of the women and no men) were of Chinese ethnic origin; and 2 per cent of the qualifiers (2 per cent of the men and 2 per cent of the women) were of mixed ethnic origin.

There was no discernible difference between those of non-white ethnic origin and others at this stage, except that one male doctor of Indian origin was one of the three men who were not working at the time of the interview, in his case because he was studying. We asked a specific question about the doctors' experience of potential or actual discrimination on the basis of ethnic origin and this is discussed in Chapter 10.

Present employment status

One of the main aims of the original study was to look at the attitudes and experience of women doctors who were not working in medicine or who were working part-time in medicine. There were concerns that the potential contribution of women doctors was not being properly exploited and the study was designed to examine ways in which this contribution could be maximised for the benefit both of the women themselves and the country as a whole. It was quite clear from the outset of the original study that many of the factors which might inhibit the development of women doctors' careers could act as constraints on the careers of men doctors.

But first it was important to establish who was doing what. There had been a broad assumption that there was a big 'pool' of non-working women doctors who, if called upon, could make a broader contribution to medicine. The last study showed quite clearly, as previous research had indicated, that the proportion of women doctors who were not working at all was very small at all stages of their careers, but that they were much more likely than men doctors to

Table 2.12   Present employment status

column percentages

	Total		Male		Female	
	1981	1986	1981	1986	1981	1986
Working full-time in medicine	86	78	99	90	73	67
Working less than full-time in medicine	10	12	1	4	19	19
Working outside medicine	0	1	0	1	0	1
Not working	2	6	0	3	5	9
Maternity leave	1	2	0	0	2	4
Working both inside and outside medicine	0	0	0	0	0	0
Working outside clinical medicine but in medically related occupation	*	1	0	2	1	1
Base: all qualifiers	*(204)*	*(229)*	*(101)*	*(105)*	*(103)*	*(124)*

be working less than full-time, or to have worked less than full-time at some point in their careers. The present study confirmed this finding, albeit with some signals that something new was occurring.

Table 2.12 compares the present employment status of the 1986 qualifiers with that of the 1981 qualifiers at the same stage in their careers. The changes are small but of interest. Among the men, 90 per cent of the 1986 qualifiers were working full-time in clinical medicine compared with 99 per cent of the 1981 men, while among the women, 67 per cent of the 1986 qualifiers were working full-time in clinical medicine compared with 73 per cent of the 1981 women.

The main difference between the 1986 men and the 1981 men was that only one 1981 male qualifier was working less than full-time in clinical medicine and none of the others was employed in any other field or was not working, while 4 per cent of the 1986 men were working less than full-time in clinical medicine (four doctors), 1 per cent was working outside medicine (one doctor), 3 per cent were not working at the time of the interview (two were studying and one was not working at all), and 2 per cent (two doctors) were working outside clinical medicine but in a medically related occupation.

Among the women, the proportion of both cohorts working less than full-time in medicine was exactly the same at 19 per cent, as was the proportion of 1 per cent working outside clinical medicine but in a medically related occupation. However, 4 per cent of the 1986 women (5 doctors) were on maternity leave, compared with 2 per cent of the 1981 women, and 1 per cent (one doctor) was working outside medicine, compared with none of the 1981 women. The more striking difference was that 9 per cent of the 1986 women (11 doctors) were not working at the time of the interview (six not working, three unemployed and two students), compared with 5 per cent of the 1981 women. (The views and experience of the men and women who were not working are considered in more detail in Chapter 7. There was little evidence that these doctors were lost to medicine in that most intended to return.)

It is not surprising that it was the presence of children which largely determined whether the women doctors were working full-time or less than full-time. Among the 23 women with children or stepchildren, 22 per cent were working full-time in clinical medicine compared with 77 per cent of women with no children, and 43 per cent were working less than full-time, compared with 13 per cent of those with no children. Nearly one fifth (4 doctors) of the women with children were on maternity leave and three were not working, compared with one woman with no children on maternity leave and eight women with no children who were not working.

It must be remembered that all but one of the women with children had children who were less than three years of age, and it is indicative of the dedication of these young women doctors that two-thirds of them were working, with more than one fifth of them working full-time.

It was interesting, but not surprising, that all the 24 men doctors with children or stepchildren were working full-time, either in clinical medicine or in a medically related occupation, but we found that among the men without children, 5 per cent were working less than full-time and 4 per cent were not working at present. It appears that the absence of children gave men more freedom in their careers, while the presence of children gave women doctors fewer options.

We were interested to see how the work of the doctors was made up. In the study of GPs we carried out after the last study of doctors' careers (Allen, 1992), it was particularly striking how complicated the packages of work were, with many male GPs having a full-time commitment made up of a full-time post combined with one or more part-time posts, while women GPs were more likely to have more complex combinations of packages of part-time posts. The 1986 qualifiers were, of course, at a much earlier stage of their careers than the respondents in the study of GPs, but nevertheless we found it an interesting exercise, particularly to see to what extent the women doctors were already experiencing the fragmentation of posts, with a number of part-time posts making up a package, which was often regarded to be useless in terms of career progression.

We found that even among these young doctors, five years after qualification, some of the typical pattern of later careers was emerging. Among the women working full-time we found that 6 per cent had more than one part-time post adding to a full-time commitment, while among those working less than full-time, over 40 per cent had more than one part-time post adding to a part-time commitment. Among the men, we found that rather more of the full-timers had a full-time post plus one or more part-time posts, reflecting the greater number

Table 2.13　Composition of work of all doctors by full-time and part-time posts (1986 qualifiers only)

column percentages

	Male			Female		
	Total	FT	PT	Total	FT	PT
Considers self to be working:						
Full-time	96	100	0	79	100	0
Part-time	4	0	100	21	0	100
Work made up of:						
One FT post with no PT work	78	82	0	67	85	0
One FT post with one or more PT posts	13	13	0	6	7	0
More than one PT post which add to a FT commitment	2	2	0	5	6	0
More than one PT post which add to a PT commitment	3	0	75	9	0	43
One PT post	1	0	25	12	0	57
Base: all in work at present (excl. those on maternity leave)	*(102)*	*(98)*	*(4)*	*(108)*	*(85)*	*(23)*

of GP principals among the men. Two of them had a package of part-time posts making up a full-time commitment, compared with five women. Three of the four men working less than full-time had a package of part-time posts and only one had just one part-time job – a quite different pattern from the women.

We look in more detail at the number of hours or sessions worked by the doctors in the next section, but we should stress that the term 'part-time' was often totally misleading when attached to the jobs of the doctors. We have noted before (Allen, 1988; Allen, 1992) that 'part-time' working in medicine is often the equivalent of more than full-time working in other occupations. We have consistently preferred the term 'less than full-time working', although we note the use of the term 'flexible working' (Department of Health, 1993). In our view, this term introduces other notions of flexibility of time or over time and does not therefore fully address the actual number of hours or sessions worked in a week by so-called part-timers. The term is a useful approach to the problems of recognising and maximising the contributions of those who do not work full-time all the time, but is not a substitute definition for part-time or less than full-time working.

Present jobs

This report is mainly concerned with the factors affecting the career progression of doctors. This section presents a snapshot of what the 1986 qualifiers were doing at the time of the interview (late summer 1991), and compares it with the 1981 qualifiers at a similar stage in their careers. Table 2.14 gives their present job or employment status and Table 2.15 in the next section shows the specialty or career in which they were working at the time. There is one important factor, which was also relevant to the 1981 qualifiers in the last study, and that is the extent to which some doctors, whose long-term aim was general practice, were actually working as SHOs in hospital medicine as part of their vocational training for general practice (*Joint Committee on Postgraduate Training for General Practice*, May 1982). Nine doctors were identified in the 1986 cohort as SHOs doing GP vocational training, although, of course, more doctors might subsequently use their experience to pursue a long-term career in general practice. It is always made clear in this report in which way these 9 SHOs are recorded. They were part of the hospital establishment, but their long-term contribution was likely to be in general practice.

At first sight, it may appear that there were few differences between the jobs of the 1981 and the 1986 qualifiers five years after qualification. Indeed, it would be unlikely that a major change would have taken place in a five year period. However, closer inspection indicate that certain trends described in interviews were apparent in this table.

The proportion of doctors working in general practice was virtually the same at 36 per cent of 1981 qualifiers and 35 per cent of 1986 qualifiers. The proportions of men and women actually working in general practice were virtually the same for both cohorts, although, as we note below, their actual grades were rather different. However, it should be noted that 28 of the 1981 qualifiers were in fact working as SHOs in hospital medicine as part of their GP vocational training at the time of the last study, compared with only 9 of the 1986 qualifiers, so that the real proportion in or entering general practice had actually declined among the 1986 qualifiers. We look in more detail at this in the discussion on Table 2.15.

The proportion of qualifiers working in hospital medicine had dropped from 56 per cent of the 1981 qualifiers to under 50 per cent of the 1986 qualifiers. This was largely accounted for by the drop from 52 per cent of the 1981 women to 44 per cent of the 1986 women, although the proportion of men working in hospital medicine also dropped from 59 per cent in the 1981 cohort to 55 per cent in the 1986 cohort. The proportion in academic medicine remained much the same at 3 per cent in the 1981 cohort and 4 per cent in the 1986 cohort, with a slight increase in the number of women.

As might have been expected, the proportion of doctors in community or public health was tiny in both cohorts, as was the proportion in other medicine (for example, private or non-clinical medicine). There was, however, an increase in the proportion of doctors who were not working, studying, unemployed, on

Table 2.14   Present job/employment/grade of doctors (main/first job)

column percentages

	Total		Male		Female	
	1981	1986	1981	1986	1981	1986
GP principal	14	16	17	23	11	10
GP assistant	1	1	0	0	2	2
GP trainee	15	7	16	5	14	10
GP locum	5	10	2	8	9	12
GP retainer scheme	1	1	0	0	1	2
Total GP	*(36)*	*(35)*	*(35)*	*(35)*	*(37)*	*(35)*
Consultant	0	0	0	0	0	0
Senior registrar	2	3	2	3	2	2
Locum SR	0	*	0	0	0	1
Registrar	29	25	29	34	29	17
Locum registrar	*	2	1	3	0	2
Senior house officer[1]	20	16	20	15	19	16
Locum SHO[1]	3	2	5	0	2	3
Clinical assistant	1	2	2	0	0	3
Total hospital medicine	*(56)*	*(49)*	*(59)*	*(55)*	*(52)*	*(44)*
Lecturer	2	*	5	0	0	1
Research fellow/asst	1	4	1	5	2	3
Total academic medicine	*(3)*	*(4)*	*(6)*	*(5)*	*(2)*	*(4)*
Clinical medical officer	1	1	0	1	3	2
Total community health	*(1)*	*(1)*	*(0)*	*(1)*	*(3)*	*(2)*
Med. officer(other)	1	*	1	0	1	1
Total other medicine	*(1)*	*(*)*	*(1)*	*(0)*	*(1)*	*(1)*
Not working/student	2	6	0	3	6	9
Maternity leave	1	2	0	0	2	4
Outside medicine	0	1	0	1	0	1
Base: all qualifiers	*(204)*	*(229)*	*(101)*	*(105)*	*(103)*	*(124)*

1. 9 SHOs who were GP trainees are included in this table as SHOs.

maternity leave or outside medicine, and this was the main difference between the two cohorts. The numbers were small overall, of course, but nevertheless they represented an increase from 3 per cent of the 1981 cohort to 9 per cent of the 1986 cohort, and, as such, gave some indication of a potential shift in employment patterns which merited scrutiny. Among the men, the increase in these categories was from none of the 1981 men to 4 per cent of the 1986 men, while the proportion increased from 8 per cent of the 1981 women to 14 per cent of the 1986 women. It should be noted that some of this might possibly have been attributed to the timing in the year of the interviews which took place in late summer in 1991, just as some of the doctors had finished their vocational training and before they had entered general practice, but not too much weight can be attached to this.

Looking in more detail at the grade of jobs of the doctors, rather more disturbing trends can be observed, particularly in the differences between men and women. For example, 23 per cent of the 1986 men were GP principals, compared with 17 per cent of the 1981 men. However, only 10 per cent of the 1986 women were GP principals. This had changed little in comparison with the 1981 women, but did not compare well with their male counterparts from 1986. At the time of the interview, only 5 per cent of the 1986 men were GP trainees compared with 10 per cent of the 1986 women, whereas among the 1981 cohort, the proportions had been more or less equal at 16 and 14 per cent respectively. The last study had indicated that women were more likely to be GP locums than men. The present study showed this trend continuing, although it should be noted that the proportion of GP locums had doubled to 10 per cent overall among the 1986 cohort compared with only 5 per cent of the 1981 cohort. There were many indications in this study that young GPs were finding it difficult to get partnerships at the time of the interviews in 1991. It appears that this trend may not have continued, although the shortage of part-time partnerships may well have continued. Only a tiny number of women were GP assistants or on the retainer scheme in either cohort, which might have been expected, given their age.

Among the doctors in hospital medicine, there was a slight difference between the cohorts in the proportion of registrars (29 per cent among the 1981 cohort falling to 25 per cent of the 1986 cohort) but these overall figures concealed a marked shift in the balance between the sexes. In the 1981 cohort the proportion of registrars was identical at 29 per cent of both men and women, but in the 1986 cohort, the proportion of men was double that of the women – 34 per cent of the men and only 17 per cent of the women were registrars, and 3 per cent of the men and 2 per cent of the women were locum registrars.

A higher proportion of 1981 men and women were SHOs compared with the 1986 doctors, although this was probably largely accounted for by the higher numbers of SHOs doing GP vocational training among the 1981 cohort. However, 19 per cent of 1986 women were SHOs or locum SHOs compared with 15 per cent of the 1986 men. 3 per cent of the 1986 women were clinical assistants.

The proportion of both cohorts who had reached senior registrar level was virtually the same at 2 per cent of the 1981 qualifiers and 3 per cent of the 1986 qualifiers, with roughly equal proportions of men and women in both cohorts. None of the doctors in either cohort had reached consultant level at the time of the interviewing, but it would have been unlikely that anyone would have done so five years after qualification.

We have already noted the fact that doctors often held more than one job. In the last study, we looked in some detail at those with more than one post, differentiating between those with academic posts who also held an honorary NHS appointment and those who held two or more completely different posts. We found that less than 10 per cent of the total number of doctors interviewed from all three cohorts (640) had more than one job. In this study we found that some 20 per cent of the doctors (24 per cent of men and 18 per cent of women) said that they did other work, either in or out of medicine. The majority of these were working in general practice which has traditionally allowed for other work, but nevertheless we were surprised to find that such a relatively high proportion of these 1986 qualifiers did other work, compared with the previous cohorts. They were mainly working as clinical assistants or as medical officers of some kind.

Specialty in which doctors working
Table 2.15 shows the specialty in which the doctors were working at the time that we interviewed them, with their sub-specialties, on which we collected details, collapsed into the main categories presented here reflecting those used in government statistics and presented annually in *Health Trends* (Department of Health). The table is presented in two ways, first showing the 9 SHOs/GP trainees in their hospital specialty and secondly showing them in general practice, to enable a longer term view to be taken of the statistics. The table should be looked at against the national statistics (*Health Trends; Department of Health Annual Hospital Staff Statistics*), but it gives a snapshot of the present specialty of the doctors and must be interpreted in conjunction with all the evidence to be presented in this report.

The choice of specialty and changes in specialty choice are discussed throughout this report. Table 2.15 shows the present specialties of the 1986 qualifiers in comparison with the 1981 qualifiers. The difference in long-term plans for general practice between the two cohorts are shown clearly in Table 2.15 (ii) where the SHO/GP trainees are coded in general practice. This shows the proportion of men in general practice dropping from 48 per cent of the 1981 qualifiers to 38 per cent of the 1986 qualifiers, while the proportion of women drops from 49 per cent of the 1981 qualifiers to 40 per cent of the 1986 qualifiers. The trends noted elsewhere of a declining interest in general practice were already apparent among these 1986 qualifiers in 1991, and there can be little doubt that they have accelerated since then.

Table 2.15(i) Specialty working in at present (main/first job) (9 SHOs/GP trainees coded in hospital specialty in this table)

column percentages

| | Total | | Male | | Female | |
	1981	1986	1981	1986	1981	1986
General medicine	5	8	4	12	6	4
Geriatric medicine	1	1	1	1	2	1
Other medical specs	2	3	3	1	1	5
Paediatrics	3	7	5	6	1	7
A and E	5	3	5	2	4	3
Surgery	8	10	14	15	2	6
Obstetrics and gynae	9	2	7	1	12	2
Anaesthetics	8	6	9	7	7	6
Radiology	5	2	5	2	5	2
Radiotherapy	*	1	0	2	1	0
Pathology	5	3	6	4	5	2
Psychiatry	9	8	7	6	11	10
Oral surgery	0	*	0	1	0	0
General practice	35	35	34	35	36	35
Community/public health	1	2	0	2	3	2
Environmental health	*	0	0	0	1	0
Others (inc occ. health govt dept.)	*	*	1	0	0	1
Maternity leave	1	2	0	0	2	4
Not working/outside med.	2	7	0	4	4	10
Base: all qualifiers	*(204)*	*(229)*	*(101)*	*(105)*	*(103)*	*(124)*

But if the doctors were not going into general practice, what else were they doing? The following analysis is based on the Table 2.15 (ii) which does give a better indication of the longer-term future. There was an increase in the proportion in general medicine, largely accounted for by an increase in the proportion of men, while women were rather more likely to be in other medical specialties. The proportion in paediatrics had increased, particularly among the women (from none in the 1981 cohort to 6 per cent in the 1986 cohort). The proportion in surgery had also increased, marginally among the men from 13 to 15 per cent, but rather more among the women from 2 to 6 per cent. However, the proportion in obstetrics and gynaecology had declined overall, remaining static among the men at 1 per cent but falling among the women from 6 to 2 per cent. The proportions in radiology and pathology had also declined, while those in psychiatry had remained much the same.

Table 2.15(ii) Specialty working in at present (main/first job) (9 SHOs/GP trainees coded in general practice in this table)

column percentages

	Total		Male		Female	
	1981	1986	1981	1986	1981	1986
General medicine	4	8	3	12	5	4
Geriatric medicine	1	0	1	0	2	0
Other medical specs	2	3	3	1	1	5
Paediatrics	2	6	3	5	0	6
A and E	1	2	2	1	1	3
Surgery	7	10	13	15	2	6
Obstetrics and gynae	4	1	1	1	6	2
Anaesthetics	8	6	9	7	7	6
Radiology	5	2	5	2	5	2
Radiotherapy	*	1	0	2	1	0
Pathology	5	3	6	4	5	2
Psychiatry	7	7	6	6	9	8
Oral surgery	0	*	0	1	0	0
General practice	48	39	48	38	49	40
Community/public health	1	2	0	2	3	2
Environmental health	*	0	0	0	1	0
Others (inc. occ. health, govt dept etc)	*	*	1	0	0	1
Maternity leave	1	2	0	0	2	4
Not working/outside medicine	2	7	0	3	4	10
Base: all qualifiers	(204)	(229)	(101)	(105)	(103)	(124)

The two tables taken together show some interesting trends, but also indicate the extent to which the SHO/GP trainees make an important service contribution in specialties such as obstetrics and gynaecology, paediatrics, psychiatry and accident and emergency. If the numbers of SHOs doing GP vocational training drop off, there may well be serious implications for the future service delivery in some of these specialties, most particularly obstetrics and gynaecology, as can be seen from the two tables. If, at the same time, fewer doctors enter such specialties for other reasons, there may well be a shortage of doctors in these specialties, and there can be little doubt that the present decline in numbers entering obstetrics and gynaecology and paediatrics can be deduced from these statistics, limited though they may be. What is more important is to examine the reasons for changing specialty choice, as discussed further in this report. And at the same time, it is important to look in more detail at the reasons for a decreased level of employment in medicine, comparing the 1981 and 1986 cohorts.

Hours of work

In the last study, there was a relatively high level of regret at the decision to become a doctor, particularly among the younger cohorts, and many indications of considerable stress among doctors in training. One of the main reasons given by doctors in all specialties was the long working hours expected of junior hospital doctors in particular. Since the publication of the last report (Allen, 1988), the hours of junior doctors have been progressively decreased, and the 'New Deal' introduced two major objectives: first, that no junior doctor should have a contract for more than 83 hours a week by April 1993, and secondly that no hard-pressed posts should be contracted to work more than 72 hours a week by December 1994. Underlying these goals was the intention that no junior doctor should have to *work* for more than 56 hours a week (Department of Health, 1991). This was certainly not the case among the doctors interviewed in the last study, and, as Table 2.16 shows, it was not the case among the doctors interviewed in 1991 for the present study.

In the last study we had found it difficult to measure in precise detail the workload of doctors, since some showed their contribution in hours and some in sessions. In this study we asked the doctors to give their weekly workload in *either* hours *or* sessions. Table 2.16 shows the number of hours or sessions worked by those in work, whether in or out of medicine – 103 of the men and 107 of the women.

Among those showing their workload in hours (84 per cent of the working men and 74 per cent of the working women), the men worked an average of 68.4 hours and women an average of 61.3 hours. Only 9 per cent of the women worked 20 hours or less a week, compared with only 1 per cent of the men, while a further 21 per cent of the women worked between 21 and 40 hours a week, compared with 15 per cent of the men. 89 per cent of the men and 66 per cent of the women worked more than 40 hours a week, and, indeed, 34 per cent of the men and 32 per cent of the women worked more than 80 hours a week. It was clear that there was an urgent need to reduce the hours of junior doctors.

Looking at those showing their workload in sessions (15 per cent of the men and 26 per cent of the women) 6 per cent of the men and 15 per cent of the women worked between 1 and 5 sessions, a further 15 per cent of women but no men worked between 6 and 7 sessions, around one third of both sexes worked between 8 and 9 sessions, while 50 per cent of men and 40 per cent of women worked 10 or more sessions. The men worked on average for 9.2 sessions and the women an average of 7.9 sessions.

It can be seen that the workload of doctors was considerable, even among those who regarded themselves as working part-time. Looking at the overall picture, it can be seen that only 8 per cent of the total doctors who were working (2 per cent of the working men and 14 per cent of the working women) were

Table 2.16   Number of hours or sessions worked per week by all those working (in or out of medicine)

column percentages

	Total	Male	Female
No. of hours			
1 - 20	5	1	9
21 - 40	18	14	21
41 - 60	18	20	15
61 - 80	23	25	19
81 - 100	29	30	28
101 - 120	5	4	4
Intermittent/sporadic	2	2	3
Average no. of hours per week	*65.1*	*68.4*	*61.3*
Base: all those giving answers in hours	*(166)*	*(87)*	*(79)*
OR			
No. of sessions			
1 - 5	12	6	15
6 - 7	9	0	15
8 - 9	32	31	32
10 and over	43	50	40
Intermittent/sporadic	2	6	0
Not stated	2	6	0
Average no. of sessions per week	*8.4*	*9.2*	*7.9*
Base: all those giving answers in sessions	*(44)*	*(16)*	*(28)*

working for 20 hours or less or five sessions or less a week. Less than half (11) of the 23 women who regarded themselves as working part-time were working less than 21 hours or six sessions. Six of these 'part-timers' were working between 21 and 40 hours a week, three were working for 6 or 7 sessions a week and three were working 8 sessions a week.

It is quite clear that 'part-time' working in medicine is by no means a limited commitment, and that full-time working is often a very great commitment, particularly among junior hospital doctors. Over half the registrars and over 40 per cent of the registrars and SHOs who gave their workload in hours were working for more than 80 hours a week at the time that we interviewed them in 1991, and two-thirds of the registrars and nearly 80 per cent of the SHOs were working more than 70 hours a week.

The workload of GPs was rather more difficult to measure since they were more likely to give their answers in terms of sessions, presenting some difficulty in interpreting the length of a session. Nevertheless, of the 75 per cent of GP principals who gave their answer in hours, over one third said that they were working for more than 60 hours a week.

Private work

In the last study we found that private work in medicine was essentially a male activity and was largely restricted to doctors who had been qualified for at least ten years. For example, we found that 47 per cent of the 1966 men working in medicine and 20 per cent of the 1976 men did some private work, compared with only 19 per cent of the 1966 women and 5 per cent of the 1976 women. The proportion of 1981 qualifiers doing any private work was very limited – 7 per cent of men and 4 per cent of women.

Although the total numbers of 1986 qualifiers concerned were small (22 doctors – 17 men and 5 women), Table 2.17 shows an interesting upturn in the proportion of recently qualified male doctors doing any private work in medicine, with little change in the proportion of women. 17 per cent of the 1986 men working in medicine said they did some private work in medicine, a fairly big increase on their 1981 counterparts, compared with only 5 per cent of the 1986 women, virtually the same proportion as that found among the 1981 women.

Table 2.17   Whether any work in medicine in the private sector

column percentages

	Total		Male		Female	
	1981	1986	1981	1986	1981	1986
Yes	6	11	7	17	4	5
No	94	89	93	83	96	95
Base: all doctors						
working in medicine	*(196)*	*(205)*	*(101)*	*(99)*	*(95)*	*(106)*

The majority of the men doing any private work in medicine spent less than six hours a week on it, while the women were spread more widely, often because they were doing little or no NHS work. More than half of those doing any private work in medicine were GP principals, although one fifth were registrars, most of whom said they only did occasional private work.

Qualifications

Finally we looked at the academic and medical qualifications held by the 1986 qualifiers. All the doctors held a primary medical qualification, and all but two had a medical degree from a UK medical school. Two, both overseas qualifiers,

Table 2.18   Qualifications

column percentages

	Total 1981	Total 1986	Male 1981	Male 1986	Female 1981	Female 1986
Primary qualifications						
Degree or conjoint	100	100	100	100	100	100
BDS	1	*	3	1	0	0
BSc/BMedSci	3	13	3	14	4	12
BA	2	8	3	7	2	9
BPharm	0	*	0	0	0	1
Doctorates						
PhD/DPhil	0	*	0	1	0	0
MD/DM	0	*	0	0	0	1
Masters						
MS/MCh	0	*	0	0	0	1
MSc	1	1	0	1	2	2
MA	0	2	0	3	0	2
Diplomas						
DRCOG	23	23	19	19	26	26
DCH	8	12	6	11	10	12
DMRD	0	0	1	0	0	0
DA	*	1	1	1	0	2
DLO	*	0	1	0	0	0
Other med dips	0	4	0	5	0	4
Memberships/Fellowships						
MRCP	14	17	14	18	14	15
FRCS	2	6	5	12	0	0
FRCA	0	0	0	0	0	0
MRCOG	0	0	0	0	1	0
MRC Psych	4	3	5	5	4	2
FRCR	0	0	0	0	0	0
MRC Path	0	0	0	0	0	0
MRCGP	12	22	13	22	12	22
FC Ophth	0	*	0	0	0	1
Base: all qualifiers	*(204)*	*(229)*	*(101)*	*(105)*	*(103)*	*(124)*

had conjoint only. Very few 1986 qualifiers had conjoint in addition to a medical degree, unlike the 1966 qualifiers where the proportion who had taken both qualifications was relatively high.

The women were rather younger than the men at the time that they passed their primary medical qualification but the age distribution was very similar to that found among the earlier cohorts with the vast majority of both men and women in the 1986 cohort having obtained their primary medical qualification at the age of 23 or 24.

Table 2.18 compares the qualifications held by the 1981 and 1986 cohorts. The proportions of each cohort holding the various qualifications are very similar. In the last study we did not record the intercalated degrees, which tended to under-represent the proportion of 1981 qualifiers with BSc or BMed.Sci. degrees.

As far as higher qualifications were concerned it was clearly early days for most people. The proportions gaining the DRCOG were the same for the 1981 and 1986 cohorts, with 19 per cent of the men and 26 per cent of the women in each cohort having achieved it. The proportions achieving the DCH were also similar in both cohorts.

In terms of membership or fellowship of the Royal Colleges, the proportions passing the MRCP were similar for men and women in the two cohorts. However, the proportion of men passing FRCS was higher in the 1986 cohort, while none of the women in either cohort had passed it. A handful of male and female doctors in each cohort had passed the MRCPsych. None had passed the FRCA, FRCR or MRCPath., but this would have been expected at this stage. None of the 1986 qualifiers had passed the MRCOG, and only one woman 1981 qualifier had done so at the time of the last study, again as would be expected. One 1986 woman qualifier had passed the FCOphth. The main difference between the 1981 and 1986 qualifiers was in the proportion who had passed the MRCGP – 12 per cent of the 1981 cohort and 22 per cent of both men and women in the 1986 cohort. Much of this difference can probably be attributed to the fact that the interviews with the 1986 qualifiers took place on average six months later in their careers than those with 1981 qualifiers, although it might well have reflected a greater interest among the 1986 qualifiers in achieving the qualification at an early stage.

3   What made them study medicine?

One of the most interesting findings of the previous study was the extent to which the decision to become a doctor has such far-reaching consequences. It was considered to be difficult to change from medicine as a student or to change career having qualified as a doctor. There were clear indications that our respondents felt that having embarked on a medical school course they were expected not only to complete it but also to remain in medicine. For some the original choice had quite obviously been wrong, and there can be little doubt that some of the disillusionment with medicine that we round among the respondents from all cohorts was related to the fact that they had chosen the wrong career and had felt themselves unable to change direction.

Reasons and motivation for studying medicine

The differences between men and women in their reasons and motivation for studying medicine which had been apparent among earlier cohorts continued for the 1986 cohort. Women remained more likely than men to have decided at a very early age that they wanted to be doctors. 15 per cent of the 1986 women qualifiers had decided by the age of ten that they wanted to be doctors, which was the same proportion we found among the 1981 women, although not as high as among the 1976 women, one fifth of whom had made up their mind by that age.

The most usual time for deciding on medicine as a career was between 10 and 15 for both men and women from both cohorts, with just over a fifth of both sexes deciding at 16, as they were about to embark on their 'A' level courses. The main difference between men and women in both the 1981 and 1986 cohorts was the higher proportion of men who decided at 19 or over that they wanted to study medicine. This accounted for 10 per cent of the 1981 men compared with 5 per cent of the 1981 women, but had decreased to 7 per cent of the 1986 men compared with only 2 per cent of the 1986 women. The pressure noted elsewhere for doctors to make up their minds about a career in medicine and to get on with it as quickly as possible is reinforced here.

Why did they want to study medicine? The previous study showed an increasing tendency among the cohorts of men to say that their main reason was because they were good at science subjects at school, with 30 per cent of the 1981 men saying this compared with less than one fifth of the 1966 men. Women were much less likely to give it as a reason and only 19 per cent of the 1981 women

Table 3.01   Age when first decided to study medicine

column percentages

	Total		Male		Female	
	1981	1986	1981	1986	1981	1986
Under 10 years	10	11	5	8	15	15
10-15	43	39	44	39	42	40
16	22	22	22	24	22	21
17	13	15	17	16	10	15
18	5	7	3	7	7	8
19	2	1	3	1	2	2
20	1	1	1	1	2	0
21-24	2	3	4	5	1	0
25+	1	0	2	0	0	0
Base: all qualifiers	*(204)*	*(229)*	*(101)*	*(105)*	*(103)*	*(124)*

mentioned it. As Table 3.02 shows, however, there was an interesting convergence among the 1986 qualifiers, with 24 per cent of the men and 21 per cent of the women citing it as their main reason. As we shall see, the 1986 women were in fact better at science subjects at school than their 1981 counterparts, and were also better than the 1986 men, not to mention the 1981 men.

But is it desirable that being good at science at school is such an important reason for wanting to study medicine? The most frequently mentioned reason given by the 1986 qualifiers as a whole was that medicine was a good and interesting career. Nevertheless, being good at science came a close second among both men and women and undoubtedly dominated the decisions of a substantial proportion of both sexes, as a woman who had just returned from abroad explained: 'It was the main career choice if you were good at science. I never really found out much about alternatives – silly really – but nobody suggested I find out either. I had no noble thoughts about doing good or helping people. Medical training was simply an extension of studying sciences...'

Her view was shared by other women: 'I was best at sciences. As a career I thought of civil engineering and mechanical engineering, but they seemed very male preserves. And medicine appealed because of the combination of science and caring for people ...' and another woman agreed: 'I found myself good at science and then you find that physics is desperately boring ... Thinking back, there's stunningly little you know about it. I wanted to try for Oxbridge and so I asked myself what I could do with science. Medicine seemed an obvious choice...'

Men also seemed to choose medicine because they were good at science without any clear idea of what kind of career they were entering, like this GP principal: 'I thought that medicine would be more science orientated throughout,

Table 3.02   Main reason for first wanting to study medicine

column percentages

	Total		Male		Female	
	1981	1986	1981	1986	1981	1986
Good interesting career	20	24	24	26	17	23
Good at science subjects	25	22	30	24	19	21
Wanted to help/work with people	14	12	10	9	17	15
Always wanted to be a doctor	10	12	4	11	16	12
Influenced/suggested by friends/relations	13	12	10	8	16	15
Suggested by school	4	4	4	1	4	6
Interest in anatomy/ how body works	1	3	1	4	2	2
Wanted to be a vet	0	2	0	2	0	2
Experience of illness/ being in hospital	3	2	4	3	3	1
Job security	2	2	3	3	1	1
Thought it would be glamorous/have status	3	1	6	3	1	0
More interesting than initial career choice	*	1	1	2	0	1
Couldn't think of anything else to do	0	1	0	2	0	0
Wanted to be a medical missionary	1	*	1	1	1	0
Lack of interest in commercial occupation	0	*	0	1	0	0
Financially rewarding	*	0	1	0	0	0
Other	*	0	0	0	1	0
DK/CR	2	1	2	2	3	1
Base: all qualifiers	*(204)*	*(229)*	*(101)*	*(105)*	*(103)*	*(124)*

and it wasn't. I mean I hadn't realised how human personality considerations take over. I just wanted to do a lot more science ...' And these views were repeated time and again in these interviews.

Women respondents from all cohorts were more likely than men to have wanted to study medicine because they wanted to help and work with people, and the 1986 women continued the trend. It was interesting that similar proportions of 1986 men and women (just over 10 per cent) said that they had always wanted to be a doctor, compared with a very low proportion of 1981 men and one in six of the 1981 women.

The proportions of women who had been influenced by friends or relations was higher than men among both the 1981 and 1986 cohorts, although it was a more frequently mentioned factor among the older cohorts, with around one fifth of both men and women 1966 qualifiers giving it as a reason. There appeared to have been a rather subtle shift in the reasons for this. A relatively high proportion of the 1966 men, for example, had been the sons of doctors and appeared to be following in the family tradition rather than making a positive choice. On the other hand, among the 1986 qualifiers, there were indications of family expectations being based on other factors, as a male qualifier said: 'My mother was keen on my doing medicine – keen for me to do the right thing. She had friends who were doctors and was terribly impressed. I'm sure this must have affected me, although I regret it now. She was desperate for me to continue in clinical medicine – "My son, the doctor"...'

There were other examples of family pressure, particularly among the few qualifiers from minority ethnic backgrounds, like this man: 'I was expected to do it – family pressure. My father instilled it into me. You know Asian families – "You will be a doctor ... He's working towards medicine ..." – I heard nothing else ...'

In relatively few cases was medicine suggested by the school attended by the respondents, which was not perhaps as surprising at it seems since schools appeared to be as poor as ever in the careers advice they were able to give prospective medical students. The opposite often appeared to be true, as this woman noted in giving her reasons for studying medicine: 'It was a reaction against the careers teacher who said that girls should become nurses and boys doctors ...'

The sprinkling of people who would have preferred to be vets continued among the 1986 cohort with the rather chilling reiteration of the belief that medicine was considered less difficult than veterinary surgery, as this man explained: 'I'd always wanted to be a vet, but when I got to 16 I realised I didn't have the ability, so I decided to do medicine. I liked the idea of being a doctor, helping people, wearing a white coat etc .. I really didn't know what being a doctor entailed ...'

On the other hand, some doctors studied medicine because of their scholastic achievements, like this female general medical registrar – 'I wanted to do physiotherapy but was discouraged because I was too intelligent ...' – and a male registrar in psychiatry – 'No-one considered anything else because I was so clever – but *I* did. If I could have swapped to something else I would have ...'

A variety of other reasons were given by doctors for wanting to study medicine, with glamour gradually fading from the scene, job security rarely mentioned by this cohort of doctors, and money not at all. Religious factors which had motivated some of the 1966 women were hardly mentioned, and experience of illness, which had been more commonly mentioned among older cohorts also seemed to have less impact among these 1986 qualifiers.

Parents and relatives

The last study showed a striking difference between the 1966 and 1976 cohorts of men and the 1981 cohort, with over a quarter of the older men being the sons of doctors compared with only 12 per cent of the 1981 men. However, the 1986 men were more likely than their 1981 counterparts to be the sons of doctors, with 18 per cent coming from a medical family as Table 3.03 shows.

Table 3.03   Whether either or both parents medically qualified

column percentages

	Total		Male		Female	
	1981	1986	1981	1986	1981	1986
Father only	8	12	8	12	9	11
Mother only	2	2	2	2	2	2
Both parents	3	2	2	4	5	1
Neither parent	86	84	88	82	84	86
Base: all qualifiers	*(204)*	*(229)*	*(101)*	*(105)*	*(103)*	*(124)*

The proportion of women from medical families gradually increased from 11 per cent of the 1966 women to 16 per cent of the 1981 women, and the 1986 women showed only a slight decrease on that figure with 14 per cent of them having at least one medical parent.

In the previous study there were interesting trends in the occupation of the doctors' parents at the time they were applying to medical school, with the proportion of fathers in the two top social classes decreasing among the men and increasing among the women, comparing the 1966 and 1981 qualifiers. As Table 3.04 shows, the proportion of fathers in social classes I and II remained virtually the same among the men at just over 70 per cent for both 1981 and 1986 qualifiers, but among the women it declined from 81 per cent of the 1981 qualifiers to 74 per cent of the 1986 qualifiers. The main reason appeared to be an increase in the proportion of women coming from a skilled manual background, accounting for 10 per cent of the 1986 cohort of women.

We looked again to see whether certain occupations were reported more than others, and found that the trend noted in the last study of the later cohorts being more likely to have a teacher or lecturer father than the older doctors had continued. 12 per cent of both men and women 1981 qualifiers had a teacher or lecturer father, compared with 9 per cent of the 1986 men and as many as 16 per cent of the 1986 women.

Table 3.04   Social class/occupation of fathers of doctors at time of medical school application

column percentages

	Total		Male		Female	
	1981	1986	1981	1986	1981	1986
Professional I	39	38	33	33	45	43
Intermediate II	37	36	39	40	36	32
Skilled non-manual IIIN	7	4	5	4	9	5
Skilled manual IIIM	7	9	11	7	4	10
Semi-skilled IV	1	1	3	3	0	0
Unskilled V	*	*	1	1	0	0
Armed forces	2	1	3	1	1	2
Retired	1	1	2	0	1	2
Unemployed	*	1	1	1	0	1
No answer/dead	3	7	2	10	5	5
Base: all qualifiers	*(204)*	*(229)*	*(101)*	*(105)*	*(103)*	*(124)*

The previous study had shown an increasing tendency for the mothers of doctors to have been working at the time they applied to medical school, although more than half the mothers were said to be housewives with the exception of the 1981 women qualifiers, only one third of whose mothers were housewives. This trend had continued among the 1986 qualifiers, taking in the men as well. We found that only 35 per cent of the 1986 men's mothers and 31 per cent of the women's mothers were housewives.

As Table 3.05 shows, 40 per cent of the 1986 men's mothers and 46 per cent of the women's mothers were in occupations in Social Classes I and II, with most of these in Social Class II occupations. 10 per cent of the men's mothers and 7 per cent of the women's mothers were in the nursing profession, while 14 per cent of the men and as many as 27 per cent of the women said their mothers were teachers or lecturers. This compared with 20 per cent of the 1981 women and only 12 per cent of the 1966 women, and must undoubtedly be seen as a significant phenomenon. We noted in the last report that having a teacher as a mother may be more important for women thinking about a medical career than having a doctor as a father, and the latest evidence suggests that it is becoming more important.

Finally, we asked again whether any other relatives or friends were doctors or medically qualified, and found that 27 per cent of both men and women mentioned some relative or friend – rather less than the previous cohorts studied, among whom around one third mentioned a relative or friend. The most frequently mentioned relatives were uncles, although the proportions among 1986 qualifiers were lower than the 10 per cent of uncles found among the older

Table 3.05   Social class/occupation of mothers of doctors at time of medical school application

column percentages

| | Total | | Male | | Female | |
	1981	1986	1981	1986	1981	1986
Professional I	6	6	5	8	7	4
Intermediate II	30	38	27	32	33	42
Skilled non-manual IIIN	17	13	13	11	21	15
Skilled manual IIIM	*	2	1	3	0	2
Semi-skilled IV	1	3	1	4	1	2
Unskilled V	1	1	2	1	1	1
Housewife	41	33	50	35	33	31
Unemployed	0	*	0	0	0	1
Student	*	*	0	0	2	1
No answer/dead	1	3	1	5	2	2
Base: all qualifiers	*(204)*	*(229)*	*(101)*	*(105)*	*(103)*	*(124)*

cohorts. Aunts were more frequently mentioned by the 1986 cohort than by the older cohorts, but 7 per cent of the 1986 cohort mentioned a medical grandfather which was rather higher than the older cohorts. As with the earlier qualifiers, around 10 per cent of the 1986 qualifiers mentioned other relatives, and around 10 per cent had medically qualified family friends.

Of the 1986 qualifiers with medically qualified parents, friends or relations, there was little evidence of really strong family influences to study medicine, unlike earlier cohorts of qualifiers. Only three 1986 qualifiers said they were highly influenced by family or friends, compared with over 10 per cent of all the cohorts in the last study. Indeed, around half the men and over a quarter of the women said that they had not been influenced in their decision to study medicine by any of these people. However, a quarter of the women and one sixth of the men had found the work of their friend or relation interesting or stimulating, and a quarter of the men but less than one in ten of the women said that they might have been influenced without being aware of it at the time.

Schools
The type of school attended by the doctors has all kinds of interesting implications. In the previous study, we saw clear evidence of the move away from independent single-sex boarding schools, particularly among the men but also among the women, from 29 per cent of the 1966 men to 14 per cent of the 1981 men and from 20 per cent of the 1966 women to 13 per cent of the 1981 women.

Table 3.06(i) Type of secondary school attended by male qualifiers

column percentages

	Boys only school		Mixed school	
	1981	1986	1981	1986
Independent boarding	14	8	5	8
Independent day	10	12	1	5
Direct grant	13	7	2	2
Grammar	22	18	11	15
Comprehensive	2	7	22	30
Technical	1	0	1	1
6th form/tertiary college	0	0	2	5
Secondary modern	1	0	1	0
Other/overseas	0	1	0	0
Base: all male qualifiers	*(101)*	*(105)*	*(101)*	*(105)*

Table 3.06(ii) Type of secondary school attended by female qualifiers

column percentages

	Girls only school		Mixed school	
	1981	1986	1981	1986
Independent boarding	13	6	4	4
Independent day	11	15	2	6
Direct grant	20	9	0	0
Grammar	28	21	12	6
Comprehensive	5	6	17	30
Technical	0	0	2	0
6th form/tertiary college	0	1	1	6
Secondary modern	0	1	0	2
Other/overseas	0	2	2	3
Base: all female qualifiers	*(103)*	*(124)*	*(103)*	*(124)*

As Tables 3.06(i) and (ii) show, the proportions who had attended such schools had declined to only 8 per cent of the 1986 male qualifiers and 6 per cent of the 1986 female qualifiers. The proportion of men attending mixed boarding schools had increased slightly to 8 per cent of the 1986 men and had remained static at 4 per cent of the 1986 women.

The proportions of men and women attending independent day schools had increased slightly between the 1981 and 1986 cohorts, while the proportion of both sexes attending direct grant schools had fallen sharply as the tables show.

On the other hand, 33 per cent of the male qualifiers from both 1981 and 1986 had attended a grammar school, compared with 40 per cent of the 1981 women and 27 per cent of the 1986 women. The most striking change, however, was in the proportion of qualifiers attending comprehensive schools, rising from 24 per cent of the 1981 men to 37 per cent of the 1986 men and rising in a similar proportion from 22 per cent of the 1981 women to 36 per cent of the 1986 women.

Another feature of interest was the presence of 6th form or tertiary colleges in the table. These took qualifiers from all types of schools. There is naturally some double counting of schools in Table 3.06, not only among those who attended 6th form colleges, but also among those who attended more than one type of school before the age of 16. Nevertheless, the trends remain clear over the years.

Table 3.07   **Proportion of medical qualifiers attending grammar or comprehensive schools (mixed or single sex)**

column percentages

| | Male qualifiers | | | |
	1966	1976	1981	1986
Grammar schools	44	45	33	33
Comprehensive schools	4	6	24	37
Total: grammar *or* comprehensive	48	51	57	62*
Base: all male qualifiers	*(108)*	*(105)*	*(101)*	*(105)*

*   9 per cent of 1986 male qualifiers attended both grammar *and* comprehensive schools

| | Female qualifiers | | | |
	1966	1976	1981	1986
Grammar schools	50	44	40	27
Comprehensive schools	4	15	22	36
Total: grammar *or* comprehensive	54	59	62	60*
Base: all female qualifiers	*(118)*	*(105)*	*(103)*	*(124)*

*   3 per cent of 1986 female qualifiers attended both grammar *and* comprehensive schools.

Table 3.07 shows the steadily increasing proportion of male medical qualifiers who had attended grammar or comprehensive schools. However, a slightly lower proportion of 1986 women than 1981 women had attended grammar or comprehensive schools, largely due to the marked drop in grammar school attendance, from 40 per cent of the 1981 women to 27 per cent of 1986 women. It will be noted that as many as 9 per cent of the 1986 men had attended both grammar and comprehensive schools, compared with 3 per cent of the women.

We observed in the last report that even if the class background of doctors had not changed greatly over the years, their schooling was beginning to reflect more closely that of their contemporaries. The present study indicates that this trend had continued, and that the traditional old-boy network said to be dominant in medicine was being replaced by an altogether more varied picture of schooling, with a considerable decline over the years in the proportions of doctors attending single-sex boarding schools, and a concomitant increase in the proportions attending mixed state schools.

'A' levels and Scottish Highers
Increasing concern has been expressed over the years at the ways in which medical students have been selected. It was generally agreed that selection based on whether a student was good at sport or had a father who had attended the same medical school was both undemocratic and unlikely to provide high quality medicine. However, in recent years, doubts have been expressed about whether selection based mainly or solely on 'A' level results necessarily resulted in good doctors who were happy in their work and provided the best patient care.

The last study showed clearly the increasing proportions of qualifiers who had studied three or four science subjects at 'A' level, with particular trends towards biology and maths. It also showed the strong improvement between 1976 and 1981 of the 'A' level grades among the men, although the women's results remained much the same.

Altogether 205 1986 qualifiers (90 per cent of the total sample – 98 men and 107 women) had passed any 'A' levels and 22 (10 per cent of the total sample – 7 men and 15 women) had passed any Scottish Highers. Again the proportion of 1986 women (18 per cent) taking Scottish Highers was more than double that of the men (7 per cent), thus continuing the tradition noted in the last report of Scottish women entering medicine. (Two doctors had overseas qualifications which qualified them for UK medical school entry.)

What subjects had they passed? Comparing their 'A' level results with those of the 1981 qualifiers, it was noteworthy that the proportion of men passing physics had changed very little at around 90 per cent, while the proportion of women had dropped from 83 per cent to 72 per cent. On the other hand the proportions passing mathematics had increased from around one third of both sexes to 45 per cent of the men and as many as 52 per cent of the women. An interesting trend among both sexes was the decline in the proportion passing

Table 3.08   Subjects passed at 'A' level

column percentages

	Total 1981	Total 1986	Male 1981	Male 1986	Female 1981	Female 1986
Physics	88	80	92	89	83	72
Chemistry	94	96	93	96	94	95
Biology	81	71	80	71	82	71
Zoology	6	3	5	2	7	5
Botany	0	*	0	0	0	1
Maths(1)	35	49	34	45	36	52
Maths(2)	*	6	*	5	*	7
Other/combined science	8	4	12	7	4	1
Arts subject(1)	28	25	30	24	26	26
Arts subject(2)	6	3	4	2	7	4
Arts subject(3)	3	1	1	1	5	2
Base: all qualifiers with any 'A' levels	*(178)*	*(205)*	*(91)*	*(98)*	*(87)*	*(107)*

biology, from over 80 per cent of the 1981 qualifiers to 71 per cent of the 1986 qualifiers.

The proportions passing an arts subject at 'A' level, mostly General Studies, remained the same among the women at a quarter, but dropped from nearly one third of the 1981 men to just under a quarter of the 1986 men. The proportion with three Arts 'A' level subjects remained very small.

Among those passing Scottish Highers, the proportion passing mathematics remained higher than among those taking 'A' levels, as did the proportion passing two or three arts subjects. All those with Scottish Highers had passed both physics and chemistry, continuing the pattern noted in the last report.

What kind of grades did they get? We have noted increasing concerns that medical students were being recruited on the basis of good 'A' level results, and there can be little doubt that there has been a strong impression among prospective students and their schools that medicine was a likely option only for those with three A grades or at least AAB grades at 'A' level.

All but one of those with 'A' levels had passed in at least three subjects. 15 per cent of the total (19 per cent of men and 14 per cent of women) had passed in at least four subjects. (In a handful of cases these were people who had retaken their 'A' levels, but the most common pattern was for people to have taken three science subjects and General Studies.)

As in the last study, we analysed the results in a variety of ways and concluded that the most meaningful and replicable analysis was a tabulation of

Table 3.09   Subjects passed at Scottish Higher

column percentages

	Total 1981	Total 1986	Male 1981	Male 1986	Female 1981	Female 1986
Physics	100	100	100	100	100	100
Chemistry	100	100	100	100	100	100
Biology	73	82	83	86	64	80
Combined science	0	9	0	0	0	13
Maths(1)	88	95	83	100	93	93
Maths(2)/other science	12	14	17	14	7	13
Arts subject(1)	100	100	100	100	100	100
Arts subject(2)	92	86	83	71	100	93
Arts subject(3)	38	41	17	43	57	40
Base: all qualifiers with any Scottish Highers	*(26)*	*(22)*	*(12)*	*(7)*	*(14)*	*(15)*

the three best 'A' level results, excluding General Studies, which is not usually given the same weight as other subjects by selectors for medical school.

The 'A' level grades were allocated points on the conventional system of A=5, B=4, C=3, D=2 and E=1. Table 3.10 presents the findings, showing those with 15 points (three A grades), those with 14 points and over, 12 points and over, 10 points and over and those with less than 10 points. We compare the 1986 results with those of both the 1976 and 1981 qualifiers.

Table 3.10   'A' level results of 1976, 1981 and 1986 qualifiers: three best 'A' levels (excluding general studies)

column percentages

	Male 1976	Male 1981	Male 1986	Female 1976	Female 1981	Female 1986
No. of points						
15	12	21	12	14	11	25
14 and over	27	34	39	29	25	42
12 and over	52	71	79	62	64	77
10 and over	73	95	95	85	89	97
Less than 10	28	4	5	14	11	3
Mean score	*11.3*	*12.6*	*12.7*	*12.0*	*12.0*	*12.9*
Base: all qualifiers with three or more 'A' levels	*(94)*	*(89)*	*(98)*	*(85)*	*(85)*	*(106)*

The most striking feature of Table 3.10 is the fact that 25 per cent of the 1986 women with 'A' levels achieved 15 points – three A grades – compared with only 12 per cent of the men, who did rather less well in this respect than their 1981 counterparts, over a fifth of whom had achieved 15 points. However, 39 per cent of the 1986 men achieved 14 points or over compared with 34 per cent of the 1981 men, and their results were slightly better overall than the 1981 men, with a mean score of 12.7 compared with 12.6. Both of these mean scores were considerably higher than the 11.3 of the 1976 men.

The 1986 women scored consistently higher than both the 1976 and 1981 women, not only in the proportions gaining high grades, but also in the mean score, which rose from 12.0 for both the 1976 and 1981 women qualifiers to 12.9 for the 1986 qualifiers. With this mean score they also outpointed the 1986 men, and, indeed did better than the 1986 men not only in the proportion gaining 15 points but also with 42 per cent of them gaining 14 points or more. There can be little doubt that the 1986 women were very high achievers in terms of 'A' level results.

These results tend to confirm the received wisdom that good 'A' results increasingly provided a passport to medical school, but to indicate that it was not necessary to gain at least an AAB in the early 1980s, since well over half the 1986 qualifiers taking 'A' levels did no such thing. However, the table shows quite conclusively that a score of less than 10 points was virtually a disqualification for medical school entry for these 1986 qualifiers, which is a sobering thought when it is noted that 28 per cent of the 1976 male qualifiers gained less than 10 points in their three best 'A' levels. Given that these qualifiers would have entered medical school in 1971 and 1981 respectively, it would be interesting to know what grades their counterparts entering medical school in 1991 had achieved.

We have already noted the shift in the pattern of subjects taken at 'A' level. Table 3.11 shows some of the remarkable changes over the years in the proportions gaining grades A and B in the four main subjects of physics, chemistry, biology and mathematics. The proportions of both men and women gaining an A or B in all four subjects increased between the 1981 and 1986 qualifiers, with the exception of men and mathematics where the proportions remained the same – at 77 per cent.

As might have been expected from the overall results, the 1986 women showed the more notable improvement, particularly in the proportions gaining A grades in physics, chemistry and maths. In fact, 48 per cent of the 1986 women gained an A grade in maths, compared with only 19 per cent of the 1981 women and 36 per cent of the 1986 men. A higher proportion of 1986 women scored A grades in each of the four subjects compared with the 1986 men, whereas the reverse had been true among the 1981 qualifiers in every subject but biology.

Table 3.11   Proportion of qualifiers passing 'A' level Physics, Chemistry, Biology, Maths with A or B grades

column percentages

	Male 1976	1981	1986	Female 1976	1981	1986
Physics						
A	24	36	24	29	18	30
B	24	35	52	31	40	31
A + B	48	71	76	60	58	61
Base: those taking						
Physics	*(89)*	*(84)*	*(87)*	*(85)*	*(72)*	*(77)*
Chemistry						
A	37	48	49	37	34	52
B	29	34	37	42	49	38
A + B	66	82	86	79	83	90
Base: those taking						
Chemistry	*(89)*	*(85)*	*(94)*	*(86)*	*(82)*	*(102)*
Biology						
A	38	41	49	48	63	63
B	32	36	44	34	25	28
A + B	70	77	93	82	88	91
Base: those taking						
Biology	*(65)*	*(73)*	*(70)*	*(65)*	*(71)*	*(76)*
Maths						
A	33	48	36	24	19	48
B	33	29	41	35	45	27
A + B	66	77	77	59	64	75
Base: those taking						
Maths	*(24)*	*(31)*	*(44)*	*(17)*	*(31)*	*(56)*

'A' levels and school

Given the increasing proportions of qualifiers attending state schools, particularly comprehensive schools, and given the increasing concern about standards in state schools over the period, we conducted an analysis for this report of the 'A' level results by type of school attended by the 1986 qualifiers.

Table 3.12 shows the points achieved in 'A' levels achieved by qualifiers attending different types of schools. We have already noted that some qualifiers attended more than one type of school, most often a comprehensive and a grammar school. For the purposes of this table therefore, we have categorised these qualifiers by those who attended a grammar school and not a comprehensive, those who attended a comprehensive and not a grammar school

Table 3.12 **'A' level results: points achieved in three best 'A' levels (excluding general studies) by type of school attended by 1986 qualifiers**

column percentages

	Total	Indep.	Dir. grant	1986 Males Grammar only	Comp. only	Comp & grammar	(Comp. or grammar)	Others*
No. of points								
15	12	10	0	33	0	0	(14)	14
14 and over	39	45	25	54	23	22	(36)	71
12 and over	79	81	88	75	81	56	(75)	100
10 and over	95	100	100	88	96	89	(92)	100
Less than 10	5	0	0	12	4	11	(8)	0
Mean score	*12.7*	*12.9*	*12.9*	*12.9*	*12.4*	*11.9*	*(12.5)*	*13.9*
Base: all male qualifiers with three or more 'A' levels	*(98)*	*(31)*	*(8)*	*(24)*	*(26)*	*(9)*	*(59)*	*(7)*

* 'Others' includes 6th form colleges and includes qualifiers who attended other schools (including grammar or comprehensive) before

column percentages

	Total	Indep.	Dir. grant	1986 Females Grammar only	Comp. only	Comp. & grammar	(Comp. or grammar)	Others*
No. of points								
15	25	27	18	23	30	0	(25)	21
14 and over	42	43	64	33	43	25	(38)	29
12 and over	77	80	82	77	77	100	(78)	64
10 and over	97	93	100	97	100	100	(98)	100
Less than 10	3	7	0	3	0	0	(2)	0
Mean score	*12.9*	*13.0*	*13.4*	*12.7*	*13.1*	*12.8*	*(12.9)*	*12.8*
Base: all female qualifiers with three or more 'A' levels	*(106)*	*(30)*	*(11)*	*(30)*	*(30)*	*(4)*	*(64)*	*(14)*

* 'Others' includes 6th form colleges and includes qualifiers who attended other schools (including grammar or comprehensive) before.

and those who attended both. (We have noted in the column in brackets the results obtained by qualifiers who attended a grammar *or* comprehensive school, ie an addition of the previous three columns.) In addition, some qualifiers took their 'A' levels at 6th form or tertiary colleges, which accounts for some double counting among the first five columns with the last column. The increasing proportion of those attending 6th form or tertiary colleges will make the analysis even less clear in future.

It can be seen from Table 3.12 that men attending independent schools achieved the same mean score of 12.9 as those who had attended both direct grant and grammar schools. One third of the men who attended grammar schools achieved three As at 'A' level, compared with 10 per cent of those attending independent schools, and over half those attending grammar schools achieved 14 points or more, compared with 45 per cent of those attending independent schools and a quarter of those attending direct grant or comprehensive schools. The mean score of those attending comprehensive schools was 12.4 but higher proportions of them achieved over 10 points than was found among those attending grammar schools.

Looking at the performance of those attending state schools (either comprehensive of grammar schools) compared with those attending independent schools it can be seen that there was relatively little difference, with a mean score of 12.9 for independent schools and 12.5 for state schools.

It should be noted that the performance of those attending sixth form or tertiary colleges was better on average than any others, but this finding should be treated with caution, since the base was tiny and the students were mostly included in the other categories in any case.

Among the women, it can be seen that 30 per cent of those attending comprehensive schools achieved three As or 15 points, compared with 27 per cent of those attending independent schools, 23 per cent of those attending grammar schools, and 18 per cent of those attending direct grant schools. Women attending comprehensive schools had a mean score of 13.1 compared with 13.0 for those attending independent schools, although the highest mean score was found among women attending direct grant schools.

A comparison of the mean scores of women attending independent schools (13.0) and state schools (12.9) shows virtually no difference, with little discernible difference in the proportions scoring the relative numbers of points.

Essentially this table indicates that there is little or no difference among the qualifiers according to the type of school they attended. If they meet the entrance requirements they can get into medical school. Independent school entrants were still over-represented among medical school entrants among the 1986 qualifiers, but there are almost certainly reasons for this other than straightforward academic achievement at 'A' level.

Careers advice at school on medicine

The last report showed the paucity of careers advice at school among qualifiers from all cohorts about a career in medicine, a fact which was all the more alarming given the considerable disenchantment with medicine found among so many of our respondents, combined with their perception that it was very difficult to change direction once a medical student.

In the last study, the proportions of those who said they had had no careers advice at all at school dropped from around three-quarters of the 1966 cohort to around 40 per cent of the 1981 cohort. However, Table 3.13 shows little or no improvement in this respect, since just over 40 per cent of the 1986 qualifiers also said they had had no careers advice about medicine at school. There was a marginal increase in the proportion who said that the careers teacher had given some, but the third most frequent comment among qualifiers was that someone at school had tried to put them off becoming a doctor, reflecting the experience of earlier cohorts.

Both men and women had been discouraged from contemplating medical school, like this male GP principal: 'The regional careers adviser for the county said – "Do you see that pile of books in the corner? Look through them and find something else because you'll never get into medical school" ...' – and a woman clinical assistant – 'They said there wasn't much chance of getting into medical school from a comprehensive school. They didn't know too much about it and had never had anyone else from that school going to medical school ...'

In some cases the discouragement only stiffened the doctors' resolve, but it is depressing that so many hurdles were put in the way of aspiring doctors, like this woman psychiatric registrar: 'I was told I shouldn't apply by my headmaster and science teachers because I was a woman and because I came from a comprehensive school and because my father wasn't a doctor. My headmaster said these factors mattered and to apply for pure science or engineering. It actually made me more determined ...'

Around one in ten of the doctors had been given written information, although this was not always thought to have been accurate, as a male locum GP remarked: 'It said that a degree in medicine opened doors to a whole variety of professions. I only found out later that this was wrong ...' There were criticisms of medical school prospectuses, some of which were said to be glossy and attractive, while others were 'just photostats' – 'It doesn't reflect the quality of the medical school, only the quality of the publicity office ...' as a male GP trainee noted.

Specialist speakers were not always found to be reliable, and there were a number of bitter remarks from our respondents, like a woman surgical SHO: 'The thing they don't tell you is how difficult it to be a doctor. They can't tell you what it's like to be up at night and on call – and the appalling career structure – and safe jobs – they don't tell you that it's not a safe job ...'

But some had received excellent advice from specialist sources, like this woman psychiatric registrar: 'My biology teacher took me to see a postgraduate dean in medicine to talk to him personally. Also there was a residential course

Table 3.13   Nature of careers advice at school about medical career/entering medical school

column percentages

	Total		Male		Female	
	1981	1986	1981	1986	1981	1986
Did not have any	39	41	40	42	39	40
Careers teacher gave some	24	28	29	30	19	26
Tried to put me off/ told very difficult to get into medical school	16	15	17	16	16	15
Written information given	7	9	5	8	9	10
Careers evening/ specialist speaker	10	9	10	8	10	10
Suggested I apply to medical school	5	8	4	5	7	11
Other teacher gave advice	2	6	0	7	0	5
Arranged visit to medical school/hospital	1	3	0	2	0	3
Told my qualifications not good enough	5	2	4	1	7	3
Gave bad/misleading advice	1	2	0	2	0	2
Told not suitable career for girl	2	1	0	0	5	2
Independent/vocational advice	1	1	0	1	0	1
Base: all qualifiers	*(204)*	*(229)*	*(101)*	*(105)*	*(103)*	*(124)*

for sixth formers in a boarding school in the Christmas holidays and doctors came and talked to you. The school put me in touch with that ...'

There was certainly evidence of misleading advice: 'The chemistry teacher said, "Under no circumstances apply to London medical schools – it's very difficult to get in." Absolute rubbish! The opposite was true – Leeds wanted three As and London would accept three Cs ...' And some qualifiers were pushed into certain directions by their schools with little thought of their aptitudes or inclinations, like this male GP principal: 'I loved science and maths. At my school it was so clearcut it was ridiculous. If you were arts you did law, and if you were science you did medicine. Dentistry was for people who didn't get the grades ...'

Some of the advice was rather opaque, such as the only words of wisdom given to a woman GP locum: 'I was told to take an umbrella with me when I went for the interview ...' She was accepted, but who knows on what grounds?

Table 3.14   Rating of careers advice on medicine received at school

column percentages

| | Total | | Male | | Female | |
	1981	1986	1981	1986	1981	1986
Very good	2	1	3	1	1	1
Good	7	6	10	7	4	5
Fair	12	14	11	13	13	15
Poor	21	15	21	15	20	15
Very poor	21	26	19	27	22	26
Had none	36	38	37	38	35	38
Didn't want/need any	2	*	0	0	5	1
Base: all qualifiers	*(204)*	*(229)*	*(101)*	*(105)*	*(103)*	*(124)*

Table 3.13 indicated that if advice was given at school it tended to be discouraging rather than encouraging, so we were not surprised to find that, like earlier cohorts, the 1986 qualifiers were overwhelmingly critical of the careers advice on medicine they had received at school. As Table 3.14 shows, only 1 per cent of both men and women rated the careers advice from school as very good and a further 6 per cent thought it good. Around one in six of both sexes thought it was fair, but over 40 per cent rated it poor or very poor while nearly the same proportion insisted that they had had none at all. There was little to choose between the different types of schools, and the main message which emerged was that careers advice on medicine at school was in great need of attention if young people are not to embark on the wrong career.

We have noted before that it may not matter too much in most subjects if students change course, and there may be few obstacles put in the way of people who wish to change. But medicine continues to be different, and there are undoubtedly many factors which operate to make it difficult for medical students to change course, particularly once they have entered their clinical training. There appears to be an urgent need for all prospective medical students to be given a realistic idea of the true implications of studying medicine, and, at the same time, for a proper exploration of the alternatives. At the moment it appears that the tradition continues and that discouraging and negative comments at schools may be putting off good prospective students, that people who are good at science are encouraged to study medicine, irrespective of whether it is a suitable career choice for them, and that far too little soundly-based information is available to the full range of sixth formers in the full range of schools. Determined efforts have been made over the past few years to improve the advice (Richards, 1990), but this is insufficient if the actual advice in schools remains as poor as it appears to be.

4 Medical school

The last report showed how little prospective medical students knew about what they were undertaking when they applied for medical school, either in terms of workload as a student, or in terms of stress, but most important, in terms of what it meant to be a doctor. The aim of most respondents had been to achieve a place at medical school with little conception of what would happen to them thereafter. Many of the later regrets we noted often appeared to have had their roots in the fact that doctors had made a decision to study medicine with little or no appreciation of the implications of this decision, which in some cases was clearly the wrong choice for them.

There appeared to be little change among the 1986 qualifiers, many of whom reflected the experience of earlier generations, with little or no careers advice at school about a medical career, with an assumption that being good at science was in some way an indication for studying medicine, and with very vague ideas of what 'being a doctor' actually entailed.

Desire to study medicine
In the previous study we found that later qualifiers appeared less highly motivated to study medicine than the earlier cohorts of qualifiers and that the women were more highly motivated than the men. This was particularly true of the 1966 women, 75 per cent of whom said that their desire to study medicine had been 'very strong' when they started medical school, compared with just over 60 per cent of the 1966 men.

Table 4.01 compares the strength of desire to study medicine on entry to medical school among the 1976, 1981 and 1986 qualifiers. It can be seen that the pattern has changed. The 1986 men were rather more likely than the 1981 men to show a strong or very strong desire to study medicine, while the 1986 women continued the trend for women to be less enthusiastic in each successive cohort. The proportion of women indicating a very strong desire to study medicine had declined steadily from the 75 per cent of the 1966 cohort to only 52 per cent of the 1986 cohort. This proportion was in fact below that of the 1986 men.

It is noteworthy that a relatively high proportion of the 1986 women indicated only a lukewarm interest in medicine, with over 10 per cent saying that their strength of desire to study medicine had been weak or not very strong at entry to medical school. This proportion was second only to that found among the 1966

Table 4.01   Strength of desire to study medicine on entry to medical school

column percentages

| | Male | | | Female | | |
	1976	1981	1986	1976	1981	1986
Very strong	60	49	55	69	63	52
Strong	11	22	24	14	17	20
Fairly strong	22	22	15	12	13	16
Not very strong	4	6	6	5	6	10
Weak	3	2	0	0	1	1
Base: all qualifiers	*(105)*	*(101)*	*(105)*	*(105)*	*(103)*	*(124)*

male qualifiers, some of whom had clearly drifted into medicine because they could not think of anything else to do.

There were interesting changes among the women. Whereas only 12 per cent of the 1966 women said their desire to study medicine was only fairly strong or weaker than that, the proportion among 1986 women was 27 per cent. There can be little doubt that the passionate desire to study medicine found among many of their counterparts twenty years before was burning far less fiercely among these young women, and the implications of this for their future careers are difficult to forecast.

Career preferences at start of medical school
One of the main features of this research has been the mapping of career intentions at particular points in doctors' careers: at entry to medical school, at qualification, at the end of their pre-registration years and at the time of the interview. In addition we collected full details of their careers in their curriculum vitae, including times when they were abroad, not working, bringing up families or working outside medicine.

The doctors' career intentions at the four main stages outlined above are brought together in Table 7.05 in Chapter 7, but Table 4.02 shows the broad outlines of their career intentions when they entered medical school.

The most marked change to be noted is the dramatic decline in the proportion of women doctors who said that they had no clear idea at entry to medical school of what specialty they wanted to pursue – from 59 per cent of the 1981 women qualifiers to only 35 per cent of the 1986 women. This trend was also found among the men – from 52 per cent of the 1981 men to 41 per cent of the 1986 men, but was not as marked as among the women. However, in both cases it represented a definite shift, in that well over 50 per cent of all the previous cohorts of both men and women had no clear career intention at entry to medical school.

Another interesting feature of the table is the increase in the proportion of men who wanted to pursue a hospital specialty – from 26 per cent of the 1981

Table 4.02   Career intention at entry to medical school

column percentages

	Total		Male		Female	
	1981	1986	1981	1986	1981	1986
Hospital specialty	20	31	26	39	14	24
General practice	22	24	19	17	25	31
Community/public health	0	0	0	0	0	0
Other[1]	2	7	3	3	2	10
None/no clear idea	56	38	52	41	59	35
Base: all qualifiers	*(204)*	*(229)*	*(101)*	*(105)*	*(103)*	*(124)*

1. Includes go abroad, choice of two specialties, research and non-clinical medicine.

men to 39 per cent of the 1986 men. This was a marked increase over all the previous cohorts. Among the 1986 women, the 24 per cent wishing to enter hospital medicine reversed the trend among the 1981 women who had shown less interest in hospital medicine than earlier cohorts of women at entry to medical school.

The proportion of 1986 men opting for general practice at this stage was more or less the same (less than 20 per cent) as that found for all previous cohorts, but the 31 per cent of 1986 women opting for general practice showed an increase over the previous cohorts.

In common with the earlier cohorts, none of the 1986 qualifiers had even contemplated public or community health, even though this was where quite a number would find themselves later in their careers.

Doctors intending to follow a hospital specialty usually opted for the most well-known specialties, as we found among earlier cohorts. 19 per cent of the 1986 men opted for a surgical specialty at this stage, compared with 5 per cent of the women. (The proportion of men was slightly more than the 18 per cent in 1981, and the proportion of women had increased from 1 per cent to 5 per cent). 7 per cent of the men and 3 per cent of the women had opted for a general medical specialty, whereas 6 per cent of the women and 3 per cent of the men mentioned paediatrics. 3 per cent of men and 5 per cent of women mentioned psychiatry, and there were a sprinkling of mentions for obstetrics and gynaecology, pathology and one potential anaesthetist.

As can be seen from the table, a number of doctors mentioned other options, including a choice of two specialties, going abroad and non-clinical medicine.

The main message from Table 4.02 appears to be that the 1986 qualifiers were making some kind of career decision at a much earlier stage than their predecessors. They might have changed their minds again, more than once in some cases, but there was a clear indication that they felt a need for some kind of early career intention in a way that older doctors had not.

Why did they want to pursue particular specialties? As we found before, the most common reason was because it was the only specialty they knew about at the time. This was mentioned more often by the women and mostly given as a reason for deciding on general practice. However, an increasingly important reason for opting for general practice was because hospital medicine was thought to be very competitive and only for very bright doctors. The replies were strikingly consistent, ranging from a woman who was now a general medical registrar – 'I didn't think I was bright enough to do hospital medicine ...' – to a woman GP principal – 'I didn't see myself as having a career in hospital medicine, partly because I didn't think I was bright enough, but also because I wasn't competitive enough. I think a woman has to be super-competitive, not just ambitious ...' – and to a male GP trainee – 'I never thought of myself as terribly brilliant and consultants all did seem to be brilliant ...'

These replies should give cause for concern, since, as we have seen, most 1986 qualifiers had very good 'A' level results and should have had no reason to consider themselves at this stage to be less than 'bright'. It was only one of many indications found in the course of this research of the need for personal counselling, including confidence building, for medical students.

As we have seen in previous studies, women usually showed little conception of the potential constraints on family life of a medical career even when they qualified, and it was fairly unusual for women to choose a specialty at entry to medical school for this reason, as this woman GP assistant did: 'I wanted to have a family and it was about the only specialty in which they weren't so prejudiced that you could have both family and career ...'

Men in particular opted for hospital medicine because they thought it would be more challenging and intellectually stimulating. Hospital specialty choice was made for much less specific reasons on the whole, although there were some who were quite clear when they started what they wanted to do, like this woman registrar in paediatric surgery: 'I liked the thought of doing this work because of practical technical reasons. And children are good to work with – as people and as patients ...'

Men were more likely than women to say that they wanted to do surgery because they were 'good with their hands ...', while women were more likely than men to say that they wanted to pursue a particular specialty because they wanted to work closely with people. Some, on the other hand, made choices for more negative reasons, even at this stage, like a woman psychiatric registrar: 'I was never attracted to medicine as such, so this was the least medical specialty...'

Influences at medical school on specialty choice
We had been assured when we started our last study that we would find that medical students were strongly influenced to enter a particular specialty by eminent doctors with 'star' qualities. We were interested not only in the potential influence of these leading medical figures but also in establishing whether there were any other positive influences on career choice among medical students.

Table 4.03   **Whether influenced/encouraged in specialty choice at medical school by anyone**

column percentages

	Total		Male		Female	
	1981	1986	1981	1986	1981	1986
Yes member of staff	19	32	21	31	18	32
Yes fellow student	1	3	1	2	0	4
Yes other	2	1	4	2	1	1
No	78	66	74	68	81	64
Base: all qualifiers	*(204)*	*(229)*	*(101)*	*(105)*	*(103)*	*(124)*

However, as we carried out our pilot study, we found that our respondents were tending to dwell on negative rather than positive influences at medical school, including the leading medical 'stars', and so we included a question on possible discouragement at medical school from particular specialties or career choices.

Table 4.03 shows interesting changes between the 1981 and 1986 qualifiers in the increasing proportion of respondents who said that they had been positively influenced by a member of staff to pursue a particular specialty. Among both men and women the proportions rose from around one fifth of 1981 qualifiers (which had been the pattern among the previous two cohorts as well) to just under one third of 1986 qualifiers. Other positive influences, such as fellow students or other medical practitioners, were mentioned far less often, but, as we have seen before, they were often very important influences.

Who were these people with influence – and what was it about them that had encouraged our respondents? Of those who mentioned any encouraging influence, nearly half the men but only one third of the women mentioned a male consultant, compared with 6 per cent of both sexes who mentioned a female consultant. It was interesting that around 6 per cent of both sexes mentioned either a male or female senior registrar, giving perhaps a little hope that role models of both sexes were to be found more equally among younger doctors. Male professors were mentioned by 13 per cent of both men and women, a big increase on the lone female qualifier who had found a professor a positive influence among the 1981 cohort.

Male GPs were mentioned by 24 per cent of the men and 13 per cent of the women, while female GPs were mentioned by 3 per cent of men and 7 per cent of women. It was perhaps not surprising that around 7 per cent of both men and women said that they had been influenced to follow a particular specialty by a fellow student.

What had they been encouraged to do? Looking at the 1986 qualifiers as a whole, only 5 per cent of both men and women had been encouraged to do surgery, compared with 10 per cent who had been encouraged to do general practice and the same proportion to do psychiatry. A further 6 per cent had found some encouragement to do obstetrics and gynaecology and 5 per cent to do general medicine. There were limited mentions for a variety of other specialties.

What was it about these people that had influenced our respondents? The overwhelming reason given by men who had been encouraged to pursue a particular specialty was that they admired the other person's skills or ideas, while this was an incentive for only half the women. On the other hand, more than half the women said they had been encouraged by the person's belief in their abilities, a factor mentioned by less than a quarter of the men, reinforcing the need to build up women's confidence in their own abilities.

It was interesting that men in particular were encouraged into a specialty because they liked the doctor's approach to their patients, a factor mentioned by a quarter of the men but only one in ten of the women, mainly, but not exclusively about GPs. The lifestyle of GPs was also an encouraging factor for one in ten of both men and women who cited positive influences.

It was perhaps reassuring to find that there were still inspirational role models to be found by medical students, as a male research registrar in general medicine explained in referring to general medical consultants: 'It was just the way they conducted their clinical medicine and the way they taught which demonstrated that they enjoyed what they were doing. They enjoyed practising the art as well as the science. They had a well-practised bedside manner as well as being very impressive medically and academically. They were what you would want to be yourself ...'

And a male psychiatry registrar was equally enthusiastic: 'I was inspired by the psychiatry teachers. I was quite cynical at first. I felt psychiatry was incarceration and straitjackets and so on. But in fact, they took these ideas on board and argued with them. They readjusted my views ...'

Those doctors who said they were inspired by GPs they encountered at medical school often found them particularly motivating, like this woman who was now a GP herself: 'I wanted to be doing what he did. It looked like it was enjoyable and interesting. You see so many consultants in hospital who have lost their humanity through the way they trained. But he hadn't. He was still down to earth and in touch with his patients ...'

There were certainly indications that this cohort of doctors were more enthusiastic about general practice than earlier cohorts – and later cohorts for that matter, and this male GP principal explained some of the reasons: 'I respected the GPs as doctors. We had a straw poll at university in our final year and 90 per cent of us wanted to do general practice – that was 270 of us ...'

It was interesting to see whether the encouragement at medical school had had a lasting effect. The pattern was surprisingly patchy. For example, of those who had been encouraged to do surgery, well over half were still in surgery, but the rest were in a variety of specialties, including general practice. None of those who had been encouraged to do general medicine were in a general medical specialty, but over half were in surgery. Of those who had been encouraged to do general practice, most were still in general practice or in a vocational training scheme. Of those who had been encouraged to do psychiatry, only one in ten were still in psychiatry, while most of the rest were in general practice. Of course, the numbers were relatively small, but, on the whole, it appears that there are much stronger factors than encouragement or role models at medical school which affect the later career choices of doctors.

There was little doubt in the last study that doctors were much more likely to have been discouraged or put off a specialty at medical school than encouraged by staff to pursue a career in a particular specialty. But even though the 1986 qualifiers were rather more likely to have been encouraged than earlier qualifiers they were also more likely to have been discouraged, as Table 4.04 shows.

Table 4.04   Whether discouraged from any specialty at medical school by anyone

column percentages

	Total		Male		Female	
	1981	1986	1981	1986	1981	1986
Yes member of staff	34	45	27	45	41	44
Yes fellow student	5	5	6	9	5	2
Yes other	0	2	0	1	1	3
No	65	49	71	48	58	51
Base: all qualifiers	*(204)*	*(229)*	*(101)*	*(105)*	*(103)*	*(124)*

The previous study had shown an increasing tendency among both men and women for students to be discouraged from certain specialties at medical school, with women in all cohorts more likely to have been discouraged than men. The 1986 cohort followed the trend of gradually increasing discouragement, but with a disquieting jump in the proportion of men being discouraged, from 27 per cent of the 1981 men to 45 per cent of the 1986 men, almost exactly the same proportion as 1986 women, whereas the 1986 women had been only slightly more discouraged than their 1981 counterparts.

Who had discouraged the 1986 qualifiers? Over half the women and nearly 40 per cent of the men who had been discouraged mentioned a male consultant. But there was also a rather disturbing trend, noted in the last report, towards mentioning junior hospital doctors, with around one fifth of both sexes saying they had been discouraged by male registrars and over 10 per cent saying they had been discouraged by male senior registrars. Staff in general at medical school were mentioned by over one fifth of the women, but far fewer men. GPs were hardly mentioned as discouraging factors, and only a few women staff were mentioned, either by men or women qualifiers.

We had established that surgery was the specialty most frequently mentioned in terms of discouragement by previous cohorts of qualifiers. It was most often

Table 4.05   Specialty discouraged from at medical school

column percentages

	Total		Male		Female	
	1981	1986	1981	1986	1981	1986
Surgery	17	33	7	30	27	35
General practice	3	7	6	10	1	5
Psychiatry	0	3	1	4	0	2
Obs and gynae	4	6	3	7	5	6
Paediatrics	0	3	0	3	1	3
Other hospital specialty	7	6	7	4	7	8
Hospital medicine in general	5	7	9	9	1	6
Medicine in general	1	1	0	0	3	1
Community/public health	0	2	0	3	0	1
Base: all qualifiers	*(204)*	*(229)*	*(101)*	*(105)*	*(103)*	*(124)*

mentioned by women with increasing frequency over the cohorts, with as many as 27 per cent of 1981 women saying they had been put off surgery at medical school compared with only 14 per cent of the 1966 women and only around 7 per cent of men from all three cohorts.

However, there had been a radical change between the 1981 and 1986 cohorts, as Table 4.05 shows. The proportion of 1986 women qualifiers indicating that they had been put off surgery at medical school had risen to 35 per cent, but, most strikingly, the proportion of men saying this had risen from 7 per cent of the 1981 men qualifiers to 30 per cent of the 1986 men. (Indeed 70 per cent of the women and nearly 60 per cent of the men who said they had been put off a specialty at medical school mentioned surgery.)

It is difficult to account for this marked change. It seems unlikely that surgeons underwent a dramatic change in their nature or behaviour in the intervening five years as far as male students were concerned. It was more likely that the students themselves reflected the changing characteristics and expectations noted elsewhere in this report. There were many indications that this 1986 cohort were not only not prepared to admire the characteristics of 'macho' surgeons, but also that they did not accept the necessity of working very long hours under the conditions that were prevalent in the early 1980s when they were medical students. It was clear that some of those who were put off surgery, particularly the men, were not so much discouraged by the characteristics of senior doctors in the specialty, which had been such a marked feature of comments in the last study, but were increasingly discouraged by the lifestyle which appeared to be the fate of people opting for a surgical specialty, as this male GP principal explained: 'It was a rat race – hard work, long hours, no rewards till 34 – that's a third of my life ...'

His views were echoed many times by women as well as men, with other issues being noted by a woman SHO in anaesthetics: 'In surgery it was the hours the senior surgeons had to work, standing on their feet – the stamina required. And the age at which they seemed to reach consultant level. And the number of senior registrars who themselves seemed fed up ...'

However, the main reason cited by respondents for being put off a specialty was that they disliked the type of people in that specialty. There were many indications that surgeons were perceived to be different from other doctors and that the specialty tended to attract people with personalities which many of those interviewed did not wish to emulate, as a woman GP trainee noted – 'They seemed to want someone who has killer ambitions ...' Men agreed, like a general medical registrar – 'They behave like god-like creatures. Things are done through habit, not because it's logical ...' – and a research pathologist – 'Surgeons were deemed to be not very nice people – rugby types ...'

They were certainly not regarded as good role models by women like this psychiatric registrar: 'The consultant surgeons made me feel *that* high ... It was their view of life and medicine really – and to a certain extent their personalities too. Whether they'd started out like that or whether the world had made them that way – their rigidity, their lack of feeling, their narrow-mindedness ...'

Some women doctors, like another psychiatric registrar, gave graphic examples of the behaviour of surgeons, which tended to confirm some of the views expressed above: 'He said women shouldn't be surgeons. They should do things where they can't *kill* people – like family planning ...' And again women frequently alluded to the view still commonly held by staff they encountered at medical school, it appeared, that women and surgery somehow did not 'mix', as a woman GP principal explained: 'There was a feeling that women were not welcome in surgery – that women couldn't possibly do what was needed to be a good surgeon ...'

General practice was the second most frequently mentioned specialty, although doctors were less likely to have been discouraged by the people in it as by the way in which it was regarded as a 'second-rate' specialty by hospital consultants and staff at medical school, as this woman GP noted: 'My whole teaching staff assumed the "clever" students should do a hospital specialty. There was almost no mention of general practice, because it did not rate at all with them ...' A male GP principal agreed: 'The surgical registrar tried to put me off general practice. He was very unpleasant and sarcastic about my interview in general practice and said, "Don't bother to come for surgery sessions then ..." He had a very old-fashioned attitude. General practice still has a lowly status with some hospital doctors. This is especially true of London teaching hospitals ...'

It was unusual for doctors to mention being put off general practice by the people in it, although one male surgical senior registrar said: 'He was a social worker as far as I was concerned – not a doctor ...'

Obstetrics and gynaecology was mentioned more frequently by the 1986 qualifiers than by the 1981 qualifiers, often for the same reasons as surgery, and indeed the two specialties were often linked together in one answer. Consultant obstetricians and gynaecologists were often deemed to be no better than surgeons in their attitude towards patients and their general approach to medicine, particularly by women doctors: 'Their attitudes to women's health, their superior attitudes towards their patients and their junior colleagues. They were rude and unsympathetic towards their patients. And their attitude towards women students – they were more interested in whether we wore skirts than if we knew what we were talking about ...'

However, some women embarked on a career in obstetrics and gynaecology having found other specialties even less attractive, like this woman registrar: 'In general medicine they have an underhand way of appointing house officers and SHOs. How dare they plot and plan like that. I didn't like it or them. I prefer surgeons – they're pigs not schemers. I did not want to be like them or work in such a set-up ...'

The later qualifiers in general were rather less likely to say that they had been put off psychiatry at medical school than the earlier qualifiers, and the 1986 cohort followed this trend, although there were references to difficulties with patients rather than senior doctors in the specialty. Paediatrics was thought to be too demanding in terms of time and dedication by some doctors. There were one or two disturbing indications of racial remarks in a couple of specialties, although it was not possible to attribute this to anything other than the personality of the reported speaker. Other specialties attracted a range of responses, and it was clear that negative influences were at work in medical schools in most specialties.

It was not insignificant that nearly one in ten of the 1986 men and 6 per cent of the women said that they had been put off hospital medicine in general at medical school, often for reasons illustrated above, but encapsulated in the comments of a male psychiatric registrar: 'I was put off hospital medicine in general. They are rude and condescending to patients, staff, nurses and students. They are really quite amazingly unpleasant people ...'

The lack of encouraging role models, especially for women, has been a marked feature of this research, and since the last report was published (Allen, 1988) there have been a number of attempts, particularly in specialties where women have been under-represented, to increase the proportion of women, not least by attempting to demonstrate that good role models can be found. (For example, the Women in Surgical Training (WIST) Scheme was set up as a result of recommendations made in *Women Doctors and their Careers* (HMSO, 1991).) There is clearly a long way to go, as was apparent from the remarks of women qualifiers from all medical schools, including some of the newer schools where it might have been thought that attitudes were more up-to-date. This woman GP trainee had been discouraged from general medicine: 'It was the fact that I was a woman. There was a very strong anti-female atmosphere and feeling. There were no female role models at all at (new medical school). A friend and I started a "Women in Medicine" group. We were going to ask prominent local women doctors – SRs and consultants – to speak to us, but after two meetings we ran out of speakers. There just weren't any more to speak to us ...'

Careers advice at medical school

The rather alarming indication that so many career decisions were taken at medical school based on unpleasant encounters with senior doctors or negative experiences in certain specialties ran through the last study, and appeared to have lost none of its strength among the 1986 qualifiers. The relative paucity of formal careers advice at medical school was found to be a matter of concern to respondents, and the last report made a number of strong recommendations on the need to improve careers advice, information and counselling at medical school, with particular facilities available for women medical students (Allen, 1988).

In the last report, we found that, although nearly 100 per cent of the 1966 qualifiers reported that they had had no formal careers advice at medical school at all, the situation had improved slightly over the years in that over one fifth of the 1981 qualifiers said that they had some formal careers advice at medical school. As Table 4.06 shows, the improvement had continued, albeit at a painfully slow rate, since as many as 70 per cent of 1986 qualifiers still said that they had had *no* formal careers advice at medical school

Table 4.06   Formal careers advice received at medical school

column percentages

	Total 1981	Total 1986	Male 1981	Male 1986	Female 1981	Female 1986
None	78	70	80	69	76	71
Careers fairs	9	19	10	21	8	17
Careers talks/lectures	10	7	8	8	12	6
Tutor available	2	5	2	6	3	5
Written information	2	*	0	1	4	0
Interview with Dean	1	2	2	2	0	2
Clinical careers adviser	0	1	0	1	0	1
Medical Women's Federation	1	0	0	0	3	0
Base: all qualifiers	*(204)*	*(229)*	*(101)*	*(105)*	*(103)*	*(124)*

The most noticeable change in careers advice was in the increase in the proportion of respondents who said that they had attended careers fairs – rising from under 10 per cent of the 1981 qualifiers to nearly 20 per cent of the 1986 qualifiers. Careers talks and lectures remained at more or less the same level, but what was more depressing was the tiny proportion of qualifiers who mentioned careers advice from tutors or other members of the staff of their medical school. But whose responsibility was this? Was the advice available but not taken up? Did the students even know that facilities for formal careers advice existed? We asked again what formal careers advice was available at medical school, and Table 4.07 shows that students were increasingly aware that careers advice was available, but nevertheless did not take it up. The proportion of those who said that no formal careers advice was available fell from over one third of the 1981 qualifiers to just over a quarter of the 1986 qualifiers, and one in six did not know whether formal careers advice was available or not.

Table 4.07   Formal careers advice available at medical school

column percentages

	Total 1981	Total 1986	Male 1981	Male 1986	Female 1981	Female 1986
None	36	26	38	26	34	26
Careers fairs	10	27	10	30	11	25
Tutor	16	24	17	25	15	23
Careers talks/lectures	7	9	8	10	6	8
Only on request	11	7	11	7	12	6
PG Dean/Adviser	6	5	4	4	9	6
Written information	5	5	3	5	7	5
No formal/but informal	1	3	0	2	3	4
Dean/Director of Studies	0	3	0	4	0	3
Don't know	14	16	14	14	14	17
Base: all qualifiers	*(204)*	*(229)*	*(101)*	*(105)*	*(103)*	*(124)*

However, it was clear that knowledge of availability by no means ensured take-up. This was particularly marked with reference to tutors. Around a quarter of the 1986 qualifiers knew that tutors could offer careers advice. It could be argued that this was a very low level of knowledge, but nevertheless it was considerably higher than that found among earlier cohorts. However, it was much more a matter of concern that only 5 per cent of the qualifiers said that they had taken advantage of the careers advice available from tutors.

It was quite clear from the last study that tutors were in an ideal position to give medical students careers advice and counselling, but that few students saw their tutors more than once a term, if that, and that tutors were not generally regarded as potential sources of advice and counselling on anything, let alone careers. We made recommendations on the development of a tutorial system at medical schools, not only to give students careers advice but also to offer personal counselling, something which many respondents would clearly have welcomed.

The findings of the present research indicate that little had changed between the early and mid-eighties. It is to be hoped that matters have changed since.

Some of the comments on tutors at medical schools confirm the need for a much more careful assessment to be made of the role and selection of tutors. A woman psychiatric registrar noted: 'We had personal tutors allocated, but mine never contacted me. He was an anatomy demonstrator and did not like contact with students – and it showed ...' Another woman had even less contact: 'I had an interview with a medical tutor – ten minutes in three years ...' Several respondents did not think that tutors were available for careers advice – 'Tutors were for if you were having a nervous breakdown ...'

The responses to this question gave little room for complacency among staff at any of the medical schools. A male SHO said: 'There was a clinical dean whom you could make an appointment to see when the test match wasn't on. He didn't know you from Adam ...' A woman GP locum from a school at the other end of the country said: 'I didn't see the clinical tutor the entire time, apart from a tea-party when I first came. You were only seen if you failed your exams. It really was "paddle your own canoe" ...'

It was not perhaps surprising that the informal system was more highly regarded than the formal system, although again the ad hoc and haphazard nature of careers advice in medicine was demonstrated: 'You get your informal advice talking to other people at night – sitting up with your registrar ...' It could be argued that talking to over-worked disillusioned junior doctors is not necessarily the best way of ensuring that doctors receive the most appropriate advice on their own career direction or how best to develop their aptitudes and skills.

The more formal career fairs or talks were often regarded as being too impersonal, and were criticised for not giving enough information on the structure of medical careers – and how to 'work the system ...'

So how did the 1986 qualifiers rate the careers advice they received at medical school? As Table 4.08 shows, they rated it as only marginally better than the 1981 qualifiers. Essentially, the 1986 qualifiers remained as critical as the earlier cohorts of the careers advice they had received at medical school, with the main difference being the lower proportion of 1986 qualifiers reporting no careers advice at all at medical school. If they had had any, they tended to rate it as poor or very poor, with only one fifth of them rating as fair or better.

The respondents stressed the inappropriate or inadequate nature of much of the advice, the lack of advice tailored to their own personal requirements, and the lack of realistic advice on the length of time required and the demands of a career in hospital medicine, particularly the acute specialties. There were also rather ominous criticisms of the lack of advice or understanding for those who had realised at medical school that they might have made a mistake in studying medicine, like this woman: 'The advice was inappropriate because I should have left medicine. They couldn't believe how so clever a student could want to give up. I got a place on a social work course at one stage in order to convince everyone. It didn't of course, so here I am. They told me not get the failure tag ...'

Table 4.08   Rating of careers advice received at medical school

column percentages

	Total 1981	Total 1986	Male 1981	Male 1986	Female 1981	Female 1986
Very good	*	2	0	2	1	2
Good	5	6	6	6	4	6
Fair	10	12	9	10	12	13
Poor	10	20	8	23	13	18
Very poor	12	15	16	13	8	17
Had none	62	46	61	47	63	45
Base: all qualifiers	*(204)*	*(229)*	*(101)*	*(105)*	*(103)*	*(124)*

The lack of sensitivity in much of the careers advice described by doctors only serves to underline the need for a much more systematic and sensitive approach to careers advice and counselling for doctors at all stages of their careers. There can be little doubt that constructive advice and counselling at medical school would have helped many of those interviewed in this research to lead less stressed lives in specialties more suited to their personalities and indeed to have helped those who were unsuited to medicine to find another career path at an early stage. On the other hand, there were several doctors who thought that careers advice at medical school was inappropriate because it was too early, like this woman: 'You've no idea what it's like until you've qualified. If people knew beforehand, they'd drop medicine. Three people from my year have gone to do something else ...'

What improvements did the 1986 qualifiers suggest? The main improvement suggested was the provision of more information and guidance on the different specialties, as it had been in the previous study. The lack of knowledge among medical students often appeared alarming. A male GP trainee said: 'I didn't know what the requirements for being a GP were until a few months ago. I had to write to the Royal College. Nobody ever tells you really – honest to God – what being a house officer is like. It's the most terrible shock when you start. You need generalised lectures telling you how career structures are organised ...'

There was thought to be a clear need for advice on the less well-known specialties, which were thought to be overlooked at medical school, as this woman SHO GP vocational trainee pointed out: 'I've had no idea of oncology, radiology etc. – the smaller specialties – for example how long it would take, job opportunities. I've only picked up information myself recently through hard work ...'

The need for personal tutors throughout the medical school course was stressed by nearly 40 per cent of the 1986 qualifiers, a big increase on the 1981 qualifiers of whom less than one fifth of both men and women thought it would improve careers advice at medical school. It was interesting that the 1986 men were even more likely than the women to mention it. The 1986 qualifiers were certainly more aware of the lack of personal advice and support at medical school than their predecessors had been, as a woman GP principal noted: 'You should have a personal tutor all through medical school, not just for one year. Nobody ever discussed with you, on a personal level, anything about your emotional response to what you're doing, or your personal aptitude, or suggested other ways of using your skills ...'

There was no doubt that the lack of personal support at medical school was felt very acutely by many of the doctors, both male and female. There was also a clear need for discussion on the range of specialties available and how these might be suited to the student's own aptitudes and preferences. Much of the tutorial advice appeared to be negative rather than positive – 'No-one ever told you if you were *good* at anything. You only got pulled up if you were bad ...'

There were yet more indications that the selection, training and approach of tutors was a matter which needed urgent attention, as this male registrar pointed out: 'Advisers should be vetted themselves. Ours were off-putting. We were scared of them and never went near them. If they are going to pay people to do it then they should be suitable ...' And a woman GP agreed: 'They need a one-to-one approach to students – less treatment as herd animals ...'

But many doctors thought there should be much more realistic advice at medical school about the demands and constraints of a medical career, like this male anaesthetic SHO: 'Anything would be an improvement on nothing. I think, when you're a student, they should tell you more about what the job involves and they ought to stress that there are no easy options any more and that you're going to have ten years of hard slog and you're going to have to give up a large chunk of your social life ...'

Women also demanded a realistic approach at medical school, although it could be argued that if all the recommendations of this woman GP principal were put into practice, more medical students might drop out: 'Attempts should be made to inform people about what they're taking on, what they need, the cut-throat nature of specialties, some kind of grasp of medical politics – who runs the show and who will run you for the rest of your life – the Department of Health, consultants, principals in general practice. The hospital medical system allows no flexibility – no year out to work in the third world. No-one tells you there's no formal postgraduate education structure and that there are horrendous exams and that you're supposed to work 100 hours a week *and* study in your spare time ...'

It was interesting that over a quarter of the women compared with one in seven of the men thought there should be more advice and guidance on higher qualifications and examinations. It was not surprising that more women than men thought there should be more advice and information on part-time training opportunities, on specialties compatible with family life and more information about the realities of life in different specialties. Nevertheless more than 10 per cent of 1986 qualifiers mentioned each of these categories.

More careers fairs or formal sessions were suggested by less than 10 per cent of the 1986 qualifiers, and confirmed the views expressed in the last report that doctors wanted more careers advice tailored personally to their own needs, preferably on a one-to-one basis, rather than the opportunity to gain information from formal impersonal events like careers fairs.

Special careers advice for women at medical school

The proportion of doctors who thought that women needed special careers advice at medical school increased from 72 per cent of the 1981 qualifiers to 81 per cent of the 1986 qualifiers, as Table 4.09 shows. It was interesting that the proportions of men and women were more or less the same among the 1981 qualifiers, but that the 1986 men were more likely than the 1986 women to consider that there was a need for special careers advice for women – 84 per cent compared with 79 per cent of the women.

Table 4.09   **Whether women need any special careers advice or information at medical school**

	Total		Male		Female	
	1981	1986	1981	1986	1981	1986
Yes	73	81	72	84	73	79
No	25	17	24	13	26	20
Don't know	2	2	4	3	1	1
Base: all qualifiers	*(204)*	*(229)*	*(101)*	*(105)*	*(103)*	*(124)*

column percentages

Table 4.10 gives a breakdown of the type of special careers advice the doctors thought women needed at medical school. Over 50 per cent of those thinking they needed special careers advice thought they needed advice on the specialties most compatible with domestic commitments. This was a considerable increase on the proportions found among the 1981 qualifiers. The second most frequently mentioned topic was advice on specialties most compatible with part-time training, closely followed by advice on the specialties offering the best career prospects for women.

It should be noted that the 1986 qualifiers also stressed the need for *information and advice* on part-time training, a topic that was hardly mentioned as such by earlier cohorts. There were some particularly interesting comments on this question, with a number of indications that it was never mentioned at medical school, as this woman GP trainee commented: 'Nobody ever tells you about senior registrar training in any specialty part-time. You only hear about it

Table 4.10   What kind of special advice women need at medical school

	Total		Male		Female	
	1981	1986	1981	1986	1981	1986
Re specialties/career						
- most compatible with domestic commitments	34	55	41	53	27	56
- most compatible with PT training	34	41	29	39	40	43
Re specs offering best career prospects for women	35	38	38	40	32	36
Advice from women drs re their experience	15	33	11	28	19	38
Re best time in career to have children	31	31	33	33	29	29
Counselled re difficulties and prejudices will have to overcome	16	14	15	19	16	9
Information re PT training	3	10	0	5	0	15
Counselled that women as good as men	2	4	3	1	1	7
Advice re legal rights/ maternity leave	0	2	0	3	0	1
Counselled re importance of family or career	0	2	0	3	0	0
Advised to choose spec. within physical capabilities	2	1	0	1	4	0
Total: all those thinking women need special advice at medical school	*(148)*	*(186)*	*(73)*	*(88)*	*(75)*	*(98)*

on the grapevine – which is very important ...' Her experience was repeated by others, including a woman research registrar: 'It's a closely guarded secret that there *is* part-time training. Most specialties could be organised part-time but they don't even *tell* you that there are part-time posts ...'

There was a considerable increase among the 1986 qualifiers – both men and women – who thought that there should be advice from women doctors about their experience. A male surgical registrar clearly spoke from experience: 'They could talk about whose career takes precedence. It needs to be decided early on which geographical location to centre on, so that both can apply for jobs within easy reach of it ...'

On the other hand, some doctors were rather sceptical about the value of advice from older women doctors, like this male GP principal: 'The problem is there were so few – and they were very old at a senior level – peculiar elderly single female consultants. The younger grade females seemed to disappear. I know why now! I didn't notice it much then. I should have been more aware ...'

In terms of specialty choice, some men and women were worried about the idea of women moving into certain specialties only because they were compatible with domestic commitments, as this woman who was currently not working pointed out: 'The advice to women at the moment is always general practice. There should be advice on what you can do with a medical degree other than clinical medicine ...'

Around one third of respondents thinking that women needed special advice said they needed advice on the best time in their careers to have children. It was a recurrent theme in the previous study, and yet it is something which appears to be little discussed in any documents on doctors' careers. Given the length of most postgraduate training in medicine, it is hardly surprising that women are concerned about when they can fit in having babies, but little attention appears to have been paid to this problem.

Men were more likely than women to say that women should be counselled about the difficulties and prejudice they would have to overcome, possibly because women took this for granted. A male surgical registrar thought women needed a lot of practical advice on the subject: 'They need to know about the business practicalities of general practice – that they need capital, that they will not get short-listed if they haven't had their children. I don't think they know that. They get a shock when they are viewed as women and not the same as men. It's quite different from student life and attitudes ...'

There were still a tiny number of men who said that women should be counselled at medical school about the importance of choosing between a family and a career, and one man thought women should be advised to choose a specialty within their physical capabilities, but essentially most qualifiers thinking women needed special careers advice referred to practical issues surrounding specialty choice, career information and timing of families.

But why did the doctors think that advice to women should differ from that given to men? The overwhelming response from both men and women was that women needed more help than men in coping with the demands of career and family life. Nearly 80 per cent of the women stating that women needed special careers advice cited this reason. The second most common response was that women needed advice early on to prevent them making an unrealistic career choice, stated by nearly 40 per cent of the 1986 qualifiers.

Prejudice and discrimination against women in the medical profession were still thought to be rife, interestingly enough particularly by men, a quarter of whom mentioned it. The 1981 qualifiers had been much more likely than earlier cohorts to mention this as a reason for providing women with special careers advice, and the 1986 qualifiers continued the trend. It appeared that the discrimination which had been taken for granted among older doctors was no longer acceptable to many of these younger qualifiers.

A woman general medical registrar was quite clear about the reasons: 'Women need more help than men about career and family and need advice to prevent unrealistic career choices. They need advice so that they can plan when to have a family – so that they know what their options are. You cannot rely on working out options as they happen – which is how it is now ...'

And a male psychiatric registrar thought special careers advice to women was important: '... because they can end up in the "sidings" – that is general practice or minor hospital specialties or married with children and not working at all ...'

It was thought that the people giving careers advice at medical school were not necessarily sympathetic to the special requirements of women, as a woman SHO observed: 'Some consultants still tend to treat their female students as second class juniors. They value you for your efficiency and hard work but you are still not supposed to contradict them and they don't see you as potential consultants – more as staff grade or GPs ...'

It was also thought that women needed to be made aware of the potential career constraints facing them so that they were better able to plan for them, as this male GP trainee pointed out: 'Women in my year were bright and plunged head-first into hospital careers. They moved on fine until they wanted families – but now lots have dropped out ...'

But some respondents were concerned about the possibility that special advice could only serve to restrict change, as another male GP trainee noted: 'You need to tell them about the pit-falls. The danger is that this advice could perpetuate the problems – meaning that women will only go into non-acute specialties ...' Many doctors, like a male SHO in anaesthetics, thought this happened in any case: 'They get the picture pretty quickly as to which options are more orientated towards a female career. It's pretty clear that surgery is a closed book to females unless they're prepared to be very thick-skinned to survive, and work very hard ...'

The need to plan the right time to have children was thought crucial in planning medical careers. A male GP said: 'Women need advice about how to time their families. Male GPs *hate* young women trainees *without* children. They're worried about maternity leave ...' But a woman GP trainee thought this problem was rather academic: 'You're forced, in medicine, to have your children late anyhow. It's difficult to find an opportunity! Out of my year only 20 per cent are married ...'

Of the relatively few doctors who thought that women did not need special careers advice at medical school, most thought that the problems of the career structure were the same for men as for women, others thought that women should be treated on equal terms with men, others thought that medical school was really too early for women to appreciate what the constraints were likely to be, while some thought that special advice was not necessary since women were usually well-informed in any case.

Difference in treatment of male and female students at medical school

In the last study we were interested to see whether doctors thought that men and women were treated differently at medical school by staff, and if so, by whom and in what way. We wanted to know what effect any difference in treatment was thought to have, both at the time and on subsequent career choice and development.

Perhaps the most interesting finding was the steady increase over the cohorts in the proportion of qualifiers of both sexes who thought that there was a difference in the treatment of men and women medical students – from 22 per cent of the 1966 men to 35 per cent of the 1981 men and from 36 per cent of the 1966 women to 45 per cent of the 1981 women. It could be seen that although the men were generally less likely than the women to think there was a difference in treatment, the trend was clear among both sexes.

The results from the 1986 qualifiers show an interesting divergence from this trend, as Table 4.11 indicates. 50 per cent of the 1986 men thought women students were treated differently at medical school – an increase from just over one third of the 1981 men – whereas 42 per cent of the 1986 women thought so – a slight decline on the proportion of 1981 women.

Table 4.11   Whether any difference in treatment of male and female students at medical school

column percentages

| | Total | | Male | | Female | |
	1981	1986	1981	1986	1981	1986
Yes	40	45	35	50	45	42
No	60	53	64	49	55	57
Don't know	*	1	1	1	0	1
Base: all qualifiers	*(204)*	*(229)*	*(101)*	*(105)*	*(103)*	*(124)*

What were the reasons for this sudden increase in the proportion of men noting different treatment? One of the most interesting findings was that one fifth of the men saying that women received different treatment were concerned about them receiving preferential treatment from senior staff, and some of the comments were lengthy, as from this male GP principal: 'They were treated differently but not in the sexist way you might expect. They slept with senior medical staff, had them to dinner at their flats, and did deals with regard to their jobs – so they said. Well some medical staff decidedly favoured the girls. We could all see that. It occurred in no particular grade or group – some at each level.

That's the way they would have been in any job I expect. Pretty girls were favoured by the consultants. Chaps didn't apply for their jobs. It's tough in the real world. It was light relief to the hassle of hospital life I expect. But one lecturer used to announce, "I shall treat you all the same. You are all chaps to me" ...'

But many women did not see it that way at all, and this question brought forth a flood of examples of practices which could only be described as discriminatory. Unfortunately, many of the examples related to surgeons, and one fifth of the qualifiers of both sexes who thought women were treated differently referred specifically to surgeons. A woman GP principal spoke of her experience: 'I've been treated badly by consultant surgeons. The nurse was off sick so he made me do her job rather than the two male doctors I was with ...' Other women resented being treated 'like nurses' by surgeons, and reported rudeness, hostility and discriminatory remarks – 'Some surgeons would say that women were denying men a place or that they were GP fodder ...' – 'They thought that women shouldn't be there – quite disparaging, hurtful and intimidating ...' – 'There was one consultant who refused to have women on his ward round ...' – 'Women used to get reprimanded for wearing trousers, particularly in surgery and orthopaedics. We had lectures where the lecturers used to put up slides of naked women in between the educational slides – just to keep the boys awake I think. On a general level, they deprecated women at all times ...'

There were clearly problems with consultants from all specialties however, as a male GP principal reported: 'Our consultant renal physician was always going off to see his private patients in tutorial time. He said he couldn't see why women tried to do medicine as they'd only go off to "breed sometime, like an old cow". Those were his exact words. And the urology SR was always making passes at girls ...'

Women reported that senior staff tended to have lower expectations of women, as this clinical assistant noted: 'They took the men much more seriously. Most of them didn't expect the women to get very far in medicine ...' Another woman, now a general medical registrar, commented: 'One of the professors said, "Why are we wasting time on you when you'll end up washing nappies?" So we told him there were disposable nappies ... In our year, more than half the students were women ...'

Other women, like this GP trainee, thought that senior staff found it difficult to know how to treat women students: 'You weren't taken so seriously if you were a woman. You were either a swot and bound to get better marks than a man, or you were a flirt. These were the two categories you were pushed into. They couldn't accept you as you were ...'

There were a number of comments on women being regarded as more conscientious than men, but that this was not necessarily a long-term advantage, as this GP locum noted: 'They tended to favour women for junior posts because they're more conscientious and work harder. But they didn't see them as *career* doctors. Their expectations were that women would drop out and have a family, but that if you did pursue an academic career, you'd be boring – not the kind of woman they'd want to socialise with ...'

As in the last report, we found that nursing staff were thought to treat women students differently from men students. However, we found in the present research that nurses were mentioned more than any other single group – 45 per cent of both sexes who thought that women were treated differently from men by nursing staff. They were certainly thought to give women students less help, if not to treat them with hostility. A woman GP remembered her own experience: 'Nurses are very hard on female doctors. You have to prove yourself to them, and take far bigger steps not to offend them. You have to do the giving in the relationship. But you can be very lonely. Married nurses and older nurses are better ...'

The types of stereotyped views among senior staff at medical schools reported by the 1986 qualifiers must give cause for concern. The comments were consistent across medical schools and were reported by both men and women. It might be thought that doctors making some of the more extreme remarks quoted in the last report by women from earlier cohorts would have died out by the time we interviewed in 1991, but these senior staff had clearly survived or had passed their views on to their successors. It is perhaps even more alarming that they seemed to feel such little inhibition in making remarks of a kind which could have been interpreted as discriminatory under the Sex Discrimination Act. It is possible that they were not aware of such legislation.

But as we observed in the last report, much of the behaviour reported as unpleasant or intimidating to women was also found upsetting by men students. 'Humiliating' was a word used quite frequently by medical students in describing their experience with some consultants, and we noted that medical students appeared to be treated in a way that no other students would tolerate. There was plenty of evidence among the 1986 qualifiers that teaching by humiliation was still common in medical schools in the 1980s, as this psychiatric registrar observed: 'It made women very annoyed and distressed. "Character building" equals character destroying – which is what medical school is all about ...'

Among those who thought women were treated differently, over one third of the women, but rather fewer men, thought that the different treatment had little or no effect. However, a quarter of the men and one in six of the women thought that it put women off surgery, while around 10 per cent of both sexes thought it put women off other specialties, and 10 per cent of women thought it put women off hospital medicine in general. One fifth of the women, but only a handful of men, thought that it made life more difficult for women, while over 10 per cent of the men, but only a handful of women, thought that it made life easier for women.

A further 10 per cent thought that it made women more determined to succeed and the same proportion thought it made women angry. Some women were fairly sanguine about their experience, like this GP trainee: 'The attention you got was far less – and that meant less teaching. It was educating. I realised what consultants could be like and for the first time I felt at a disadvantage as a woman ...' But others became disillusioned after trying to 'buck the system', like this GP locum who was not sure what specialty she now wanted to pursue: 'It made me angry and inspired at first. I was very ambitious at first and it made me want to do gynaecology because I felt they needed more women in the specialty. But then I realised that I didn't want to spend the rest of my life on the defensive ...'

12 per cent of both sexes thought the difference in treatment made women less confident and ambitious, and this theme ran as an undercurrent through the research. Here were these exceptionally well-qualified young women feeling undermined by their treatment at medical school. Some of them would continue to under-achieve, and medicine would fail to maximise on the contribution of people who did not fit into a mould which was increasingly seen by both men and women as ill-fitting for the modern world.

Career intention at qualification

And so the doctors qualified and embarked on their house jobs. What had happened to their career choices in the five years of medical school? As Table 4.12 shows, there were remarkable similarities between the 1981 and 1986 qualifiers in their career choice at qualification, with around half the men and one third of the women from both cohorts opting for hospital medicine, and around one third of the men and just over 40 per cent of the women from both cohorts opting for general practice. There was a decline among both men and women in the proportion who still had no clear idea of what they wanted to do, with the 1986 women in particular having firmed up on their ideas by the time they left medical school rather more than the 1981 women had.

Table 4.12   Career intention at qualification

column percentages

	Total		Male		Female	
	1981	1986	1981	1986	1981	1986
Hospital specialty	41	42	50	51	32	34
General practice	37	37	33	30	41	42
Community/public health	0	0	0	0	0	0
Other[1]	2	7	3	6	4	8
Not work in medicine	*	0	0	0	1	0
None/no clear idea	18	14	14	12	22	16
Base: all qualifiers	*(204)*	*(229)*	*(101)*	*(105)*	*(103)*	*(124)*

1. Includes go abroad, choice of two specialties, research and non-clinical medicine.

Table 4.13   Career intentions from entry to medical school to qualification

column percentages

	Total		Male		Female	
	1981	1986	1981	1986	1981	1986
Intention both at entry and qualification	42	56	46	55	38	57
- Same specialty	(25)	(30)	(27)	(30)	(24)	(31)
- Different specialty	(17)	(26)	(19)	(26)	(14)	(27)
No idea at entry but intention at qualification (made up mind)	41	29	41	32	40	27
Intention at entry but no clear idea at qualification (became undecided)	2	6	2	4	3	7
No clear idea both at entry and qualification (undecided at both stages)	16	9	12	9	19	9
Base: all qualifiers	*(204)*	*(229)*	*(101)*	*(105)*	*(103)*	*(124)*

What kind of hospital specialties had the 1986 qualifiers decided on at qualification? 12 per cent of both men and women qualifiers had opted for a general medical specialty, which was an increase on previous cohorts. 19 per cent of the men and 7 per cent of the women had opted for a surgical specialty. The proportion of men was a slight increase on the proportion of 1981 men but rather lower than that found among earlier cohorts. The proportion of 1986 women opting for surgery at qualification was rather higher than the 4 per cent of earlier cohorts of women at this stage. It was also an increase on the proportion of 1986 women opting for it at entry to medical school although the proportion of men remained the same as at entry to medical school (although not necessarily the same people).

The proportion of 1986 qualifiers opting for paediatrics at qualification was marginally down on the 5 per cent of earlier cohorts at 4 per cent. 3 per cent opted for obstetrics and gynaecology, 3 per cent for psychiatry and 2 per cent for anaesthetics, the same proportions as found among earlier cohorts. The proportions of men and women were similar to those found among earl[i]er cohorts, with women slightly more likely to opt for paediatrics and anaest[hetics], men for obstetrics and gynaecology and equal proportions for psychi[atry].

We found again, as we had found in the last study, that cert[ain] were hardly mentioned at qualification, like radiology, pathology, and some, like accident and emergency and public/community health, were not mentioned at all. It was quite clear that very little information or encouragement was given to medical students to contemplate the less well-known specialties.

We were interested in seeing how far experience at medical school had affected career choice. Table 4.13 summarises career intentions from entry to medical school to qualification, and Table 4.14 shows more clearly what had happened to those who had stated a career preference at both entry to medical school and qualification.

Table 4.14   Whether changed specialty choice if intention stated at entry to medical school and at qualification

column percentages

	Total		Male		Female	
	1981	1986	1981	1986	1981	1986
Same specialty at entry and qualification	61	53	59	53	64	54
Different specialty at entry and qualification	39	47	41	47	36	46
Base: all those stating a career intention at entry and qualification	*(85)*	*(129)*	*(46)*	*(58)*	*(39)*	*(71)*

It can be seen from Table 4.13 that well over half the 1986 qualifiers expressed some kind of career intention at both entry to medical school and qualification, compared with just over 40 per cent of the 1981 qualifiers. Similar proportions of men and women 1986 qualifiers expressed an intention, compared with 46 per cent of the 1981 men and only 38 per cent of the 1981 women. One of the main reasons for the higher proportion of 1986 qualifiers falling into this category is, of course, the higher proportion of them who expressed a career preference at entry to medical school, but, in addition, as we noted in Table 4.12, a higher p⁓‿ ‿⁓ ‿ expressed an intention at qualification.

‿at one third of the 1986 men and just over a quarter of

r mind at medical school about what they would like to

⁓0 per cent of the 1981 qualifiers. However, 6 per cent

me undecided at medical school having had some idea

e that under 10 per cent of the 1986 qualifiers had no

nted to do both at entry to medical school and at

one in six of the 1981 qualifiers.

r minds early did not necessarily mean that doctors

hose who had expressed a career intention at entry

to medical school, only 53 per cent of the 1986 qualifiers wanted to pursue the same career or specialty by the time they qualified, compared with over 60 per cent of the 1981 qualifiers in the same position. It was striking that the proportion of those who changed their minds at medical school about a chosen specialty increased steadily over the four cohorts among both men and women. For example, in the 1966 cohort, only 32 per cent of the men and 27 per cent of the women who expressed a career intention at both entry and qualification changed their minds at medical school, compared with 47 per cent of the 1986 men and 46 per cent of the 1986 women.

What were the changes? Of the 71 doctors (31 per cent of the total) who had chosen a hospital specialty at entry to medical school, two-thirds still wanted to pursue a hospital career at qualification, although often not in the same specialty, one fifth wanted to enter general practice, a tiny number wanted to do something else and over 10 per cent now had no clear idea of what they wanted to do.

Of the 56 doctors (24 per cent of the total) who had opted for general practice at entry to medical school, one in six now thought they wanted to do hospital medicine, nearly three-quarters wanted to stay with general practice, one doctor wanted to do something else and just under 10 per cent had become undecided by the time they qualified.

Among the 15 who had opted for something other than hospital medicine or general practice only a quarter had stuck to this intention while nearly half of them had opted for hospital medicine and just over a quarter for general practice.

Of the 87 doctors (38 per cent of the total) who had had no idea of what they wanted to do at entry to medical school, nearly 40 per cent had opted for hospital medicine, just over a quarter for general practice and 10 per cent for something else by the time they qualified. Nearly a quarter of them remained undecided.

What was it that made nearly half the doctors with a career intention at entry change their minds at medical school? The main reason was that the doctors, particularly the men, found that they were good at or enjoyed a subject at medical school. Women agreed, but were more likely than the men to say that they had changed their minds either because they thought they might find their previous idea boring in the long-term or because they no longer wished to pursue a hospital career because of the conditions in hospital medicine. Men were more likely than women to say that they had changed their minds because they thought there would be less competition in their new specialty. Both men and women had found some aspect of hospital medicine more intellectually stimulating than their original choice of general practice, and similar proportions had found good teaching in their new specialty. A variety of other reasons were given for changing their preferred specialty, reflecting the reasons given in the previous study, including those who found general practice at medical school unsatisfactory, those who found they preferred clinical to non-clinical medicine and the other way round, those who disliked the teaching staff or other staff or their attitude towards patients, and those who wanted to offer practical help to people. Only two women mentioned marriage or family constraints and only two women mentioned that they wanted a specialty without on-call commitments or long hours – factors which were to loom much larger in the lives of many doctors at a later stage in their careers.

The change in choice often reflected a process of becoming more realistic, and in some instances was clearly beneficial to the doctors, like this women who changed from wanting to be a medical missionary to a GP: 'I suppose it was going on my elective to Africa for three months which made me realise that going abroad wasn't all roses. It brought me down to earth I think. I also realised that I didn't enjoy medicine that much and didn't want to go for a top career job. I decided to go for an easy option ...' (She was now a part-time clinical assistant.)

In other cases, there was evidence of a complete misconception among doctors at entry to medical school of what a specialty was like. Two women doctors had wanted to do psychiatry when they started medical school. One had changed her mind to haematology, in which she was now a registrar – as far away from patients as possible: 'Having done sessions in psychiatry I disliked it intensely. Patients were stressful to look after. I didn't like the role of consultant psychiatrists – making decisions to lock people up or not ...' The other had changed her mind to general practice, although she was now a clinical assistant: 'My perception of psychiatry was totally different when I left from when I started. I didn't realise how much other people irritated me. Some drove me crazy and I wanted to slap their faces and say, "Pull yourself together!" ...'

Some doctors had been completely put off hospital medicine at medical school, like this woman, now a GP: 'I didn't really like hospital medicine. I thought it was a rat-race – sucking up to consultants – patients on a conveyor belt ...'

But some doctors changed their minds for more positive reasons, including a man who changed from microbiology at entry to psychiatry at qualification: 'As a post hoc rationalisation – because psychiatry was intellectually demanding and you could do something useful. But really – because I enjoyed it. It's a real privilege to deal with people – to talk to them about intimate problems. I enjoy the process – I'd never thought about the *process* of being a doctor before ...'

And another man had changed his mind from hospital medicine to general practice: 'It was the GP attachment – getting to know patients and realising the opportunities for following up patients and families and the great opportunity for education – and the variety of general practice ...'

Just under a third of the men and nearly half the women said they thought their original idea had been unrealistic, mainly because they realised that they had a rather romantic notion of what the specialty would be like, or, more candidly, they acknowledged, like the doctors quoted above, that the original option had been a totally unsuitable choice for them personally. Only two women said that they realised that their original choice was incompatible with family life, but others said that they had not realised that their original choice would make such demands in terms of time, hard work and commitment. There were other reasons for acknowledging that the original choice had been unrealistic, as this GP noted: 'My face didn't fit to be a general surgeon ...'

And some doctors realised that medicine was not really for them, although they might not have made this decision until a bit later, like this woman who had left medicine in her pre-registration year: 'By the time I qualified you had to do the vocational training scheme – three years of changing jobs. Just when you'd got to feel on top of the job you had to change. I might have made a good GP but I couldn't stand the life and death decisions in hospital medicine. I worked hard and got good grades. They couldn't understand why I felt such stress. The locum house job in my final year was the last straw ...'

One third of the 1986 men and just over a quarter of the women made up their minds about a specialty at medical school, as Table 4.13 shows. The main reasons they gave were, not surprisingly, similar to those given by doctors for changing their minds – because they were good at or enjoyed the subject, because they were well taught, and because they thought they were likely to be successful in the specialty. There were also complaints about hospital life and conditions from both men and women, like this woman GP: 'I was disillusioned with hospital medicine. The hours were grim – and the way you were treated – total lack of respect – not even any clean bed-linen when you were on call. My on-call room wasn't cleaned for six months. I slept in the labour ward most of the time ...'

But it was not only conditions in hospital medicine that influenced doctors towards general practice. Some doctors, especially the men, liked the autonomy of general practice, the breadth of practice and the lifestyle they thought it offered. Others wanted more contact with patients, like this woman GP trainee: 'I didn't like the fact that the only contact with patients was in hospital. After they left you never saw them again, as though what happened to them after that didn't really matter ...'

But other doctors realised that patients were not really their cup of tea, like this research pathologist: 'I became aware that I couldn't really see myself as a clinician. I'm not that kind of person. I'd wanted to be, but I found the whole thing of having to look after people too difficult. I didn't care enough and I wasn't confident enough. I felt I couldn't do them any good – and I didn't give a damn anyway. I had a problem being responsible for *myself*, let alone other people ...'

It is fortunate that medicine is a broad church which can accommodate so many different types of personalities and aptitudes, and it is fortunate that some doctors have the insight to recognise at an early stage that they are not suited to certain specialties. The problem arises when they embark on a career for which they find out later that they are totally unsuited, or when they persevere with a specialty in which they are only mildly interested. The life of a young doctor is stressful and hard, and it is becomingly increasingly important that people make up their minds at an early stage about their later career choice. With the implementation of the Calman Report (Department of Health, 1993) an early choice of specialty may become even more important. The need for more focused and sensitive careers advice, information and counselling, which has been such a recurrent theme in this research will become even more pressing.

5　Pre-registration year

Graduates from United Kingdom medical schools have to spend a year in pre-registration house jobs, usually six months in a medical specialty and six months in a surgical specialty, before they can be admitted to the Medical Register as fully registered doctors. In the last report we observed that there was nothing like house jobs for putting doctors off hospital medicine. What was the experience of the 1986 qualifiers?

Type of hospitals in which pre-registration posts held

We asked the doctors about the hospitals in which they held their pre-registration house jobs. There has been a tradition that the types of hospitals in which doctors have their house jobs have an important influence on their future careers. We had thought that this was probably increasingly less important than it had been assumed to be, but in the last study we found that the later cohorts thought it even more important than earlier cohorts. As many as 89 per cent of the 1981 men and 79 per cent of the 1981 women thought it mattered for the subsequent careers of doctors in general. It was interesting that a much lower proportion of doctors from all cohorts thought it had had any effect on their own careers.

The traditionally held view was that the very best students had both their house jobs in their own teaching hospitals, and that it was important to have at least one house job in a teaching hospital. We found, in fact, that a relatively high proportion of doctors had done neither house job in a teaching hospital. It appeared to have made little or no difference to the jobs of the more senior doctors we interviewed, but younger doctors in hospital training posts appeared rather more likely than older doctors to have held at least one house job in a teaching hospital.

It was early days to say what was likely to happen to the 1986 qualifiers, but we established where they had held their pre-registration house posts and asked them their views on the importance of the types of hospital in which house jobs were held.

Table 5.01 indicates that there was a decline between the 1981 and 1986 qualifiers in the proportion of doctors holding both house posts in their own teaching hospital. It is probable that this was related more to the policy of the teaching hospitals than anything else. There was an increase in the proportions holding both their house jobs in a general hospital linked to their own teaching hospital, again probably illustrating a general change in policy in which teaching

Table 5.01   Doctors holding both pre-registration posts in same type of hospital

column percentages

	Total		Male		Female	
	1981	1986	1981	1986	1981	1986
Both pre-reg posts						
Own teaching hospital	17	10	18	11	17	10
Other teaching hospital	1	3	0	4	2	3
General hospital linked to own teaching hospital	7	14	4	14	10	14
General hospital in same RHA as own teaching hospital	7	2	8	2	7	2
General hospital in other RHA	13	11	15	10	11	11
General hospital linked to teaching hospital in other RHA	1	2	1	3	1	2
Other hospital	*	0	0	0	1	0
Qualifiers *not* holding pre-reg posts in same type of hospital	53	57	54	55	52	58
Base: all qualifiers	*(204)*	*(229)*	*(101)*	*(105)*	*(103)*	*(124)*

hospitals made greater use of local general hospitals for teaching purposes, rather than a complete change in the type of hospitals used for house jobs.

There was a continuing trend away from qualifiers doing both their house jobs in a general hospital in a different region from their teaching hospital – something which had been much more common among the 1966 qualifiers. The other types of hospitals in which qualifiers held both pre-registration house jobs were similar to those found in the previous study, while the proportion of qualifiers *not* holding both house jobs in the same type of hospital had increased slightly on the 1981 qualifiers, continuing the trend recorded in the last study. The big change was from the experience of the 1966 qualifiers, only one third of whom did not hold both posts in the same type of hospital.

Table 5.02 shows that there was little difference between the 1986 men and women in the proportions who held both posts in their own or another teaching hospital, and compares the proportions with the qualifiers of 1976 and 1981. The trend is clearly away from holding both posts in a teaching hospital, from 24 per cent of the 1976 men and 27 per cent of the 1976 women to 17 per cent of both men and women in the 1986 cohort. However, at the same time, there has been a slight movement towards one house job in a teaching hospital among the men

Table 5.02   Whether both, one or no pre-registration posts held in a teaching hospital

column percentages

		Male			Female	
	1976	1981	1986	1976	1981	1986
Both in own TH	19	18	11	14	17	10
One in own TH	36	39	40	39	27	41
None in own TH	45	44	49	47	56	49
Both in another TH	2	0	4	5	2	3
One in another TH	8	7	4	10	6	7
None in another TH	90	93	92	86	92	90
Both in a TH	24	20	17	27	18	17
One in a TH	38	42	40	33	33	40
None in a TH	38	39	43	40	49	43
Base: all qualifiers	*(105)*	*(101)*	*(105)*	*(105)*	*(103)*	*(124)*

and a more marked increase among the women, from 33 per cent of both the 1976 and 1981 cohorts to 40 per cent of the 1986 women.

The proportions holding *no* pre-registration jobs in a teaching hospital increased from 38 per cent of the 1976 men to 39 per cent of the 1981 men to 43 per cent of the 1986 men, but showed a rather more complicated pattern among the women, from 40 per cent of the 1976 qualifiers to 49 per cent of the 1981 qualifiers back to 43 per cent of the 1986 qualifiers, exactly the same proportion as the 1986 men.

To what extent did the doctors think it had made any difference to their subsequent careers where they had done their house jobs? The 1986 qualifiers could be compared directly with the 1981 cohort in the last study. Table 5.03 indicates that the proportions of both men and women thinking that the type of hospital had had an effect on their subsequent careers was almost identical in both the 1981 and 1986 cohorts, with over 60 per cent of the men and under 60 per cent of the women noting some effect. The table compares the figures with the 1976 cohort, who had had a ten-year career at the time of the last study. The proportion of 1976 men thinking it had had an effect was very similar to that of the two later cohorts, while the 1976 women were more likely than the later women to think that it had no effect on their subsequent careers.

However, the question was left open so that doctors could describe what kind of effect they thought the type of hospitals in which they had done their house jobs had had on their subsequent careers. The last study showed that our respondents by no means interpreted this question only to support the theory that house jobs in teaching hospitals were a sign of high-flying doctors, and the respondents in the present study reacted in the same way.

Table 5.03   Whether type of hospitals in which pre-registration posts held had any effect on doctors' subsequent careers

column percentages

| | Male | | | Female | | |
	1976	1981	1986	1976	1981	1986
Yes	61	63	62	49	56	57
No	36	36	36	49	41	40
Don't know	3	1	2	3	3	3
Base: all qualifiers	*(105)*	*(101)*	*(105)*	*(105)*	*(103)*	*(124)*

On the one hand, we found that just under a quarter of both men and women who thought the type of hospital had affected their careers said that at least one house job in their own teaching hospital had been important for them. And just over 10 per cent of both sexes said that they had found teaching hospital house jobs stimulating and they had made them want to stay in hospital medicine.

On the other hand, we found that as many as 20 per cent of 1986 women answering the question said that house jobs in a teaching hospital had put them off working in a teaching hospital – a view shared by only 8 per cent of the men. We also found that just over 10 per cent of both sexes said that getting away from a teaching hospital had given them broader experience which they had found beneficial, and a similar proportion said that general hospital house jobs had offered them better training and experience for general practice and other non-hospital specialties than teaching hospitals were able to offer.

Nevertheless over 10 per cent of the men, but hardly any women, thought that house jobs in a general hospital had not been as beneficial for their careers as those in teaching hospitals. On the other hand nearly 10 per cent of the women said that their experience in general hospitals during their house jobs had made them want to work in hospital medicine in a general hospital.

In the last study we found that the most frequent comment was that it was not so much the type of hospital itself but the working conditions and the attitude of the staff which had had most effect on our respondents during their house jobs. Among the 1986 qualifiers this comment was made much less often, but one in seven of both men and women mentioned it.

It was interesting that the most vociferous comments about house jobs came from those who had disliked their house jobs in teaching hospitals. Even among those who thought that having had a house job in a teaching hospital was important for their careers, there were numerous criticisms of them. Doctors said they were 'treated like clerks' or 'like the little ant at the bottom of the heap ...' One woman GP said – 'It put me off hospital medicine. The teaching hospital was just awful – badly run, too busy and you're just an underdog ...' – and a male GP agreed – 'I found the working atmosphere in a teaching hospital unpleasant

– fiercely competitive resulting in unfriendliness. I did not want to spend a large chunk of my working life in such an establishment. It's basically back-stabbing ...'

There were numerous comments about competition and lack of cooperation among staff at teaching hospitals. A male GP noted: 'The prevailing atmosphere in teaching hospitals is "Get on and suck up to everyone" ...' And his words were echoed by a male surgical SHO: 'You had to basically lick the boss's boots to get on. I just couldn't do that ...' It had put some people off medicine altogether, like this woman who had left medicine: 'You're very vulnerable in the first years, and if you don't get the back-up you need you lose confidence and become unable to fulfil your career. That's what happened to me ...'

There were others comments about the 'rarefied' atmosphere of teaching hospitals, which had discouraged people from hospital medicine, like this woman GP – 'In a teaching hospital you're cut off, behind glass doors. No importance is attached to patients' outside lives ...' and a woman GP trainee – 'There's not a good team spirit and the patients are at the bottom of the list of priorities ...'

The wider range of experience possible in a general hospital was clearly important for many doctors, and there was emphasis on the opportunities for developing independence and autonomy, not always without its hazards it appeared, according to a woman GP locum: 'As a houseman in (....) general hospital you were on call on your own. The system was dangerous but, boy, you did learn. It was too pressurised though. Some people did crack up ...'

An interesting theme running through a number of interviews, particularly with women, was the confidence given to doctors in their house jobs in general hospitals, as this woman ophthalmic registrar noted: 'There was a different and more accessible relationship between all sorts of staff and I was busier than I would have been in a teaching hospital job. I quickly gained confidence and experience. I saw more patients and I did a lot more than the others who had stayed at my teaching hospital ...'

But although only around 60 per cent of 1986 qualifiers thought that the kind of hospitals they had done their house jobs in had mattered for their own subsequent careers, over three-quarters of them thought it mattered in general, as Table 5.04 shows. The 1986 men were much less likely than their predecessors to think that it mattered, while the proportion of women remained much the same for all three cohorts shown in Table 5.04. Nearly half the 1986 men thinking that it mattered in general said that house jobs in their own teaching hospitals were important for ambitious doctors, a view held by just over a third of the women. However, one third of both sexes thought that references from teaching hospitals carried more weight than those from general hospitals, with a number adding that it looked good on doctors' CVs to have had a house job in their own teaching hospital. One in six of both men and women said that house jobs in teaching hospitals were only important if doctors wanted to continue in hospital medicine, and 10 per cent thought that they were important for success in certain competitive specialties. However, the same proportion thought that doctors could

Table 5.04 **Whether type of hospitals in which pre-registration posts held matters in general for subsequent careers of doctors**

column percentages

	Male			Female		
	1976	1981	1986	1976	1981	1986
Yes	88	89	76	81	79	78
No	11	8	22	15	15	20
Don't know	1	3	2	4	7	2
Base: all qualifiers	*(105)*	*(101)*	*(105)*	*(105)*	*(103)*	*(124)*

get more clinical experience outside teaching hospitals, and it was noted that better training might be available in general hospitals. Some doctors thought that a mixture of teaching and general hospitals was a good idea, and, as can be seen from the tables above, this is what many of the doctors had had.

Again, the atmosphere of the different types of hospital was thought to be an important factor, as this woman SHO noted: 'Quite a lot of people are put off working in hospital if they are in a teaching hospital and all the time looking for beds and not looking after their patients. A lot of people say that in teaching hospitals they have no social relationships with their senior colleagues, whereas in a district hospital they do. They see you as a person – not just a doctor – so you enjoy it more ...'

Her view was repeated time and again, as by this woman GP: 'The rigid sterile environment in teaching hospitals can put people off academic medicine. The back-scratching, bowing and scraping in teaching hospitals puts people off hospital medicine. District general hospitals were more pleasant and friendly and consultants were often more approachable. Men do better because there is a "machismo of coping" that men go along with – although less now than they used to ...'

But as we have seen, the most frequent comment was that it mattered for ambitious doctors, and many felt that they did not fall into that category, like this respondent who had left medicine: 'If you can take the hours and responsibility, you may thrive in a teaching hospital environment and like that atmosphere. In provincial hospitals you're more likely to get more of a slice of real life – more contact with reality – normal people with normal illnesses. There's a place for both, but if you're academic a teaching hospital is better ...'

Essentially there appeared to be little difference between men and women in where they did their house jobs. The proportions were much the same, as they were among the previous cohorts. The location of house jobs had made no marked difference to the long-term careers of the majority of doctors in the last study it appeared. There was no real reason to think that this had changed, but the view remained firmly fixed that at least one house job in a teaching hospital was a 'must' for a doctor who was going anywhere.

Career intention at registration

But where were the doctors going? By the time a doctor reaches registration nowadays, there is a fairly strong imperative for some kind of firm career choice to have been made – at least provisionally. The last study showed a steady decline over the three cohorts in the proportion of doctors who still had no clear career intention at registration. However, as Table 5.05 shows, the proportion of 1986 qualifiers with no clear idea at registration remained much the same as that found among the 1981 qualifiers, although the 1986 men were rather more likely to have made up their minds, at least initially. A tiny proportion of 1986 qualifiers had decided not to work in medicine after their pre-registration year.

Table 5.05   Career intention at registration

						column percentages
	Total		Male		Female	
	1981	1986	1981	1986	1981	1986
Hospital specialty	46	48	52	57	39	41
General practice	41	39	38	35	44	42
Community/public health	0	0	0	0	0	0
Other[1]	*	3	0	2	3	3
Not work in medicine	1	1	0	1	2	1
Stop working	1	0	1	0	1	0
None/no clear idea	10	9	9	5	12	13
Base: all qualifiers	*(204)*	*(229)*	*(101)*	*(105)*	*(103)*	*(124)*

1. Includes go abroad, choice of two specialties, research and non-clinical medicine.

Comparing Table 5.05 with Table 4.12, it can be seen that the gradual shift towards hospital medicine in the pre-registration year which was noted in previous studies had continued among both sexes, while the proportions intending to enter general practice had remained much the same among the women but had increased among the men, when compared with their choice at qualification.

However, the steadily increasing trend towards opting for general practice at registration noted in the last report had been halted, and indeed rather fewer 1986 qualifiers were intending to enter general practice than had been found among 1981 qualifiers. This trend has clearly continued among later qualifiers, and has been a cause of much concern in general practice.

The difference between the 1986 men and women was rather more marked than it had been among the 1981 qualifiers, with 57 per cent of 1986 men but only 41 per cent of women opting for hospital medicine at registration, compared with 35 per cent of men and 42 per cent of women opting for general practice. The women from all three previous cohorts had been consistently more likely than the men to opt for general practice at this stage of their careers. The big change over the years among the women was the big drop in the proportion who still had no clear career intention at registration. The consistent factor was the total lack of interest among qualifiers at this stage in a career in public or community health.

What were the main changes in specialty which had taken place in their pre-registration year? 12 per cent of doctors had now opted for general medicine, 5 per cent for anaesthetics and psychiatry, 4 per cent for paediatrics and pathology, 2 per cent for obstetrics and gynaecology, and in all these specialties, the proportions of men and women were roughly the same. However, 12 per cent of the 1986 qualifiers had opted for surgery, representing 17 per cent of the men but only 7 per cent of the women.

The overall proportions of 1986 qualifiers opting for specific specialties at registration remained much the same as those found in the last study, although the proportion opting for general medicine was slightly higher among this cohort. The main difference found in comparison with earlier cohorts was that the proportions of men and women were more or less evenly balanced in the 1986 cohort, with the exception of surgery. In the previous cohorts far more women than men had opted at this stage for obstetrics and gynaecology, anaesthetics, pathology and psychiatry, for example, even if they did not end up in these specialties. It was difficult to foretell what was going to happen to the 1986 women.

Changes from qualification to registration
We were interested to see to what extent the pre-registration year had affected career choice and Table 5.06 summarises the changes between qualification and registration. The proportions of both men and women from the 1981 and 1986 cohorts who had expressed a career intention at both qualification and registration were almost identical at over 80 per cent of the men and just over three-quarters of the women. Again the proportions of these who stuck to the same specialty and those who changed were remarkably similar. It can be seen that the men were more likely to have changed specialty in their pre-registration year than the women – 60 per cent of the total number of 1986 men stayed in the specialty they had chosen at qualification while 23 per cent had changed their minds, compared with 65 per cent of the 1986 women staying with the same specialty and only 12 per cent changing their minds. As Table 5.07 shows, over a quarter of the 1986 men who had chosen a specialty at qualification had changed their minds after the pre-registration year, compared with only 15 per cent of the women.

12 per cent of the 1986 men and 10 per cent of the women had made up their minds on a specialty at registration, having been undecided at qualification. 6 per cent of the 1986 qualifiers became undecided during their pre-registration year, having had some idea at qualification. But the proportion who were undecided at both stages had dropped to none of the 1986 men and only 6 per

Table 5.06   Career intentions from qualification to registration

column percentages

	Total 1981	Total 1986	Male 1981	Male 1986	Female 1981	Female 1986
Intention both at qualification and registration	79	80	83	83	76	77
- same specialty	(62)	(63)	(61)	(60)	(62)	(65)
- different specialty	(18)	(17)	(22)	(23)	(14)	(12)
No clear idea at qualification but intention at registration (made up mind)	11	11	9	12	13	10
Intention at qualification but no clear idea at registration (became undecided)	2	6	3	5	3	6
No clear idea both at qualification and registration (undecided at both stages)	7	3	5	0	10	6
Base: all qualifiers	*(204)*	*(229)*	*(101)*	*(105)*	*(103)*	*(124)*

cent of the 1986 women. The doctors might not have known what they were going to do at registration, but they had known once.

What specialties did they stay with and what did they change to? 86 per cent of the 96 who had chosen hospital medicine at qualification stayed with a hospital specialty, although not necessarily the same one, but 9 per cent changed to general practice, and 4 per cent became undecided. Of the 84 who had opted for general practice at qualification, 81 per cent were still intending to stay with it at registration, but 13 per cent had changed to a hospital specialty, and 6 per cent had become undecided.

Of the 16 who had wanted to do something else at qualification, a quarter had now decided on a hospital specialty, just over 10 per cent had changed to general practice, the same proportion had decided to leave medicine, a quarter had no clear idea of what they wanted to do, and only a quarter were still sticking with their idea at qualification. Of the 33 who had had no clear idea at qualification, nearly 40 per cent had now opted for hospital medicine, just under a third for general practice, two doctors for something else, but a quarter of them were still undecided.

What reasons did they give for their change of mind? Once again, the main reason, given by over a third of those who had changed their choice, was that they enjoyed their new specialty or were good at it. Other reasons were far less

Table 5.07 **Whether changed specialty choice if intention stated at qualification and registration**

column percentages

	Total		Male		Female	
	1981	1986	1981	1986	1981	1986
Same specialty at qualification and registration	78	80	74	74	82	85
Different specialty at qualification and registration	22	20	26	26	18	15
Base: all those stating a career intention at qualification and registration	*(162)*	*(183)*	*(84)*	*(87)*	*(78)*	*(96)*

important, but included the appraisal that they thought there was less competition in their new specialty, that they thought a hospital specialty was more challenging than general practice or that they had had good teaching in their new specialty during their pre-registration year.

As we found in the last study, there were very few mentions of domestic factors in influencing the change in specialty. No women mentioned marriage constraints, although one man did, and two women said they wanted a specialty without long hours, which might not necessarily have been related to domestic responsibilities.

There can be no doubt that personalities and good teaching played an important role in influencing specialty change in the pre-registration year, as this male surgical registrar explained: 'As a pre-reg houseman I had this wonderful senior registrar. He told me I *had* to do surgery, said he'd support me. He used to let me choose to do one operation a week. He wouldn't start any operation, day or night, unless I was there ...'

But not everyone was so lucky in their house jobs, as this male anaesthetics registrar noted: 'I'd had the stuffing knocked out of me in house jobs, so I didn't know what I wanted to do ...'

As we have seen, the pre-registration year sometimes made doctors realise that hospital medicine was not for them, like this woman who had changed her mind from surgery to general practice: 'Surgery precluded all other life. I wanted to have my cake and eat it. I saw that general practice was a worthwhile career ...' But sometimes it gave doctors the opportunity to find a specialty they really enjoyed, like this male surgical registrar: 'I thoroughly enjoyed surgical practice. There are so many aspects I enjoyed – for example, manual dexterity, the creative side, a lot of young patients, it's instantly gratifying. People came in – had the operation and went out ...'

Among those who made up their minds during their pre-registration year, again the main reasons for choice of specialty were because the doctors enjoyed the subject or found that they were good at it. Only two doctors – one man and one woman – mentioned marriage or domestic constraints, and two women said that they wanted a specialty without long hours or on-call responsibilities. However, one in six of the doctors who made up their minds during their pre-registration year said that their experience as house officers had made them decide against hospital medicine.

In the last study we noted the extent to which the doctors embarked on their careers at registration with what appeared to be little thought of the possible constraints which might be placed on them by domestic commitments or the careers of their partners. Women appeared to be as little concerned about their future needs in terms of hours or geographical location as the men when they were discussing their possible choice of career. And yet, as we saw so clearly in that study, many constraints were placed on the development of the doctors' careers which seemed external to their ability or potential within their chosen specialty.

There was little wonder that when we interviewed them so many of the older cohorts were no longer in the specialty they had chosen at registration, with only one third of the 1966 qualifiers and less than half the 1976 qualifiers still in the same specialty they had started out on. Even among the 1981 qualifiers, less than two-thirds were still in the same specialty they had embarked on less than five years earlier. Men were more likely than women in all three cohorts to have remained in the same specialty, but even so there was evidence of considerable change of career among men as well as women.

The 1986 qualifiers were even less likely than the 1981 qualifiers to be working in the same specialty they had chosen at registration. We examine the reasons for this and track their careers since registration in the next chapters.

6   Doctors' careers and their present jobs

One of the main measures of success in doctors' careers is whether they reach career grade jobs which have full clinical autonomy. This category has become a little blurred in recent years, but career grade jobs are usually taken to be principals in general practice, consultants and senior managers in public health. There is a problem surrounding public health doctors in management roles in that they are usually not strictly within clinical medicine, but for the purposes of the last study they were included in career grade posts. Senior clinical medical officers (SCMOs) and clinical medical officers (CMOs) also have limited clinical autonomy but were not included in the analysis as career grade doctors in the last study on the advice of the Department of Health.

We were particularly interested in the last study in establishing whether there was any difference between men and women in the age at which they reached career grade, if they had actually attained that level. We were mainly trying to establish whether the women who reached career grade (a much lower proportion than men) took longer to do so than their male counterparts. Looking at the three cohorts as a whole, we found that there was little difference in the age at which men and women became consultants (34.8 for men and 34.5 for women) and that men were slightly younger than women in becoming GP principals (29.2 for men and 30.2 for women). The number of doctors in other categories of career grade jobs was really too small to make any meaningful comparison.

We found, however, that, although there was little difference between men and women in the age at which they reached career grade, the 1966 women qualifiers took rather longer to reach consultant status and considerably longer to reach GP principal status than the men, while the 1976 women qualifiers took much the same length of time as the men to reach consultant status, but rather longer to reach GP principal status (Allen, 1988, see Table 6.02).

There were a number of reasons for this. First, the women in all cohorts were rather younger than the men when they qualified, so that the fact that they reached career grade at much the same age disguised the fact that they took longer to do so. Secondly, particularly among the GP principals, there was evidence that women, especially in the 1966 cohort, tended to do other things before they settled on a specialty. Thirdly, the difference between men and women consultants in the 1976 cohort was almost certainly less marked than in the 1966 cohort because the 1976 qualifiers who had reached consultant level by 1986 when we interviewed them were the high flyers or 'early achievers'. Women consultants in fact outnumbered the men in the 1976 cohort at that time by 9:7, a ratio which had changed considerably by the time of the follow-up study carried out concurrently with this study in 1991.

We drew three main messages from the data collected in the last study on the age at reaching career grade. The first was that, if women reached career grade, they did so at roughly the same age as men, although they might have taken longer to get there. Secondly, the actual numbers of men and women reaching GP principal level were similar for all three cohorts, but only just over half the number of women in the 1966 cohort had reached consultant level compared with the men, while men and women were level-pegging at consultant level in the 1976 cohort. Thirdly, and perhaps most important, it was clear that if doctors were going to reach career grade, especially in hospital medicine, the age at which they reach it may be determined by the expectation that doctors will have reached a particular stage by a particular age. Doctors not conforming to that expectation may well find it more difficult to make progress.

This linking of age to grade in medical careers was one of the most important findings of the last study and had particular implications not only for the careers of women doctors, but also for mature entrants to the profession, overseas-qualified doctors, and others who might not be able, or willing, to conduct a career in which certain stages or grades are reached within certain rather inflexible age-bands. In terms of our study, it was clearly a potential constraint on the development of the careers of women who might have wanted to work less than full-time at any point in their careers, or to follow a more flexible career path than the norm.

We were aware of the fact that few of the 1986 qualifiers would have reached career grade at the time of the present study, and that it was likely that all of these would be GP principals, as had been the case with the 1981 qualifiers in the last study. We found that among the 1986 qualifiers 37 doctors had become GP principals (25 men and 12 women), all but one of whom (a male GP locum) were currently working as GP principals. Four of the 12 women GP principals were working part-time.

The average age at which the doctors had achieved career grade status was 28.8 for the men and 29.6 for the women, although the median age was 28 for both sexes. The figures were skewed for the women by two older women who had achieved career grade status in their late thirties or early forties. The distribution of ages was otherwise similar among men and women. It is therefore difficult to draw any firm conclusions from the figures, other than to say that if the 1986 women had become GP principals, which they had done in relatively fewer numbers than the men, they had done so at very similar ages. In the last report we found that around 40 per cent of both men and women of the total sample had become GP principals over the age of 30. Since the majority of 1986 qualifiers were still under the age of 30 at the time we interviewed them, it is clearly too early to make any real assessment of the relative ages at which they achieved career grade.

Curricula vitae

As in the last study the doctors were asked for their curricula vitae, accounting for each month of their careers from the date they started after full registration as a doctor. Our method of collecting the data was to record the starting and finishing date of each job or activity from the start of their careers post-registration until the date they were interviewed. For all medical jobs in Britain, we recorded the grade, the specialty, whether it was full-time or part-time and the RHA in which it was held. For all hospital jobs we recorded whether it was a teaching or non-teaching hospital. We recorded whether jobs were part of an organised GP vocational training scheme or whether they were put together by the doctors as part of a self-constructed GP vocational training scheme. We recorded whether the jobs were part of a rotation of any other kind.

We also recorded whether jobs were in any way concurrent with one another. We had found considerable evidence of more than one job being held at a time, but there were serious problems in analysis, particularly since a number of jobs could be held concurrently or overlapping each other, with different start and finishing dates.

In addition to recording details on every medical job held in Britain, we also recorded the exact periods of time the doctors spent working abroad in medicine, working abroad in any other capacity, travelling, working outside medicine, not working (with no other information given), unemployed, ill, on maternity leave, having babies or bringing up children, and studying. None of the periods of time on any of these activities was allowed any concurrence or overlap with another period of time.

This method of recording meant that we had a full career profile for all but one of the 640 doctors interviewed in the last study. We repeated the exercise with 100 per cent success in this study of 1986 qualifiers.

Length of time to achieve certain grades

We were interested to know whether there were any differences in the actual length of time that men and women took to reach certain grades from the start of their careers. Table 6.01 measures the length of time from the start of the doctors' careers (the first date recorded on their individual curriculum vitae), to the first time the grade in question is coded. We have noted before that this is a relatively crude measure in that it makes no allowance for other activities the doctors might have been engaged in, for example, working abroad or having children, and it can be misleading, in that a doctor might, for example, have reached the grade of registrar and then changed direction completely, in some cases returning to SHO level.

We have looked at four selected posts in Table 6.01: registrar, senior registrar, consultant and GP principal. We have compared the three cohorts of 1976, 1981 and 1986 qualifiers, taking the data for the first two cohorts from the last study. We show the 1976 data simply to give a benchmark against which to measure the achievements of the latter two cohorts. Even so, a better benchmark

Table 6.01   Elapsed time from start of career to attaining selected posts

	Male			Female		
	1976	1981	1986	1976	1981	1986
Mean time to reach grades (in months)						
Registrar	49.7	30.8	29.6	37.9	30.9	38.8
(Nos reaching grade)	(56)	(41)	(46)	(49)	(37)	(33)
Senior Registrar	69.0	33.3	50.5	71.3	43.0	47.7
(Nos reaching grade)	(29)	(3)	(2)	(23)	(2)	(3)
Consultant	84	0	0	85.9	0	0
(Nos reaching grade)	(7)	(0)	(0)	(9)	(0)	(0)
GP principal	50.9	39.5	44.0	67.7	39.5	43.3
(Nos reaching grade)	(43)	(15)	(25)	(42)	(11)	(12)
Base: all qualifiers	*(105)*	*(101)*	*(105)*	*(105)*	*(103)*	*(124)*

is the experience of the 1966 qualifiers, since the careers of the 1976 qualifiers were only ten years long in 1986, and not only were the consultants very early achievers, the senior registrars were also relatively early achievers.

In addition, we should note that we interviewed the 1986 qualifiers at a point on average six months later in their careers than the 1981 qualifiers (see Table 6.02). It would therefore be expected that the average length of time to reach a grade would be longer for the 1986 qualifiers (since more months would be available). It would also be expected that a higher proportion of qualifiers would have reached various grades, but, as Table 6.01 shows, this was not necessarily true.

First of all, none of the 1981 or 1986 qualifiers had reached consultant grade at the time that we interviewed them around five years after qualification – four years after registration. This was not surprising, given the fact that the 1966 men had taken an average of over 11 years to reach consultant level. We found that 25 men and 12 women from the 1986 cohort had reached GP principal grade, with an average of 44 months for the men and 43.3 months for the women. Given the fact that they were six months further into their careers, they had taken rather less time to reach this grade on average than the 1981 cohort. However, a higher proportion of 1986 men had reached GP principal grade than we found among the 1981 men, while a lower proportion of 1986 women had done so compared with the 1981 women. (The numbers were roughly the same, but the proportion was lower).

There was virtually no difference in the length of time taken to reach senior registrar level between the 1986 men and women, while the 1981 women had taken slightly longer. However, the numbers were so small that little can be deduced from these early arrivers.

Looking at registrar level, and allowing for the fact that the 1986 qualifiers were six months further on in their careers, it can be seen that there was virtually no difference in the length of time taken between men and women in both cohorts, but that a considerably lower proportion of 1986 women had reached registrar status than 1981 women in the last study, who were interviewed six months earlier in their careers. This reflected our finding that far fewer 1986 women were currently working as registrars than we found among the 1981 cohort (see Chapter 2, Table 2.14).

We noted in the last report that a great deal of caution must be exercised in interpreting these figures for a variety of reasons. This is particularly true of the later cohorts, in that in all cases we are looking at the early achievers, and cannot make allowances for the 'tail' of arrivers. It could well be misleading to extrapolate from the experience of the 1966 qualifiers, particularly the women, since so many circumstances were different in their careers. As we noted in the last study, among the women 1966 qualifiers, we found some very resourceful women who had managed to reach consultant status at a relatively late age, having changed specialty, sometimes more than once, moved around the country, had a number of children and led very chequered careers by any standards. There was general agreement when we interviewed in 1986 that these careers were no longer possible except in very exceptional circumstances. It appeared that by 1991 such careers were even more unusual.

However, comparing the careers of the 1986 cohort with the 1981 cohort, there were certain indications that not everything was going as well for the women as they were for the 1981 women when we interviewed them last time. The 1986 women might be similar to the 1981 women in that they were level-pegging with the men in terms of the length of time taken to reach certain grades, but relatively fewer of them had actually reached the two crucial grades of GP principal and registrar.

In terms of longer term predictions, it is necessary to examine the subsequent careers of the 1976 and 1981 qualifiers analysed in the study carried out in 1991 in parallel to this study. It will be seen that some of the bright hopes of the 1981 women were not fulfilled.

Time spent in careers on various activities

In looking at the activity and participation rates of doctors, it is important to assess how much time they spend actually working in medicine in their careers. Table 6.02 looks at the average length of the doctors' careers, the average time they have spent in medical jobs in Britain, the average time they have spent in full-time and part-time medical jobs in the Britain, and the average time they

Table 6.02   Time spent in careers on medical jobs in Britain and other activities

	Total		Male		Female	
	1981	1986	1981	1986	1981	1986
Average length (in months) of career	42.8	48.8	42.9	48.8	42.7	48.9
Average time (in months) spent in medical jobs in Britain	39.7	45.6	41.3	46.8	38.1	44.6
(As proportion of total career)	*(93%)*	*(93%)*	*(96%)*	*(96%)*	*(89%)*	*(91%)*
Average time (in months) spent in full-time medical jobs in Britain	39.4	43.8	41.3	45.7	37.6	42.1
Average time (in months) spent in part-time medical jobs in Britain	0.2	2.0	0	1.4	0.5	2.5
(Time in part-time jobs as proportion of time in medical jobs in Britain)	*(<1%)*	*(4%)*	*(0)*	*(3%)*	*(1%)*	*(6%)*
Average time (in months) spent doing other things	3.2	3.2	1.7	2.0	4.7	4.3
Base: all qualifiers	*(204)*	*(229)*	*(101)*	*(105)*	*(103)*	*(124)*

have spent doing other things, like working abroad, travelling, having children, studying and so on.

We found in the last study that this analysis showed quite conclusively that the vast majority of men and women qualifiers from all years had spent most of their time since registration working in medical jobs in Britain. It completely ruled out any idea that women doctors were likely to drop out of medicine in large numbers for any length of time.

Table 6.02 compares the careers of the 1986 qualifiers in this study and 1981 qualifiers in the last study. It can be seen that the average length of the 1981 qualifiers' careers from registration at the time we interviewed them in 1986 was 42.8 months and the average length of the 1986 qualifiers' careers at interview in 1991 was 48.8 months – six months longer. There was no real difference between men and women in either year.

We can see that the qualifiers from both years had spent an identical average proportion of their careers in medical jobs in Britain – 93 per cent. The men from both cohorts had spent an average of 96 per cent of their careers in medical jobs in Britain, compared with the 1981 women who had spent 89 per cent and the 1986 women who had spent 91 per cent of their careers in medical jobs in Britain.

In both cohorts, the men had spent slightly longer than the women in full-time medical jobs in Britain, and rather less in part-time medical jobs. The 1986 qualifiers had spent rather longer in part-time medical jobs, but this was almost certainly related to the fact that they were six months further into their careers. However, looking at time spent in part-time medical jobs as a proportion of their total time in medical jobs in Britain, we found that this averaged 6 per cent for the 1986 women, compared with 1 per cent for the 1981 women, 3 per cent for the 1986 men and nil for the 1981 men.

It can be seen that the differences between men and women from these two cohorts four years after registration in the proportion of their careers spent in part-time medical jobs were minimal, mainly because nobody had spent much time in part-time medical jobs. However, as the last report showed, this was by no means true of the earlier cohorts, where we found that the big difference between men and women lay in the extent to which jobs were full-time or part-time. The 1966 women qualifiers had spent virtually half the length of time on average in full-time medical jobs in Britain as their male counterparts, and the 1976 women qualifiers had spent just over two-thirds the length of time in full-time medical jobs in Britain as the men from the same cohort. (43 per cent of the time spent in medical jobs in Britain by the 1966 women had been in part-time jobs, compared with 27 per cent of the time of the 1976 women.)

Would things change for the young women from the 1981 and 1986 cohorts who had spent so little time so far in part-time jobs? We will see in Chapter 15 that, although the 1986 women might not have worked part-time to date they were certainly intending to do so, and the parallel study to this shows that the 1981 women had done so. The main pattern of women doctors' careers continues, with the not surprising move towards part-time or less than full-time working when they are in their early thirties.

But if the doctors had not been working in medicine, what else had they been doing? Table 6.02 shows that in both cohorts only about 3 months had been spent on average in their careers doing anything other than work in medicine. Women in both cohorts were rather more likely than the men to have spent time out of medical jobs, but even so, the time they had spent was minimal.

In Table 6.03, the average time spent on various specified activities other than medical jobs in Britain is given in two ways: first by the total sample and secondly by those who had ever spent time in this way. It also gives the percentage of the sample who had actually ever spent any time in this way. The most relevant comparisons are between the men and women in each cohort rather than across cohorts, because of the slight difference in the length of the careers between the two cohorts.

Table 6.03 **Time spent in careers post-registration on activities other than medical jobs in Britain**

	Male		Female	
	1981	1986	1981	1986
Average time (in months) spent:				
not working				
- by total sample	0.4	0	1.1	0.3
- by those ever not working	2.8	0	7.4	6.8
(% of sample)	(14%)	(0)	(16%)	(5%)
unemployed				
- by total sample	0.6	0.2	0.4	0.4
- by those ever unemployed	3.3	3.2	2.8	3.4
(% of sample)	(19%)	(5%)	(16%)	(14%)
maternity leave				
- by total sample	0	0	0.3	0.6
- by those ever mat. leave	0	0	5.2	5.0
(% of sample)	(0)	(0)	(5%)	(12%)
bringing up children				
- by total sample	0	0	0.6	0.6
- by those ever brought up children	0	0	5.9	13.8
(% of sample)	(0)	(0)	(10%)	(4%)
studying				
- by total sample	0.2	0.9	0.4	0.4
- by those ever studied	3.8	7.5	7.4	7.6
(% of sample)	(6%)	(11%)	(5%)	(6%)
travelling				
- by total sample	0.2	0.3	0.7	0.5
- by those ever travelled	5.3	4.0	15.0	4.2
(% of sample)	(3%)	(8%)	(14%)	(12%)
working abroad in medicine				
by total sample	0.3	0.4	1.2	1.0
by those ever worked abroad in medicine	5.4	5.2	9.9	10.1
(% of sample)	(5%)	(9%)	(12%)	(10%)
working abroad not in medicine				
- by total sample	0	0	0.1	0
- by those ever worked abroad not in medicine	0	0	4.0	0
(% of sample)	(0)	(0)	(1%)	(0)
working outside medicine				
- by total sample	0	0.2	0.1	0.4
- by those ever worked outside medicine	0	10.5	4.0	52.0
(% of sample)	(0)	(2%)	(1%)	(1%)

The figures are perhaps not as markedly different as they were for the earlier cohorts, since the 1981 and 1986 qualifiers had had relatively short careers in which the vast majority of their time had been spent in full-time medical jobs in Britain as we saw in Table 6.02.

However, there were some interesting findings. The 1981 cohort were rather more likely to have spent some time not working than the 1986 cohort, with the women in both cohorts who had spent any time not working to have been out of work for a slightly longer average time. Unemployment times were similarly low for both cohorts although fewer of the 1986 men had spent time unemployed.

A higher proportion of 1986 women than 1981 women had had maternity leave, but the average length of time spent on maternity leave was virtually the same. On the other hand a slightly higher proportion of 1981 women had spent time bringing up children. The average time spent by the sample as a whole was identical, while the average time spent by the 1986 women who had taken time out to bring up children was rather longer than for the 1981 women.

The 1986 men were rather more likely to have spent time studying than any other group, but the average time out for studying for all groups was very short. We had noted before that the 1981 women were the group most likely to travel, and this was similar for the 1986 women. However, the 1986 women who had travelled had spent a similar amount of time doing so to the 1981 and 1986 men and less than the 1981 women.

Around 10 per cent of the 1986 men had worked abroad in medicine, compared with 5 per cent of the 1981 men and just over 10 per cent of the women from both cohorts. The women who had done so had spent longer on average abroad than the men. (We know that some of the qualifiers whom we could not interview for this study were working or travelling abroad at the time of the fieldwork – see Appendix).

We found that only tiny proportions of the 1981 cohort had worked outside medicine, but 2 per cent of the 1986 men and 1 per cent of the 1986 women had done so. The average times were clearly related to individual circumstances, with some doctors having worked outside medicine from registration onwards.

In summary, Table 6.03 can only illustrate in more detail the very limited amount of time spent by doctors in the early years of their careers in activities other than medical jobs in Britain. It is useful as a base-line to the later careers of the doctors and as a comparison with Table 6.04 in the last study (Allen, 1988).

The information in this chapter must be read in conjunction with the data on present jobs and future intentions given elsewhere in this report. The CVs of the doctors give a wealth of information about actual career paths and the complicated road to the top. As we note in Chapter 15, one of the most interesting aspects of these studies is the importance attached by most doctors to their CVs. Given the present career structure in medicine this is not surprising. What is surprising is how little help and guidance most doctors are given not only in ensuring that their CV does them justice, but also in maximising their own potential in career terms.

7　Present job and changes since registration

Most of the qualifiers had registered a year after qualification, so that at the time we interviewed them in the late summer or autumn of 1991, it was usually four years since they had registered, about six months longer on average than the 1981 qualifiers, who had mainly been interviewed in the spring of 1986.

We recorded whether their present specialty or job was different from the decision they had made at registration, and Table 7.01 shows the shifts in their careers. We found in the last study that the 1981 qualifiers were more likely than earlier qualifiers to have still been in the specialty they had chosen at qualification. This was partly due to the fact that they were more likely than earlier cohorts to have actually come to some decision at registration, but also, of course, their careers had been much shorter and they had had less opportunity for changing course. However, we found that as many as 24 per cent of the 1981 qualifiers were already in different specialties from those they had chosen at registration, less than four years earlier.

We should note that we recorded a change of specialty as a change even if doctors were working in another specialty as part of a longer-term plan, for example to give them wider experience, with the intention of returning to their original choice. We also recorded for this analysis a change from a broad choice of specialty to a specific sub-specialty as a change of specialty. However, we did not record a change of specialty for doctors who had chosen general practice at registration but were doing a hospital specialty as part of their GP vocational training package, but we did record a change if doctors were adding to their experience in hospital having completed their GP vocational training.

The patterns and intentions were extremely complex, so that we had to lay down some guidelines on what was and what was not a change of specialty at this stage. There was no guarantee that doctors would return to their original choice once they had changed specialty, even if they regarded it as temporary. The discussion in this chapter underlines the danger of making simplistic remarks about career intentions or career changes. The reality is that doctors' choices and .changes of specialty do not follow a neat path, and career intentions may not be any real guide to behaviour at all.

The 1986 qualifiers were even less likely than the 1981 qualifiers to have remained in the specialty they had chosen at registration by the time we interviewed them four years later. As Table 7.01 shows, the proportions of those in the same specialty had dropped slightly from 67 per cent of the 1981 to 60 per

Table 7.01   Whether present specialty/job is different from decision at registration

column percentages

	Total		Male		Female	
	1981	1986	1981	1986	1981	1986
Same specialty	62	54	67	60	56	49
Different specialty	24	28	25	30	22	25
Made up mind since registration	10	8	7	5	14	11
Not working at all	2	6	0	3	5	9
Working outside medicine	0	1	0	2	0	1
Maternity leave	1	2	0	0	1	4
Still no clear idea	1	*	1	0	1	1
Base: all qualifiers	*(204)*	*(229)*	*(101)*	*(105)*	*(103)*	*(124)*

cent of the 1986 men, and from 56 per of the 1981 women to 49 per cent of the 1986 women. Just under one third of the 1986 men, compared with a quarter of the 1981 men, were in a different specialty, while this was true of a quarter of the 1986 women compared with just over a fifth of the 1981 women. The proportions who had made up their minds since registration were similar for both cohorts, with women rather more likely than men in both years to have made up their minds since registration.

The main difference between the two cohorts was the rather higher proportion in 1986 of both men and women who were not working at all or were working outside medicine, and the higher proportion of women on maternity leave. The differences were slight but reflect some of the trends we have noted elsewhere in this report.

Of those who had chosen a hospital specialty at registration, 71 per cent (78 per cent of the men and 63 per cent of the women) were still in hospital or academic medicine, although not necessarily in the specialty chosen at registration. (In the last study we did not present an analysis of the material by cohort since it was so complicated, but the proportions found in the 1986 cohort are slightly higher than we found for the sample as a whole last time, which is not surprising, given the fact that they were only four years into their careers.) 17 per cent of the 1986 cohort (18 per cent of the men and 16 per cent of the women) who had chosen a hospital specialty at registration had changed to general practice, 2 per cent of both men and women had changed to community/public health, 3 per cent were on maternity leave (6 per cent of the women) and 7 per cent were not working (2 per cent of the men and as many as 14 per cent of the women).

Looking at those who had chosen general practice at registration, the proportions were really very similar. 73 per cent (76 per cent of men and 71 per

Table 7.02   Present specialty/job status compared with specialty choice at registration

column percentages

| | CHOICE AT REGISTRATION | | | | | | | | |
| | Hospital specialty | | | GP | | | No clear idea | | |
	Total	Male	Female	Total	Male	Female	Total	Male	Female
Present specialty/ job status[1]									
Hospital specialty	71	78	63	20	22	19	62	80	56
General practice	17	18	16	73	76	71	29	20	31
Community/ public health	2	2	2	2	0	4	0	0	0
Maternity leave	3	0	6	1	0	2	5	0	6
Not working	7	2	14	3	3	4	5	0	6
Base: all those choosing specialty at registration	*(111)*	*(60)*	*(51)*	*(89)*	*(37)*	*(52)*	*(21)*	*(5)*	*(16)*

1. 9 SHO/GP trainees counted in general practice

cent of women) were still in general practice. 20 per cent (22 per cent of men and 19 per cent of women) were now working in hospital medicine, 2 per cent were working in community/public health (none of the men and 4 per cent of the women), 1 per cent were on maternity leave (2 per cent of the women) and 3 per cent (3 per cent of the men and 4 per cent of the women) were not working.

Of those who had made up their minds since registration, 62 per cent (80 per cent of the men and 56 per cent of the women) were now in hospital medicine, 29 per cent (20 per cent of the men and 31 per cent of the women) were now in general practice, 5 per cent were on maternity leave (6 per cent of the women) and 5 per cent were not working (none of the men and 6 per cent of the women).

Looking at the grades of the doctors' current jobs, we found an interesting pattern. Nearly 90 per cent of GP principals were in the same specialty they had chosen at registration, compared with less than 40 per cent of the SHOs not on a GP vocational training scheme and 47 per cent of GP trainees. However, 60 per cent of the registrars were still in their specialty choice at registration. There can be little doubt that early career decisions can help speed up career progression among doctors. No doubt there was still scope for those doctors who had changed direction after registration to catch up, but nevertheless the perceived stress on progress linked to age and grade remains a formidable force in medical careers. Early decisions on career direction may become even more crucial with the implementation of the Calman Report (Department of Health, 1993) although there is some debate about this.

Table 7.03   Comparison of specialty choice at registration and numbers still working
in same specialty[1]

column percentages

Specialty	TOTAL Choice at reg Nos	Still in spec Nos	%	MALES Choice at reg Nos	Still in spec Nos	%	FEMALES Choice at reg Nos	Still in spec Nos	%
General medicine	28	12	43	12	9	75	16	3	19
Geriatrics	0	0	0	0	0	0	0	0	0
Other medical specialties	3	0	0	3	0	0	0	0	0
Paediatrics	10	4	40	3	1	33	7	3	43
A&E	1	0	0	0	0	0	1	0	0
Surgery	27	19	70	18	13	72	9	6	67
Obs & gynae	5	2	40	1	0	0	4	2	50
Anaesthetics	11	8	73	5	5	100	6	3	50
Radiology	3	3	100	2	2	100	1	1	100
Radiotherapy	1	1	100	1	1	100	0	0	0
Pathology	9	4	44	7	3	43	2	1	50
Psychiatry	11	9	82	5	4	80	6	5	83
Total hospital specialties	*109*	*62*	*57*	*57*	*38*	*67*	*52*	*24*	*46*
General practice	85	62	73	35	27	77	50	35	70

1. 9 SHO/GP trainees counted in general practice

We looked in more detail at the specialties chosen at registration compared
with their present jobs. Table 7.03 shows the numbers of those choosing a
particular specialty at registration and looks at the numbers still working in the
same specialty as a proportion of those who had chosen it at registration. (It must
be remembered that the numbers do not represent all those in the specialty but
only those who had chosen it at registration.) The analysis is by broad specialty
choice and reflect the findings of the last study, although it should be noted that
the comparable table in the last study took the sample of doctors as a whole as
the base (Allen, 1988, p137), so that greater change might have been expected
among them, given the length of the careers of the older doctors. A greater change
was found, but the differences between the earlier findings and Table 7.03 were
not perhaps as marked as might have been expected.

Among the 1986 qualifiers we found that, taking the hospital specialties as
a whole, 57 per cent were still in the same broad specialty, but that this
represented 67 per cent of the men compared with only 46 per cent of the women.

Women were much less likely than the men to stay in the same hospital specialty chosen at registration. (The comparable figures for all qualifiers in the last study were 53 per cent for the men and 43 per cent for the women.) Looking at general practice, we found that 73 per cent of those choosing general practice at registration were still in the specialty (77 per cent of the men and 70 per cent of the women). This reflects the finding in Table 7.02 above, although the figures were arrived at in a slightly different way.

The 1986 qualifiers, like the earlier cohorts, were more likely to have stayed in some specialties chosen at registration than others. For example, although the numbers were small, all those choosing radiology and radiotherapy at registration were still in the specialties. Over 80 per cent of those choosing psychiatry were still in the specialty as were over 70 per cent of those choosing anaesthetics and surgery. However, only around 40 per cent of those choosing general medicine, pathology, paediatrics and obstetrics and gynaecology were still in these specialties, and none of those choosing other medical specialties or A and E had survived in them.

There were some interesting differences between men and women in the proportions still in particular specialties. In general medicine, which was a popular choice at registration among all cohorts, 75 per cent of the men choosing it at registration were still in the specialty compared with less than one fifth of the women. However, women were more likely to have stayed in obstetrics and gynaecology than the men but much less likely to have stayed in anaesthetics. Similarly high proportions of both men and women had stayed in psychiatry if they had chosen it at registration. Interestingly, if women had chosen surgery at registration they were almost as likely as the men to still be in the specialty, which, although the figures were relatively small, was a major change on the last study. However, it remains to be seen whether these young women surgeons are able to progress above SHO or registrar level.

Why did the doctors change specialty? There were certain interesting differences between the 1981 and the 1986 cohorts, as illustrated in Table 7.04. The main reason for both sets of doctors was a greater interest in their present specialty – a factor of particular importance to the 1986 men. The second most frequently cited reason overall was the need for work to fit in with family or domestic commitments, but it was interesting to note a drop from nearly one third of the 1981 women saying this to one in seven of the 1986 women. The assumption has often been that women mention this factor because they want a specialty to fit in with their child care demands. This was clearly still important, but there were other factors, such as geographical mobility and the demands of a dual medical career family which were equally important, as this woman who had changed her intention from general practice at registration to paediatrics explained: 'Although long term I still want to do general practice, I want to see how far in paediatrics I can go. But if a perfect GP post came up I would probably opt out. The main problem is my husband, because if I wasn't married I could get a GP post anywhere, but because he's doing surgery, it's going to be seven

Table 7.04   Most important factor since registration which made doctors change direction/specialty

column percentages

	Total		Male		Female	
	1981	1986	1981	1986	1981	1986
Greater interest in present specialty	25	29	24	34	26	23
Need for work to fit in with family	17	11	4	6	30	16
Needed exp. in (sub) spec. for main specialty	0	11	0	13	0	10
Dissatisfaction with hospital life/work	16	8	24	13	9	3
Failed higher exams	6	6	8	13	4	0
Stop-gap post/looking for GP post	0	6	0	6	0	6
Wanted spec. without long hours	5	6	0	0	9	13
Bored with previous specialty	0	5	0	0	0	10
Opps better in present specialty	8	5	8	9	9	0
Didn't want to study more	0	3	0	3	0	3
Job in present spec. came up when needed	2	2	4	0	0	3
Base: qualifiers with different spec/job from registration decision	*(48)*	*(63)*	*(25)*	*(32)*	*(23)*	*(31)*

years before he can say he's going to be in one place. I don't think, from my knowledge of general practice, that they're going to offer me a partnership if I say I'm going to move in five to six years ...'

The question of geographical mobility is discussed in more detail later in this report, but it appears of increasing importance particularly where both partners are doctors (see Allen, 1992), as a male orthopaedic registrar explained: 'My wife is looking for a job at the moment. She's GP trained but can't get a partnership – I'm too mobile ...'

A factor which had not been mentioned in detail by the 1981 cohort was the need for experience in another specialty or sub-specialty to help their careers in their main specialty. This was mentioned by over 10 per cent of both men and women in the 1986 cohort.

Men in both cohorts were more likely than women to say that they had changed from hospital medicine to general practice because of dissatisfaction with hospital life in general. However, the proportion of 1986 men mentioning this was lower than the quarter of 1981 men who had changed specialty after registration. Nevertheless, it was still an important consideration, as this male GP explained: 'The job was *grim*! After I got MRCP and I became a registrar, the workload was so grim, very long hours, job satisfaction low. I hadn't been married very long – and I couldn't see any prospect of things improving. The desire wasn't there any more. I couldn't see myself as a consultant, and no single specialty attracted me ...'

The 1986 men were just as likely to say that they had changed specialty because they had failed or had difficulty with higher professional examinations. Two new phenomena among the 1986 qualifiers were the number saying that they were using their present post as a 'stop-gap' post while looking for a partnership in general practice and the number saying that they did not want to spend any more time studying for examinations.

Women in both cohorts mentioned that they had changed because they did not want a specialty with long hours, and a number of 1986 women said they had changed because they were bored with their previous specialty, while men were more likely to say that they had changed because the prospects were better in their present specialty. A woman GP trainee gave her reasons for changing from anaesthetics: 'It was the realisation that I couldn't do the job for the rest of my life. I was bored with it after two years. If I had continued to do anaesthetics and then decided five years on that it wasn't for me after all, I would have been stuck with it because I would have had to go back to being an SHO for other careers ...'

Many of the doctors giving reasons to explain their change in specialty such as a greater interest in their present job or boredom with a previous specialty, had clearly chosen the wrong specialty at registration, often with little idea of what it entailed. A woman who had changed from pathology to general practice had evidently had a misconception both of the specialty and her own preferences: 'I hated doing post mortems – just being faced with a dead body on a Monday morning. You're on your own. The morticians are a bit peculiar and they spend the whole morning telling you jokes. You didn't have any patient contact at all – just sitting in front of a microscope. I couldn't face it for the rest of my life. People who knew me said, "I never thought you'd like it." I like *talking* to people ...'

But the reason for career or specialty change often related to a combination of factors, as summarised by a male GP principal who had set out with the intention of becoming a consultant physician: 'It's a combination of things. I detested the long hours in hospital. You're expected to work totally unreasonable hours. You're working flat out for long periods of time and I don't think you can expect any human being to work like that. I didn't like the insecurity in that every twelve months you have to get your contract renewed, and once you've got a mortgage and everything I find that very unsettling. And finally, the career structure is non-existent. I met doctors during my time in hospital who were very competent, who had passed all their exams but were still stuck at registrar level, and I didn't want that to happen to me ...'

There was one interesting difference between both the 1981 and 1986 cohorts and earlier cohorts, which was the tiny proportion saying that a job in their present specialty had come up when they needed one. This had been much more frequently mentioned by earlier cohorts when explaining their change of specialty. It must be seen as part of the tightening job market and the decreasing extent to which chance and serendipity can influence the careers of doctors.

We observed in the last report that doctors from earlier cohorts had often changed specialty more than once but had still managed to reach career grade with apparent ease. This might perhaps have been expected of the men, but there were indications that a relatively high proportion of the 1966 women had changed specialty more than once, fitted in having children with few problems to their careers, followed their husbands around the country, but had still reached consultant or GP principal status by their middle or late thirties. We noted that this appeared to be a pattern which was no longer possible, and that younger doctors interviewed were very much aware of the dangers of changing specialty if they wished to keep their feet firmly on the career ladder. Many of these comments were reinforced in the present study, but women in particular often found it difficult to remain in the specialty they had chosen at registration for reasons outlined above. Some, however, had not yet changed specialty, but were at a crossroads in their career.

Present specialty and changes since entry to medical school
We recorded the career intentions of the doctors at entry to medical school, at qualification, at registration and recorded their present job. This section traces the changes in career intentions recorded by the doctors. Table 7.05 brings together the career choices at the three stages of their careers discussed so far and compares them with the specialty or branch of medicine they were working in or had chosen at the time we interviewed them. Their present job is shown in two forms, first with the SHO/GP trainees in the general practice category, which was their actual career intention, and secondly, in the hospital specialty they were working in at the time of our interview with them.

The table shows aggregated figures and does not indicate the changes among the individual doctors which have been discussed in previous chapters. It takes men and women together, and can be examined in conjunction with the comparable table in the last report which looked at all years of qualifiers together (Allen, 1988, p.145).

Essentially, the table confirms the pattern found in the last study, with the proviso that the last table included doctors from all three cohorts so that present specialty was perhaps more firmly fixed for the two older cohorts. The last study showed a clear drift to general practice after registration, whereas this table indicates that a choice of general practice was more often made at qualification

Table 7.05   Career/ specialty choice of doctors at different stages of career and present job (1986 qualifiers only)

column percentages

	At entry to med. school	At qual.	At reg.	Present job[1]	Present job[2]
General medicine	3	10	12	8	8
Geriatric medicine	0	0	0	0	1
Other medical specialties	1	2	1	3	3
Paediatrics	5	4	4	6	7
A&E	0	0	*	2	3
Surgery	11	13	12	10	10
Obs & gynae	1	3	2	1	2
Anaesthetics	*	2	5	6	6
Radiology	0	*	1	2	2
Radiotherapy	0	1	*	1	1
Pathology	3	3	4	3	3
Psychiatry	4	3	5	7	8
Oral surgery	*	*	0	*	*
General practice	24	37	39	39	35
Community/public health	0	0	0	2	2
Others[3]	7	7	3	*	*
No clear idea	38	14	9	0	0
Not working/out of medicine	0	*	1	9	9
Base: all qualifiers	*(229)*	*(229)*	*(229)*	*(229)*	*(229)*

1. 9 SHO/GP trainees counted in general practice
2. 9 SHO/GP trainees counted in hospital specialty
3. Includes go abroad, choice of two specialties, research and non-clinical medicine

(35 per cent of 1986 qualifiers compared with 28 per cent of all qualifiers in the last study). The actual proportion of 1986 qualifiers working in general practice at present (39 per cent including the SHO/GP trainees) was slightly lower than that found among all qualifiers in the last study (42 per cent), and may have longer-term implications for general practice, when taken in conjunction with other evidence in this report.

The table repeats the findings of the last report of interest in general medicine peaking at registration but falling off by the present job. There were slightly more 1986 qualifiers currently working in paediatrics and surgery than found among all qualifiers in the last study, fewer in obstetrics and gynaecology, radiology and pathology and about the same in psychiatry. The numbers and proportions are tiny, but may be indicative of trends, even allowing for the fact that the last table included qualifiers from all years. The last study showed more than double the proportion of doctors currently working in community or public health than among the 1986 qualifiers, but this is probably largely accounted for by the older women qualifiers in the last study. It is also likely to reflect the trend away from community health into general practice demanded by young women both in the last study and in the present research.

Doctors who were not working or who were working outside medicine
There were 14 doctors (3 men and 11 women) who were not working at the time that we interviewed them. They represented 6 per cent of the total sample of 1986 qualifiers (3 per cent of the men and 9 per cent of the women), which was an increase on the proportions found in the last study of 5 per cent of women in each cohort of doctors studied and one man in the total sample of 640 doctors.

There were two doctors who were working outside medicine – one man who was a teacher and one woman who was managing a health-related unit. Five women were on maternity leave. There were no doctors who were working both inside and outside medicine, but there were three doctors who were working outside clinical medicine but in medically related occupations: a female senior registrar in public health, a male registrar in public health and a male research fellow in pathology. For the purposes of most of the tables in this report these three have been included in the grades and specialty counts, and are only mentioned here to complete the picture of those working outside clinical medicine.

This section is devoted to the doctors who were not working or were working outside medicine at the time that we interviewed them. This is the group who might potentially be 'lost' to medicine and we wanted to explore the reasons why they were not currently working in medicine and to see whether they intended to return. In addition, we comment briefly on the women who were on maternity leave at the time of the interview, who were found in the last study to be quite different from the other doctors who were not working when we interviewed them. The present research replicated these findings.

The two doctors who were working outside medicine had both left medicine because they did not enjoy it and preferred non-medical work. Both felt they had made the wrong decision to enter medicine, and one explained why he had left after registration: 'I came out late rather than early in the course because I was afraid of failing in my father's eyes and disappointing him. However, perhaps it was good to actually qualify and get the house jobs done. I'm not sure. The stress and hurt of the last years – I'm not sure that they were worth it. It might have been better to come out early ...' Neither of them intended to return to medicine, and one hoped to become a missionary.

We found in the last study that it was impossible to present the material about the doctors who were not working at the time that we interviewed them in any tabular form. Their experience and reasons were so diverse that it was not really possible to draw firm conclusions from them. We found the same thing to be true in this study. Among the 14 doctors who were not working when we interviewed them, 7 simply said they were not working or were between jobs (6 women and 1 man), 4 were studying (2 men and 2 women) and 3 (all women) said that they were unemployed, although these women also felt themselves to be between jobs.

Looking at the last jobs of the 7 who were not working, 2 had been GP trainees and, in fact, were both waiting for partnerships, 4 (including the man) had been SHOs, and 1 had been a registrar. Among the 4 who were studying, 3 had been SHOs and 1 had been a locum registrar, while the 3 women who said they were unemployed had all been SHOs, one of whom had only returned from abroad the week before we interviewed her.

The last jobs of the 14 doctors who were not working, studying or unemployed were scattered across the specialties, although 3 had been in obstetrics, 2 in paediatrics, 2 in a surgical specialty and 2 in general practice. They had all been working full-time, on average nearly 80 hours a week.

Three of the women who were not working had children while the other 3 women and the man had no children. All 4 of the doctors who were studying and all 3 of the unemployed doctors had no children.

Half the non-working doctors had given up their last job in the previous six months, a further 3 within the last year and 4 women had given up between one and two years before.

Only 2 of the 14 non-working doctors said they were not working at the moment for family or child care reasons. Two said they were just taking time out to study and one had found it difficult to pass higher professional examinations. Two wanted time out to decide on their future and one was finding difficulty in getting part-time work in general practice. Three wanted more time for other interests, while two said they did not enjoy working in medicine.

All but two said they definitely intended to return to medicine: one said he did not know whether he would or not and one was sure she would not. One third of those intending to return said they would return within a year, while the others were less sure when they would return. Half of them said they would return when suitable posts became available. The doctors split fairly evenly between those who intended to return to general practice and those who wanted to continue in hospital medicine. The doctor who was sure she did not want to return to medicine intended to pursue a career in accountancy or computing.

It would be fair to say that only three of the 229 qualifiers from 1986 were really lost to medicine by the time we interviewed them in 1991, although it was quite possible that some of the others, not only among those who were not working at the time, would leave medicine. It may appear remarkable that so few doctors had abandoned medicine, given the levels of dissatisfaction and regret we found among those interviewed. We have observed before how difficult it was for doctors to change direction at any stage in their careers, and there can be little doubt that it became increasingly difficult the older they got.

Looking briefly at the women on maternity leave at the time of the interview, all but one intended to return to medicine as quickly as possible after their maternity leave. They had given up working on average three months before the interview. All had been working full-time, three as GP trainees, one as an SHO/GP trainee and one as an SHO, with an average of 70 hours or ten sessions a week. Four of them already had one child and one had no children. The doctor who did not intend to return to the same job at the end of her maternity leave already had a child, but did not intend to leave medicine.

Like their counterparts in the last study, the women on maternity leave were usually satisfied with their work, thought they had had a successful career in medicine and had every intention of working in career grade posts. They were typical of many of the 1976, 1981 and other 1986 women qualifiers who intended to combine a career and family. It remains to be seen how successful they will be. Evidence from the follow-up study of 1976 and 1981 qualifiers indicates that it is more difficult than some of the women respondents had expected to attain success both in career and family terms.

We observed in the last report that it is very difficult to draw any firm conclusions about doctors who are not working in medicine in order to develop a policy of keeping doctors in medicine. The reasons given by doctors for not working in medicine at the moment were diffuse and often rather vague. Some had clearly made a mistake in choosing medicine at all, but so had some who were still working in medicine. Most regarded their status outside medicine as temporary, and perhaps it should not be regarded as surprising that some people want a breather from a career which everyone regarded as demanding and many regarded as exhausting.

We have noted before that many people change direction or change careers in other professions, but it is only in medicine that such a change is regarded as so unusual or unlikely. The evidence from this report suggests that the vast majority of men and women remain in medicine, that few leave it for any length of time and that the 'pool' of doctors outside medicine is tiny and of little significance in manpower planning. It is much more important to ensure that those remaining in medicine feel satisfied and secure in their work and that they are able to fulfil their potential and maximise their contribution.

8 Influences on doctors' careers – 'patrons' and 'sponsors'

In the last report we explored in some detail the question of whether doctors' careers were influenced by the patronage or 'sponsorship' of individual senior doctors who helped to advance the careers of their protegees by encouraging them to apply for certain jobs, giving personal references and generally offering guidance and support as well as making personal behind-the-scenes 'word-of-mouth' recommendations to potential employers. The research uncovered widespread evidence that personal patronage in medicine, far from being a thing of the past, was generally perceived as being alive and well and an integral part of the medical career structure.

We had assumed at the start of our last study that patronage would be dying out, particularly with the general stress on equality of opportunity in employment backed up by legislation which had been introduced in recent years. We had also assumed that younger doctors would have had more access than earlier generations to independent systematic careers advice and information so that the need for informal help and guidance from a personal patron or mentor would have diminished. We very quickly found that our assumptions were wrong. Far from fading away, we found that patronage was thought to be flourishing. Indeed, the youngest cohort of doctors, the 1981 qualifiers, were much more likely than the older doctors to think that patrons were very important in furthering doctors' careers.

After the last report was published, some senior doctors commented that 'patronage' is found in every profession and that medicine is simply following the generally accepted pattern of making sure that the best person is appointed for the job. It was also said that our research reported on 'perceptions'. We discussed in the last report how important it was to report on perceptions, since doctors' careers may well be as much affected by beliefs about how to advance in medicine as by how the system really works in practice. However, the data collected in the last study suggested that many of the 'perceptions' were based on hard experience and that there were employment practices in medicine which would not stand up to close scrutiny by those wishing to ensure that the legal requirements surrounding equal opportunities were being met.

These factors were compounded by other practices in appointments and job interviews which were clearly discriminatory. The most recent evidence on this is discussed in Chapter 10. The Department of Health followed up the recommendations of the last report by referring to them in their guidance on equal opportunities in recruitment and selection procedures for hospital and community doctors (Department of Health, 1991). The British Medical Association was concerned enough about the issues surrounding patronage identified in the last report to make *Patronage in the Medical Profession* the subject of one of the reports from the Career Progress of Doctors Working Party (BMA, 1993).

Importance of patrons and sponsors

We had found in the last study that over 50 per cent of the 1981 qualifiers had thought that having patrons or sponsors in the medical profession was very important in furthering the careers of doctors, compared with 38 per cent of both the 1966 and 1976 cohorts. Identical proportions of 1981 men and women held this view, while among earlier cohorts men were more likely than women to find patrons and sponsors very important. It was difficult to determine whether the 1981 cohort felt that patronage was more important than earlier generations because of their particular stage of their career, which was at a time when they were usually changing jobs frequently and therefore more likely to be aware of the need for references, or whether there was a genuine shift in perception or behaviour. There is another factor which was found to be important, which was the greater dislike found among the 1981 qualifiers for the system of patronage, which many of them deplored. This could equally well have influenced their answers in assessing the importance of patronage.

Table 8.01   How important patrons or sponsors are in furthering doctors' careers

column percentages

	Male			Female		
	1976	1981	1986	1976	1981	1986
Very important	44	52	45	32	52	45
Important	21	21	23	19	21	22
Fairly important	14	10	24	12	6	19
Not very important	10	6	1	12	6	4
Not important	2	3	4	8	4	3
Don't know	10	8	4	16	11	7
Base: all qualifiers	*(105)*	*(101)*	*(105)*	*(105)*	*(103)*	*(124)*

Table 8.01 compares the views of the 1986 qualifiers with those of the 1976 and 1981 qualifiers. We found that among both the 1981 and 1986 qualifiers men and women held very similar views, with 52 per cent of the 1981 qualifiers of both sexes finding patronage very important in furthering doctors' careers and 21 per cent finding it important – giving a total of nearly three-quarters of the

1981 qualifiers regarding patronage as important or very important. Among the 1986 qualifiers, the relative proportions were 45 per cent of both sexes finding patronage very important, and 23 per cent of men and 22 per cent of women finding it important – nearly 70 per cent of the 1986 qualifiers – a decrease on the 1981 total. However, fewer 1986 qualifiers thought patronage unimportant. (It should be noted that some 10 per cent of the 1986 qualifiers thought that patronage or sponsorship referred to some kind of financial support by helping to get money for research. This interpretation was found less often among the older cohorts of doctors.)

Among the 1976 qualifiers there was a difference between men and women with 44 per cent of men but only 32 per cent of women regarding patronage as very important, and 21 per cent of men and 19 per cent of women regarding it as important – a total of two-thirds of the 1976 men but only just over half the women.

Views on patronage and sponsorship

We had found in the last report that men were rather more likely to approve of patronage than women, but that the proportion of those disapproving increased steadily through the cohorts, with the older doctors much more tolerant of the system than the 1981 qualifiers. As Table 8.02 shows, in the present study we found an interesting increase among those who approved of the system, with 38 per cent of the men and 30 per cent of the women saying that it was a good thing generally. However, the proportion of men disapproving remained the same as that found among the 1981 men at 32 per cent, but the proportion of women disapproving declined from 39 per cent among the 1981 women to 32 per cent among the 1986 women. The 1986 men were more likely to be neutral than previous cohorts, with a quarter saying that they neither approved nor disapproved, compared with one third of the 1986 women.

Table 8.02   Doctors' assessment of system of patronage in careers

column percentages

| | | Male | | | Female | |
	1976	1981	1986	1976	1981	1986
Approve	26	30	38	25	23	30
Disapprove	27	32	32	30	39	32
Neither approve nor disapprove	35	30	26	30	28	32
Don't know	12	9	6	16	10	6
Base: all qualifiers	*(105)*	*(101)*	*(105)*	*(105)*	*(103)*	*(124)*

What were the reasons given by the 1986 qualifiers who thought patronage was a good thing? A quarter of both men and women thought that everyone needed a helping hand or someone to be interested in them. They often interpreted the question to refer to a personal mentor, like a male research registrar: 'I approve generally. It means that people are promoted for their recognised ability to do a job rather than how they appear on paper. I think that's crucial ...' Another male registrar cast a little more light on how patronage still worked in practice: 'It's a good thing. The short-listing system is so pathetic – a little CV, a 10-minute interview. How can they assess you on that? They talked to me about my rowing career! So a word from your consultant is vital. Of course, the old-boy network works as well ...'

Others valued the personal help they felt they had been given, like a male GP principal: 'On balance it's a good thing. You can get one-to-one careers advice, and you're pushed to do things you hadn't thought of doing ...' Others thought it the best system in an unfair world, like a male psychiatric registrar: 'I would disapprove except that without it more unsuitable people would advance. I generally disapprove of that sort of thing, but you cannot really disapprove in medicine as it works better with it than without it ...'

Another male psychiatric registrar strongly disagreed: 'It's very bad – it benefits people like me – white, male, middle-class. I haven't ever solicited or sought it but it's worked for me. It puts me at a distinct advantage. It's important for people who haven't got patrons to have references read afterwards ...'

A male locum GP was quite clear where he stood: 'It stinks. People get chosen on who they know rather than what they can do – jobs for the boys ...' And a male trainee GP agreed: 'I think it's a dreadful thing, maybe because I've never had a patron. They become like godfathers, you know ...'

A number of women were even more vociferous in their condemnation of a system they saw as perpetuating the old-boy network, like a woman psychiatric registrar: 'In medicine it's mainly white, middle class and male. Personally I've seen very good people who don't fit a personality stereotype with the consultant surgeon, whose careers have floundered – and more worryingly because of race ...' A woman GP trainee agreed: 'At the moment it works as an old-boys' network. I think there's a sort of "if you're white, middle-class, male and play rugby and fit into a nice little pigeon-hole", then you're more likely to be taken notice of ...'

There must be some concern at the number of comments from both men and women respondents that stressed the greater ease experienced by 'white, middle-class males' in acquiring patrons. No references were made in the last study to difficulties experienced by qualifiers from minority ethnic groups in acquiring patrons, but it was commented on by a number of doctors in the present research.

A male research registrar summarised the views of a number of doctors who felt that patronage was acceptable if it worked in their favour but that it could be a double-edged sword: 'It discriminates against people who have less forthcoming or less influential contacts. I've seen a huge change in my own circumstances from being in the situation where no-one supported me to now, when everyone's behind me. It's very unfair on those who don't have that backing ...'

Around one in six of both men and women commented on what they saw as the unfairness of the 'old-boy' network, which was thought to take many forms, from encouraging people to act as 'good blokes' to 'creeping to seniors' to 'getting in on the St Thomas's cocktail circuit ...' There was concern that the constant need for references, particularly in the early years of postgraduate medicine, not only encouraged sycophantic behaviour but also, as a female medical researcher noted, could discourage doctors from 'making any complaint for fear of "the reference". You're gagged and bound. For example, I never dared say I was interested in general practice in case they saw it as a lack of commitment ...'

Over one in ten of the 1986 qualifiers thought that the system might not be fair but that it was inevitable. Others were concerned about the secrecy and behind-the-scenes way in which it worked, like a male research fellow: 'It's not formally structured and therefore no-one knows how it works until you're in it...' A woman registrar could have enlightened him: 'It's mainly done by phoning up – or a discussion over dinner. I've even heard discussion over the operating table ...'

The perceived unfairness of the system was commented on by a number of doctors who had benefited from it themselves but had seen others 'as competent as me who had no-one to help them ...' It was said that the system 'favours those who shout loudest' and operated in a very personal way, with little allowance for personality clashes in what was referred to as the 'single reference system'. Others thought it was much more important in hospital medicine than in general practice.

But a small number of doctors were clearly totally oblivious of anything that could be called patronage, like a woman GP trainee: 'I've never heard of it. It sounds very nice ...'

In the last study we found that the 1966 qualifiers, many of whom were operating the system of patronage, gave a fascinating insight into how it worked, particularly in hospital medicine. The 1976 and 1981 qualifiers had less first-hand experience of what actually went on, but gave graphic accounts of how they thought it worked. In reading the interviews from all cohorts it was striking how frequently informal chats were said to precede oral or written references, and how often powerful consultants pushing for their protegees were said to distort the fairness of the system of appointments.

We asked the 1986 qualifiers how they thought the patronage system worked in practice. Over 50 per cent of the men but only 40 per cent of the women said it worked by providing good references. Around 50 per cent of both sexes said that it worked by the provision of oral as well as written references. Around 40 per cent of both men and women said it worked by the patron providing personal advice to young doctors, and over one third of the men and women said that it provided useful contacts.

A male general surgical registrar summarised how he thought patronage worked: 'Backers will look at your career, advise you on good and bad jobs, influence good career moves, will write references and also speak personally to people you apply to. Backers have to be well-known, respected, important and generally heads of departments in teaching hospitals, for example professors of surgery ...'

Advancement in medicine was often described by all cohorts of qualifiers as dependent on personal relationships and contacts to an extent which was somewhat unusual in other fields of employment. Part of this appeared to be related to the traditional role of senior doctors in teaching their juniors the craft of their profession. A woman psychiatric registrar described how patronage worked in her experience: 'They give people jobs. They get people jobs. They teach them more when they're actually in a job. They socialise together, so they introduce them socially to people who could help them. On rotations they'll give them the better jobs ...'

The last study noted the emphasis placed by respondents from all cohorts on the importance of patrons telephoning other consultants or members of interviewing panels to push their candidate. Telephone contact alone was mentioned by over a fifth of the 1986 respondents and seemed to be as influential as ever, according to many of them, from a male general medical registrar – 'He has to ring – otherwise you won't get on the short list ...' – to a female locum SHO – 'Consultants will phone up the interviewing panel and put in a good word for you. People will often take personal recommendations by word of mouth. Reputations are very important in medicine ...' – to a male GP principal – 'It's like the masons. People phone up and get them a job. The people who get the jobs are those who know the most people ...'

The reputation and contacts of the patron were thought to be of paramount importance – as a woman research fellow pointed out – 'People are employed because of the person giving the reference rather than what the reference contains ...' And the personal contacts of the patron were seen as vital by many doctors including a male trainee GP who had changed specialty from general medicine: 'They know the right steps to get you through the maze. It sounds malevolent and devious, but it doesn't come across as that – at the time they seem nice. In fact the only way to get a research job is through a consultant. Research jobs aren't advertised usually ...'

Personal experience of patronage or sponsorship
We asked the doctors whether they themselves had ever had anyone who had helped to further their careers by acting as a patron or sponsor. As Table 8.03 shows, among the 1986 cohort, 58 per cent of men and 57 per cent of women said they had, compared with a similar proportion of 1981 men but fewer 1981

Table 8.03   Whether doctors had ever had 'patrons' or sponsors

column percentages

| | Male | | | Female | | |
	1976	1981	1986	1976	1981	1986
Yes	50	59	58	48	53	57
No	50	41	42	52	47	42
Base: all qualifiers	*(105)*	*(101)*	*(105)*	*(105)*	*(103)*	*(124)*

women, and around half the 1976 men and women. Again we were surprised to find that patronage appeared to be increasing rather than decreasing in medicine.

We found in the last study that men doctors with patrons tended to have rather more than women, but Table 8.04 shows that this pattern was changing among the 1986 qualifiers. Among the men from 1976 and 1981 nearly two-thirds of those with patrons mentioned more than one, while the proportion had increased to nearly 70 per cent among the 1981 men. Among the women, well under half the 1976 and 1981 cohorts had more than one patron, but this proportion had increased to nearly 60 per cent among the 1986 women.

Table 8.04   How many 'patrons' doctors have had

column percentages

| | Male | | | Female | | |
	1976	1981	1986	1976	1981	1986
One	36	38	30	56	56	41
Two or three	41	52	50	30	34	42
Four or more	22	8	19	12	9	15
Not stated	2	2	2	2	0	2
Base: all qualifiers with patrons	*(53)*	*(60)*	*(61)*	*(50)*	*(55)*	*(71)*

In the last study we found that the most frequently mentioned patrons were male consultants, cited by over 60 per cent of the 1981 qualifiers with patrons, compared with less than half the earlier qualifiers. The increasing importance of male consultants was shown by the fact that two-thirds of the 1986 qualifiers with patrons mentioned one as their most important patron. On the other hand, male professors were mentioned by a quarter of the 1966 qualifiers compared with 11 per cent of both 1981 and 1986 qualifiers. Around 12 per cent of all cohorts in the previous study mentioned a male GP or GP trainer, a pattern

Table 8.05   Most important occasion on which 'patron' helped

column percentages

| | Male | | | Female | | |
	1976	1981	1986	1976	1981	1986
Pre-reg posts	6	5	3	0	2	7
First SHO post	13	12	18	16	20	15
Subsequent SHO post(s)	11	37	21	20	25	37
Registrar post(s)	21	18	30	10	22	20
Sen. registrar post(s)	21	3	2	12	0	1
Consultant post(s)	4	0	0	8	0	0
GP VTS advice	15	17	3	18	27	3
GP trainee post(s)	0	0	5	0	0	15
GP principal post(s)	8	5	10	6	4	7
Academic post(s) (research/lecturer)	6	5	10	4	0	4
Clinical asst. post	0	0	0	2	2	1
Comm/public health post	0	0	0	4	2	0
At every stage	2	0	3	2	0	0
Base: all qualifiers with patrons	*(53)*	*(60)*	*(61)*	*(50)*	*(55)*	*(71)*

repeated among the 1986 qualifiers, although women were more likely to cite a GP trainer than men.

In the last study we found that women were rarely cited as the most important patrons, although 4 per cent from all cohorts mentioned a female consultant. This compared with 5 per cent of the 1986 qualifiers. Women GP trainers were mentioned by 2 per cent of the 1986 qualifiers. It can hardly be said that women were emerging as important patrons in medicine.

We asked the doctors to name the most important occasion on which their patron helped them. Table 8.05 shows that the 1976 cohort, who were five years further on in their careers, were more likely to mention senior registrar or consultant posts than the two later cohorts. Comparing the 1981 and 1986 cohorts, it can be seen that the 1981 men were more likely to mention subsequent SHO posts and GP vocational training advice than the 1986 men, and that the 1981 women were more likely to mention GP vocational training advice than the 1986 women and less likely to mention subsequent SHO posts. It can be seen by the way the most important occasions for help are spread across the grades that personal patronage in medicine is by no means restricted to one type of job or grade, but is very much related to personal circumstances.

What kind of help did these patrons give? More than half the 1986 qualifiers said that they gave good references, and a similar proportion said they gave person to person recommendations, which meant something rather different. One fifth of the men but over one third of the women said the patron had given general advice and encouragement in their careers. Nearly a quarter of the men, but less than one fifth of the women said their patron had told them whom to approach for a job. Ten per cent of both men and women said their patron had told them that a job was available and had put them forward for it. A scattering of other patrons had helped doctors fill in forms, obtained money for them to do research, had offered them jobs, had used their influence when sitting on appointments boards, had helped them with part-time training or had encouraged them to get higher qualifications.

These findings were similar to the findings from the last study, with one rather surprising exception. We had found that the 1981 qualifiers appeared to be seeking and finding rather functional help from patrons, rather than general advice and encouragement in their careers. This trend was reversed in the 1986 cohort, and is perhaps symptomatic of the need expressed throughout these interviews with 1986 qualifiers for someone to take a more personal interest in them as individuals.

The power of personal recommendations was highlighted by many doctors in the last report. The system was still thought to operate in very much the same way, as a male orthopaedic registrar pointed out: 'He helped me get my current job. He was on the interviewing committee and there was some informal nobbling of the rest of the committee ...' His view was repeated by a male GP principal: 'He encouraged me to go for the post, gave me a reference and got me short-listed. It was done by the panel, but if he recommended you, you got the job. He was very well-respected ...'

The most important result from the help of patrons was that doctors got the post they were seeking, as we found in the last study. However, an interesting development among the 1986 qualifiers was that over a quarter of the women and around one fifth of the men said that the most important way in which the patron had helped was to encourage them to stay in the specialty they were working in. There was little doubt among this cohort that the lack of personal encouragement and support was felt much more acutely than in previous generations, and this was one indication of how good 'patrons' could achieve beneficial results, both for individual doctors and for medicine as a whole.

Negative patrons

In the last study we came across many instances of respondents who described the negative influence that powerful senior doctors could have on the careers of junior doctors. We decided to add some questions asking whether the 1986 qualifiers had ever had anyone who had had a particularly negative effect on their careers, and what effect this had had.

We found that 12 per cent of both men and women in the 1986 cohort said that they had had a 'negative patron'. Most of them had had only one, but a handful said they had had more than one. In most cases, the patron with a negative effect had been a male consultant, although there were mentions for female consultants and other grades of doctors, and, interestingly, 2 per cent of all women mentioned nurses.

Of the 28 qualifiers with negative patrons, one third said they had affected their pre-registration posts, over one in ten mentioned their first SHO post and over 40 per cent mentioned subsequent SHO posts, while one in ten mentioned a GP trainee post.

What did they do? It was interesting that only around one in eight mentioned bad references. It appeared that it was much more common for 'negative patrons' to be generally unsupportive and unhelpful, mentioned by nearly three-quarters of the women but less than half the men. Around one in eight said their negative patron had prevented them from getting a post they had applied for.

The numbers of doctors who openly admitted to negative influences in their careers might have been relatively limited, but their anger and frustration was not. In some instances it appeared that doctors had been unaware of the fact that someone had a low opinion of them, and were not even aware of poor behind-the-scenes references until someone had told them. There was a general feeling of powerlessness in the face of unknown 'blackballing'. A woman GP principal spoke of her negative patron: 'He was a surgeon and gave me a bad reference for the vocational training scheme. I had no idea of his opinion at all. It was completely unjustified. It was a power issue between a consultant surgeon and a consultant anaesthetist. Each thought he was God ...' She felt she had been squeezed between the competing demands of two powerful consultants and had ended up with a poor reference. She had managed to become a GP principal, but was concerned about a system in which personal preferences and animosities could play so large a part, particularly in a secretive way.

Many of the doctors with negative patrons reinforced her description, with a number of references to rivalry between consultants. The power of individual consultants in giving references, whether oral or written, with little or no recourse to the opinion of others, was thought to play an unduly important role in the advancement of doctors, particularly at an early stage. A male anaesthetic SHO felt his career had been blighted in his pre-registration year by a consultant surgeon: 'He sent in a very critical negative report on me to the postgraduate dean and basically tried to get me failed for my first house job ... It made me very angry and very cynical. It made me very distrustful of the NHS and of consultants who can wield such influence. It was one of the factors that influenced me to quit for a year. It made me very bitter ...'

Doctors also felt powerless in the face of what they saw as personality differences between them and consultants, and there were a number of allusions to the recurring theme of the last report – the perception that 'successful' doctors would fit a particular conventional mould. Women often felt they would never fit in, like a woman locum SHO, who felt that she had lost her way: 'A consultant general surgeon in my pre-registration post sapped my confidence. I am quietly spoken and it stopped me speaking out. He also said I would do better in a shorter skirt. I did not feel so confident as a woman, and I actually split up with my first fiancee – a medic. I didn't think I could ever have a medical career. It was awful – I was wrong, but so was that surgeon. Possibly things went wrong from that point ...'

We have noted before what a high proportion of 1986 qualifiers thought that nurses treated women doctors differently from men. A particularly negative influence was cited by a woman GP principal: 'A ward sister in my pre-registration post stuck the boot in and made my life difficult in general. She reported me to the consultant for something trivial and I got blown up. I felt victimised. She didn't like me and so made my life difficult. I was very unhappy in the job and I got put off surgery. I went to another job in the hospital and really enjoyed it, so I know it was just her ...'

The importance of personal relationships in medicine was a constant feature of this research, and so was the emphasis on the success of 'conventional people with conventional careers'. Men were thought much more likely to fit this description than women. Were they more likely to acquire patrons as well? In the last study we found that around one fifth of men from all cohorts thought that they were, but that, although this view was held by over one third of the earlier cohorts of women , the proportion of 1981 women thinking this dropped slightly. As Table 8.06 shows, however, the proportion of 1986 women considering that men were more likely to acquire patrons than women had risen to 37 per cent, and, interestingly, their view was shared by a quarter of the 1986 men.

Table 8.06   Whether men doctors more likely to acquire 'patrons' than women doctors

						column percentages
	Male			Female		
	1976	1981	1986	1976	1981	1986
Yes	18	20	25	38	28	37
No	50	51	56	44	51	41
Don't know	31	29	19	18	20	22
Base: all qualifiers	*(105)*	*(101)*	*(105)*	*(105)*	*(103)*	*(124)*

Why did the doctors think that this happened? Over 40 per cent of the men holding this view and just under one third of the women said it was because of the old-boy network and that men looked after men. However, well over one third of the women thought that it was because men were seen as a better investment because they were thought to stay longer in the job. This view had been shared more or less equally by a similar proportion of the 1981 qualifiers, but it was hardly mentioned by the 1986 men. One third of the 1986 men but only one fifth of the women thought that the system favoured patronage of men because of the traditional dominance of men in certain specialties like surgery.

A quarter of the men and around one in ten of the women thought it happened because men congregated together, while around one in ten of both sexes thought it was because men shared the same leisure interests. The two often went together, as a male research fellow noted: 'They tend to do more sports together and to go drinking together. They just become "mates". It's a very different relationship with a female ...'

The old-boy network in medicine was seen as very deep-rooted, and the literal interpretation was still thought important, in spite of the fact that increasing proportions of men and women qualifiers were from state schools. A woman SHO explained: 'In teaching hospitals it perpetuates the old boy network. It's particularly noticeable at (my London medical school) where a very large percentage of people in my year had been privately educated, so a lot of people, particularly men, were *used* to the system. They'd seen it used, not just in medicine but in other walks of life ...'

A male SHO reinforced her comments: 'In London it's the background of the students. A lot of public schoolboys go to London to train and a lot of the consultants are ex-public schoolboys and a lot of the activities are very masculine. It's the old boy network, rugby club and beer-drinking. And the women either have to join in the wild excesses or not be part of the scene ...' A male anaesthetic registrar drew attention to the differences between Scotland and the south of England: 'It put me off general medicine as a career. It's much worse down here. The old-boy network is so strong. I'm out of it anyway because I went to a comprehensive ...'

But some respondents thought that men tended to offer patronage to men rather than women because of the possibility that their 'patronage' of women might be misinterpreted – 'Consultants who "patronise" a girl must be careful because of their reputation ...' was the view of a male GP principal shared by others.

The continuing importance of patronage in particular specialties was taken as a fact of life by many, including a registrar in general surgery: 'If I was a woman and/or not white, I wouldn't go into surgery. You're immediately disadvantaged. You would fail ...' A woman GP on the retainer scheme agreed: 'It tends to make surgery and orthopaedics in particular much harder to enter as a female ...'

It was observed that there were not enough women to act as patrons to women, that men were more likely to 'toady up' to consultants than women and that men were more single-minded than women. Some one in six of the women but far fewer men thought that the reason for greater patronage of men doctors was that women were not taken seriously in medicine.

So what were the main effects of all this? Over a third of both men and women who thought men found it easier to acquire patrons than women thought it meant that men had an easier career path than women. One third of the men and a quarter of the women thought that it meant that men were more likely to get the better jobs in medicine, while around one fifth of both sexes thought that it perpetuated the system which kept medicine male-dominated. One fifth of the women thought that it meant that women had to try harder and be better at their jobs than men, and more than one in ten women said it discouraged women from trying for hospital medicine or certain hospital specialties. Essentially, it was thought by most men and women to have the effect of putting women at a disadvantage in career terms. A woman registrar who was about to leave medicine thought it had potentially disastrous effects: 'It will either make you more determined to prove that you do the job as well as a man – *or* it will make you realise that you are fighting a losing battle, and that you should try an easier or less demanding specialty. This is why I decided A and E would be a more sensible option than general surgery ...'

There was a general confirmation of the view expressed in the last report that the system of patronage tended to reinforce the perpetuation of certain behaviour patterns and to encourage a conventional and standardised image of how to 'get on' in medicine. A male GP trainee thought that the system had a stultifying effect on medicine: 'It means really that certain personality types are favoured. It favours the outgoing conformists ...' It appeared that a lot of men did not fit this mould but that women found it even more difficult.

We observed in the last report that the main criticism of patronage was its secrecy and lack of openness. It was clearly unfair as it operated and open to legal challenge in terms of equal opportunities. We were disturbed to find that it still appeared to be flourishing in a climate where so much was supposed to have changed. Equal opportunities guidance had been issued, the whole system of patronage had been brought out into the open and debated (BMA, 1993) and yet many of the accounts supplied by the young doctors interviewed in this follow-up study replicated the accounts given by their counterparts five years earlier. We have noted that custom and practice in medicine are very firmly rooted and that they represent a very powerful structure. There are undoubtedly many members of the medical profession who find the present system inequitable and unacceptable. And yet it persists, to many eyes totally unchanged. If it continues with the same strength, there can be little doubt that many able doctors will fail to achieve their potential, which will not only be their loss, but also a loss to the medical profession and the general public.

9 Constraints and difficulties in careers

The Department of Health's first aim in commissioning the last study was to be able to project more accurately the contribution women doctors would make in future towards the total supply of doctors, with particular attention to changes or trends in activity or participation rates. An important additional aim of the research was to identify the main obstacles, whether institutional or domestic, which prevented women from participating as fully as they would like in medicine. In designing the study, we therefore looked for any potential constraints on women's careers which might prevent them from playing as large a role as possible in the future pattern of medical manpower. At the same time we stressed the importance of looking at any potential constraints on the careers of men doctors. It is clearly necessary to be able to plan medical manpower so that the best use is made of the talents of all doctors.

Although the traditional view has been that domestic commitments caused by marriage and children have been the main reason why women have not done as well as men in career terms in medicine, we explored in the last study the extent to which other factors, some of which were general to most professions, but others of which were found almost uniquely in medicine, acted as constraints on the careers, not only of women but also of men doctors. We had quickly become aware of the fact that not everything in the medical career structure was conducive to ensuring that all doctors fulfilled their potential and were able to maximise their contribution to medicine.

We therefore asked a series of questions on whether any of the following factors had imposed any constraints on doctors' careers, and, if they had, in what way this had affected them: marriage, having children/child care, care of relatives other than children, a break of more than six months in their careers, the necessity of doctors in training to be geographically mobile, the requirement for hospital doctors in training to be on-call and to work long, unsocial hours, and part-time working. We also wanted to know whether there were any other factors which doctors saw as having imposed constraints on their careers. We commented on the very mixed bag of other reasons which emerged in the last study. The list was even longer in the present study. And finally, we wanted to know, which, if any, was the single most important factor which had imposed constraints on their careers.

Table 9.01 **Proportion of doctors reporting factors imposing constraints on their careers**

column percentages

	Total		Male		Female	
	1981	1986	1981	1986	1981	1986
Marriage	26	28	27	23	26	32
Children/childcare	11	13	9	8	13	17
Care of relative other than child	2	2	1	2	4	2
Break of more than 6 months	5	3	4	1	7	5
Necessity of geographical mobility	32	35	33	34	31	35
On-call/unsocial hours	45	62	38	51	52	71
Any part-time working	1	3	0	0	2	5
Other factors	25	33	21	36	28	30
None of these/no constraints	27	18	33	24	22	14
Base: all qualifiers	*(204)*	*(229)*	*(101)*	*(105)*	*(103)*	*(124)*

Table 9.01 shows the composite response to this series of questions, and identifies the proportions of doctors who said that the various factors had imposed a constraint on their careers. It does not, however, shows the proportions for whom the question was relevant, for example, marriage would not have imposed a constraint for an unmarried doctor. These issues are considered below.

We noted in the last report that many of the constraints were interrelated. For example, constraints caused by marriage were often closely related to the need for geographical mobility for doctors in training posts. Both were seen as constraints, but it was often difficult for the doctors to say that one constraint was more important than another. Interestingly, as we shall see, the main constraint identified in the present study by both men and women was seen as being imposed by the demands of the medical career system itself rather than by any domestic factors alone. This repeated the finding among the 1981 qualifiers in the last study, and it should be remembered how structural constraints can have a huge impact both on the careers and on the domestic and personal lives of doctors. The interrelationship of the constraints was not only found in their effects on the careers of doctors as such but also in how they impinged on each other. We therefore explored the ways in which the doctors reacted to the constraints they experienced, with the main aim in this study of identifying how the 1986 cohort differed from earlier generations.

Marriage and children

In the last study we found that 30 per cent of the men and 50 per cent of the women interviewed reported that marriage had been a constraint on their careers, although the proportions varied from nearly two-thirds of the 1966 women to only just over a quarter of the 1981 qualifiers of both sexes. Table 9.01 shows that the proportions among the 1986 qualifiers were 23 per cent of men and 32 per cent of women.

The extent to which marriage was a constraint was obviously related to whether the doctors had been married. We found that the proportions of ever-married men who had found marriage a constraint increased from 30 per cent of the 1966 men to 38 per cent of the 1981 men, a similar proportion to the 36 per cent of 1986 men. On the other hand we found that among women the trend was in the other direction, with 74 per cent of the ever-married 1966 women reporting marriage as a constraint, compared with 68 per cent among the 1976 cohort, 56 per cent among the 1981 cohort and, as Table 9.02 shows, 54 per cent among the 1986 women.

Table 9.02   Proportion of doctors ever married or with children reporting these factors as constraints on their careers

column percentages

| | Male | | | Female | | |
	1976	1981	1986	1976	1981	1986
Ever married doctors reporting marriage as a constraint on career	37	38	36	68	56	54
Base: ever married doctors	*(97)*	*(71)*	*(67)*	*(89)*	*(48)*	*(72)*
Doctors with children reporting children as a constraint on career	31	39	29	76	81	91
Base: doctors with children	*(75)*	*(23)*	*(24)*	*(68)*	*(16)*	*(23)*

There are a number of factors which need to be taken into account when interpreting these figures. It should be remembered that relatively lower proportions of doctors of both sexes in the later cohorts were married. What we do not know is in what way the women who had got married by the time we interviewed them were different from those who had not got married, for example, whether they were more resilient, or had made other compromises in their careers to allow for the potential constraint of marriage. We do not know whether those delaying marriage were doing so for reasons connected with their careers or for other reasons, and whether those marrying later (if at all) would have different career patterns from those who were married five years after qualification.

It also appears that marriage as such was seen as less of a constraining factor on the careers of the younger married women than of the older qualifiers. It is possible that the younger women were less prepared to let marriage get in the way of their careers, or that they were married to more amenable men, or that there were other imperatives for them to continue an unconstrained career, which meant that their careers were less constrained by marriage than those of older women. It is likely that the reasons are complex. However, in spite of the fact that relatively fewer women in the later cohorts reported marriage as a constraint, it should not be forgotten that well over half of the 1981 and 1986 women doctors who had been married did report marriage as a constraint on their careers. It may be much lower than among the 1966 women qualifiers, but it is still a substantial proportion.

In the last study we found that 19 per cent of the men and 44 per cent of the women reported that children or child care had imposed a constraint on their careers. Again, the highest proportion was found among the 1966 women, over two-thirds of whom said that having children had been a constraint on their careers, compared with only a quarter of the 1966 men. The proportions overall dropped to 9 per cent of the 1981 men and 13 per cent of the 1981 women, and, as Table 9.01 shows, were similar among the 1986 qualifiers with 8 per cent of the men and 17 per cent of the women.

Again, the proportions were different when measured against those who had actually had children, particularly in relation to the very small numbers of the 1981 and 1986 cohorts who had children at the time of interview. Table 9.02 shows a steadily increasing trend among the women, so that over 90 per cent of the 1986 women with children reported it as a constraint. Although the proportion of men with children reporting it a constraint dropped from 1981 to 1986, it is still important that nearly 30 per cent of them found it an inhibiting factor in their career development.

We noted in the last report that it might have been expected that a relatively high proportion of married women or women with children would find them constraints on their careers, but we questioned whether over one third of married men or men with children of similar educational and social status as these doctors would find marriage or children a constraint on their careers.

What were the constraints imposed by marriage? The most important constraint in the last study was found even more important in this study – the need to get a job where their spouse was working. This was cited by nearly 60 per cent of women and nearly a quarter of the men in the last study who had found marriage a career constraint, but had risen to three-quarters of the women and nearly one third of the 1986 men, which reflected the findings among the 1981 cohort. The younger qualifiers were increasingly finding it difficult to plan dual careers, particularly, but not only, if they were married to other doctors. A male surgical registrar summarised the problem: 'We got SHO jobs together.

Whoever got first to a location, the other applied in that locality ...' But it was not always that easy, particularly as careers advanced, as a woman GP locum explained: 'It's making it more difficult to get a full-time partnership. GPs think you're going to have a family immediately. And/or they think you'll move away with your husband somewhere. They don't think your intentions to get full-time work are serious ...'

The second most frequently mentioned reason among the 1986 qualifiers for finding marriage a constraint was that it restricted the amount of time they were able or prepared to put into their careers. Interestingly, this was hardly mentioned by the earlier cohorts. It was closely followed by the observation that marriage was a constraint in that the doctors had to consider their spouse's jobs when choosing their own. This was mentioned by nearly 40 per cent of the men who found marriage a constraint. It might not have been essential for them to get a job where their spouse was working, but it was clearly a very important factor to ensure that both could pursue their careers. As we saw in Chapter 2, dual career families were very much the pattern among the younger cohorts, and medical careers were found to be inhibiting to this. Nevertheless a quarter of the women, and none of the men, said that marriage had been a constraint because their spouse's career came first when career moves were considered.

Other ways in which marriage was thought to impose constraints included a limiting of ambition or risk taking, mentioned by nearly one fifth of the men thinking marriage a constraint, the choice of a job or specialty which allowed a reasonable amount of home life, a restriction on the amount of time available for studying, the decision to leave hospital medicine on marriage, and a general restriction on job opportunities in general.

What about children? We had noted in the last study that the timing of the birth of the first child was a particularly crucial decision for women doctors, and that many would have liked advice on whether to delay having a baby until higher professional training had been completed or to complete a family before starting postgraduate training. We found that most women who had had children had done neither, but had started a family while in training posts. The relatively small number of 1981 qualifiers with children had mainly had their first child as SHOs or at the end of their GP vocational training, with the men rather more likely to have had a first child as GP trainees. The 1976 cohort, who were more likely to have children, had mainly delayed their first child to a later stage in their careers, (as the 1981 cohort were to – see the follow-up study of 1976 and 1981 qualifiers), with one third of the men having their first child when they were registrars, and over one fifth of the women having their first child when they were GP principals. (It should be remembered that less than two-thirds of the 1976 women qualifiers had children at the time of the last study, even ten years after qualification (Allen, 1988)).

Table 9.03 shows that the trend had changed among the 1986 qualifiers. Nearly three-quarters of the women with children had had their first child as SHOs, as had nearly 60 per cent of their male counterparts. Over 10 per cent of the men but nearly a quarter of the women had had their first child as GP trainees.

133

Table 9.03   Grade of jobs of doctors when first child born

column percentages

	Male			Female		
	1976	1981	1986	1976	1981	1986
Medical student	4	4	13	0	0	0
House officer	8	13	0	2	14	0
SHO	17	30	57	17	36	73
Registrar	35	17	13	12	14	0
Senior registrar	7	4	0	6	0	0
Consultant	1	0	0	2	0	0
Clinical assistant	0	0	0	3	0	0
GP trainee	14	22	13	9	7	23
GP assistant/locum	0	0	0	8	0	0
GP principal	14	0	0	22	0	0
Clinical medical officer	0	0	0	5	7	0
At end of GP training	0	0	0	9	21	5
Medical officer (other)	0	9	0	0	0	0
Lecturer	0	0	4	0	0	0
Research fellow	0	0	0	4	0	0
Base: all qualifiers with children of own	*(72)*	*(23)*	*(23)*	*(65)*	*(14)*	*(22)*

What were the constraints of having a child? We found that over 40 per cent of the 1986 women with children said that they had stopped working when their baby was born, but an identical proportion said that they had changed to part-time work, and a quarter said they had restricted their work commitment. These proportions were similar to those found among the 1981 women with children.

Around one fifth of the 1986 women with children said that they found that having children had affected their rate of progress in their careers. Women also thought that having children had affected their choice of jobs and made their work more stressful. The few men who thought that children had affected their careers mentioned their choice of jobs, limiting of ambitions, difficulties in studying, greater stress, the need for shorter hours and a need to leave hospital medicine.

We had found in Chapter 2 that the 1986 women were less likely than women from any other cohort to have had regular help with child care, particularly living-in help. There were a number of factors which were clearly important, not least the rising costs of such child care. There was little doubt that the demands of hospital medicine were seen as increasingly difficult for doctors trying to compete for child care in a market where other mothers and families could offer more attractive conditions. A woman locum SHO in paediatrics explained the constraints on her career, repeated a story found elsewhere among these young women doctors: 'We had one nanny and eight child-minders in six months because of my anti-social hours. Then they went. They worked from 8 am to 6 pm, but sometimes I had to phone and say I would be later. They could not accept it, especially on a Friday night. Well yes, I am very particular and fussy I suppose. Also I cannot continue with work on neonates because of my child and my husband's career too ...'

Given role models like this, it is perhaps not surprising that so few of these young women doctors had children, and that those who were contemplating it were often worried about the impact that it would have on their careers, as well as on other aspects of their lives.

Care of a relative other than a child

Only 2 per cent of the 1986 qualifiers of both sexes said that care of a relative other than a child had had a constraining effect on their careers, although a further 5 per cent thought that it would in future. These findings were similar to those found in the last study.

Breaks in careers

Some 15 per cent of the men and over 30 per cent of the women said that they had had a break of more than six months in their medical careers. In some cases the doctors had left medicine, in other cases they had spent time abroad or studying, while in other cases, women were referring to maternity leave or child care breaks.

We found that only 1 per cent of the total sample of 1986 men and 5 per cent of the women thought that a career break had been a constraint on their careers, representing 6 per cent of the men and 16 per cent of the women who had a career break of more than six months. These were much lower proportions than we found among the total sample last time, where we found that nearly 40 per cent of the women who had had a break thought that it had had imposed a constraint on their careers. However, the impact was much greater on the 1966 women than others, mainly because they were more likely to have had breaks than other cohorts, but also because the effects appeared to have been greater in any case, causing loss of confidence, loss of contacts, and great difficulties in getting back on the career ladder. We saw in Chapter 6 of the last report (Allen, 1988) that, although the 1966 women had taken relatively little time out of medicine in their careers, it was still longer than later cohorts. It did appear that career breaks were possible, as long as they were not too long, but that 'too long' could actually be a very short length of time.

We have noted before that some 1966 women qualifiers had had very chequered careers, combining career breaks, babies and geographical moves with successful careers. But there was also another side to the coin, with many 1966 women complaining of lack of success for all these reasons. The later cohorts were more likely to try and avoid lengthy career breaks. The 1986 cohort appeared to be following that trend. The few who thought that a career break had had an effect on their careers mainly spoke of the difficulty of getting back on the career ladder and the loss of confidence and personal contacts cited by earlier generations.

We explored the question of career breaks in some detail in our study of *Part-time Working in General Practice* (Allen, 1992) in which we looked at the experience of nearly 1300 qualified GPs who were mainly in their thirties at the time of the research. We found that 14 per cent of the men and 41 per cent of the women had had a career break of more than six months at some point in their careers, with the younger doctors less likely than their older counterparts to have done so. Nearly 40 per cent of the women and 30 per cent of the men who had had a break thought it had had no effect on their careers, and one fifth of the women and nearly half the men thought it had had a positive effect on their careers. However, nearly half the women thought that the career break had had a negative effect on their careers, mainly because of difficulty in getting back into the system, loss of confidence and a delay in their career progress. It should be noted that the average career breaks among these GP were rather longer than those found in the last *Doctors and their Careers* study, and that, of course, these doctors were older than the present cohort.

It remains to be seen what will happen to these young doctors as they get older. Their main intention seemed to be to keep working and to take as little time in career breaks as possible. That had certainly been the pattern among their most recent counterparts in this cohort study. Whether it made for happier doctors is another matter.

Part-time working

We found in the last study that around 10 per cent of men from each cohort had worked part-time at some point in their careers, but that the proportion of women who worked part-time declined from 78 per cent of the 1966 qualifiers to 67 per cent of the 1976 qualifiers to 22 per cent of the 1981 qualifiers. The comparable figure for the 1986 cohort were 15 per cent of the men and 28 per cent of the women. (19 per cent of the women were working part-time at the time we interviewed them.)

Around one fifth of the women and none of the men who had worked part-time thought it had been a constraint on their careers but, of course, the numbers involved in the 1986 cohort were small and few had worked part-time for very long. We look in more detail at part-time working in Chapter 11 of this report. The main reasons put forward for considering part-time working to have been a constraint were very much related to training posts, not surprisingly given the age of these doctors. The main comments were that part-time training was not taken seriously, took too long and that part-time work in jobs other than training posts was boring and less interesting than full-time work. Good part-time jobs were also though to be more difficult to find than full-time posts.

Geographical mobility

Table 9.01 showed that 35 per cent of the 1986 qualifiers, with virtually identical proportions of men and women, thought that the need for doctors in training to be geographically mobile had been a constraint on their careers. We noted in the last report the increase in the proportion of men who held this view, from only 6 per cent of the 1966 cohort to 18 per cent of the 1976 men to 33 per cent of the 1981 men, almost the same proportion as the 1986 men. Among the women we found that around 40 per cent of both 1966 and 1976 qualifiers regarded geographical mobility as a constraint, compared with 31 per cent of the 1981 women, rather less than the 35 per cent we found among the 1986 women.

It looks as though the need for geographical mobility has increasingly become an issue for both men and women, but that the older women found themselves more disadvantaged by it than the younger women. Although it could be argued that it could become more important for the later cohorts of women as they grow older, it is possible that it may be in the earlier stages of doctors' careers that the need for geographical mobility has its greatest impact. On the other hand, constraints imposed by geographical mobility often had a major impact on marriage or children, or the other way round. The younger women were less likely to be married or have children, so that it is possible they were rather less likely to have suffered constraints caused by geographical mobility. Certainly among the 1986 women, nearly half the women with children said that the need for geographical mobility had been a constraint on their career, compared with one third of the women without children. It was interesting that over 40 per cent of the men with children had found geographical mobility a constraint compared with less one third of the men without children.

The most important factor imposing a constraint because of the need for geographical mobility was rather different from the last study, and was perhaps a reflection of the time at which the interviewing took place. One third of the men and a quarter of the women regarding geographical mobility a constraint said it was because they had bought a house and wanted to stay in the same area. An important reason for this was clearly the fact that many of them had bought their house at the height of the market and found themselves in a 'negative equity' situation, unable to sell their house even for the price they had paid for it. But there were other reasons which were implicit – and repeated in a different form in answers to this question – the increasing reluctance of young doctors to see the need to move around. They wanted to stay in one place. A quarter of the men and a fifth of the women said that there were limited places to which they were prepared to move. A male registrar in general medicine said: 'I want to stay in London. If I were pushed desperately I might move, but I would have to be desperate ...' And another male psychiatric registrar said: 'I didn't want to leave Glasgow, and I accepted a temporary post in an alternative specialty until psychiatry became available ...'

On the other hand, one third of the 1986 women finding geographical mobility a constraint said that it was because of the difficulty of getting jobs in the same place as their husbands in medicine, while a further 20 per cent said the difficulty lay in getting jobs in the same place as their non-medical husbands. In other words, over half the women citing geographical mobility as a constraint did so because of the difficulty of getting jobs in the same place as their husbands. A woman senior registrar pointed out some of the difficulties: 'We've had to move four times in the last five years for my job. It was harder for my husband ...' And a woman psychiatric registrar said: 'It's the same as being married really. For instance, if I had stayed in paediatrics I would now be a senior registrar. I would have had to be very flexible but I wasn't prepared to travel around without my husband ...'

This may seem a reasonable enough thing to say, but there can be little doubt that inability or unwillingness to move around the country was thought by young doctors to be seen as a distinct black mark. Even ambitious and successful doctors deplored the system, like this male general medical registrar: 'As a junior doctor you have to move all your possessions in no time at all. You can finish a job at 9 am, having been up all night, and then start a job, maybe 300 miles away, right away ...'

There were many indications that the constant moves were found very demoralising, not least by those who were aiming high, as another male registrar, this time in neurology, explained: 'You have to go where the jobs are. There's no job security for junior doctors; sick leave is cut when you leave one job for another; maternity leave is disgusting; and you're on a short-term contract until you get a consultant post ...'

There were many indications that geographical mobility was regarded as inimical to forming stable relationships and was found personally disruptive and stressful by both men and women. It is really not surprising that one third of the 1986 qualifiers thought that the need for geographical mobility was a constraint on their careers. Many of the others disliked it, but had managed in some way to come to terms with it. It must be asked how necessary it is for so many doctors to move so often and so far. It does not appear to be laying the foundations for the stability and happiness that these young doctors should be achieving in their lives.

The requirement for doctors in training to be on-call and work long hours
We found in the last report that the constraint caused by the necessity for hospital doctors in training to be on-call and work long hours was the factor mentioned most often by the doctors, although it was not necessarily thought to be the most important constraint. We found that overall nearly half the women mentioned it, compared with a quarter of the men, but that this proportion rose to nearly 40 per cent of the 1981 men and over half the 1981 women. One of the most important findings of the present study was a marked and distinct increase in the proportion of 1986 qualifiers saying that long hours and on-call commitments constituted a constraint on their careers – 51 per cent of the men and 71 per cent of the women.

What were the reasons for this great increase? The main reason, given by nearly 60 per cent of both sexes was that it affected their family or social life too much. Both men and women painted pictures of fatigue and despair, and the interviewers involved in this study who had worked on the last study all commented on the changes they observed among the young doctors they interviewed. There had been many sad stories in the last study, but there appeared to be a much more general malaise among the 1986 qualifiers who felt affected by the long hours and responsibilities of hospital medicine.

A woman GP assistant who had recently had a baby spoke of her experience: 'You just viewed patients as objects to get out of casualty. It was dreadful, just awful. It wrecks the best years of your life. We had an awful first year of marriage – both doing one in twos at the same time. It made me ill on occasions. It certainly affected our social life and our friendships. It's made us bitter against the system. But you're too tired to make a fuss ...' Her description was repeated time and again by doctors of both sexes. A woman medical researcher said: 'It's extremely difficult when you've got a close relationship, for example when I was trying to pass MRCP. It's hard to maintain a relationship when you keep falling asleep all the time. It's considered boring ...'

Some doctors thought it was almost easier to maintain a relationship with another doctor, since at least they understood the problems, and probably shared the fatigue, as a woman trainee GP said – 'You're so tired. It ruins your marriage if you're not married to a doctor ...' But it was not only marriages and relationships which were affected. A male GP principal commented on other aspects of family life: 'I lost contact with my parents and had to make a great effort to see them at all. My parents made great sacrifices. Now they don't see much of me. It seems a poor reward ...'

A number of doctors thought that it had adversely affected not only their social or family lives but also their personal development, like a male anaesthetic registrar – 'I put up with it but it destroys you as a person. You can't develop. Everybody misjudges my age – two years of my life is only worth one year outside ...' – and a woman locum GP – 'You do all this work, you get all the stick and you're not valued. I wasn't prepared to hand my life over completely. It doesn't make you a balanced person ...' – and a woman paediatric registrar – 'I've done the worst possible – the one in two – 135 hours a week. I just think that's unnecessary. It adversely affects your development ...'

It could be argued that the worst excesses of long hours are now a thing of the past, but there can be little doubt that many doctors found even 80 hours a week far too long, particularly with the on-call responsibilities and intensive workload. The second most frequently cited reason for considering long hours a constraint was fatigue and the need for sleep. A woman trainee said tersely: 'Everybody's killed somebody through lack of sleep. It's dreadful ...' The health of the doctors was thought to be affected as much as the health of the patients, as a woman locum GP explained: 'It's awful. You don't learn anything at 3 in the morning when you're exhausted. It killed me! I couldn't have done it much longer ...'

One third of the men and a quarter of the women citing long hours as a constraint on their careers said it affected their study opportunities too much. A male GP trainee commented: 'You feel sometimes that you don't know any more than you did two years ago. You never have a chance to open a book because you feel too nackered ...'

Over a quarter of both men and women said that they did not want a specialty with heavy rotas of one in three, nearly one fifth of both men and women said that they had decided they did not want a specialty with on-call duties, and a quarter of the men and one in six of the women said that the long hours had made them decide to leave hospital medicine. A woman on maternity leave having completed her GP vocational training had not forgotten the horrors: 'I hate on-call, being tired, getting unhappy – and it never got easier. I will do anything to avoid it. It affects me so badly, physically and mentally ...'

A woman GP trainee described the effects it had had on her: 'I wouldn't have gone into general practice if it hadn't been for the on-call. Otherwise I'd have done paediatrics. It was so exhausting you couldn't live a normal existence. And it wasn't temporary. It would go on for ten years or more ...' A woman SHO in paediatrics agreed: 'I don't want to be doing those long hours when I'm 38. I don't think our marriage would survive if both of us were doing it ...'

A woman clinical assistant had found it too much for her – 'I've had enough of it. I'm sick to death of it. I must say if it was a 9 to 5 job I would still be pursuing some sort of career, but it's the out-of-hours that kills ...' – and a woman GP trainee appeared to be on the verge of opting out – 'It's made me want to give up medicine altogether – to jack it in. I hate it ...'

A male doctor had left medicine because of the long hours – 'My career wasn't constrained but *I* was. I could easily have progressed in medicine, but I wasn't happy ...' And many men echoed his sentiments, without having decided to leave, like a GP principal: 'There's more to life than medicine. I don't mind working hard. I object to being exploited and that's basically what it is ...'

There were many indications in the answers to these questions that the cut in junior hospital doctors hours was not really great enough to put an end to the complaints and fatigue suffered by these young doctors. It has been argued that doctors at this stage in their careers have always been in this position, and that these younger doctors appear to have a lower threshold of tolerance than their older counterparts. However, others agree that the duties in hospital medicine are considerably more demanding than they were when many consultants were in training, that patients are iller and in for a shorter period of time, that the technical skills needed are far greater and that the workload is much more intense. In addition, the conditions in which the doctors were working were said to be far inferior to those enjoyed by older doctors. Perhaps the younger generation of doctors are more feeble than their older counterparts, but the fact remains that nearly three-quarters of the women and nearly two-thirds of the men considered the long hours and on-call duties of hospital medicine to have been a constraint on their careers. A very close look needs to be taken at this magnitude of discontent, which often barely concealed stress which would be considered clinically unsafe in other professions.

Other factors imposing a constraint on careers

As table 9.01 shows, over one third of the 1986 men and nearly one third of the women said that there were other factors which had imposed a constraint on their careers. A very wide range of reasons was given, amounting to 25 different additional factors, most of which were mentioned by at least three doctors.

The most common factor, mentioned by nearly one third of the women and over 10 per cent of the men citing other constraining factors, was the difficulty they had found in passing higher examinations. A woman locum SHO epitomised the problems: 'I failed MRCP Part 1 three times and I do not understand why. I have never failed exams. I am brighter than my husband. It's a disaster. I couldn't get another job. I am stuck with these locums and the problems of child care seem insurmountable ...' Another woman registrar was leaving medicine because she felt that the postgraduate examination system did not accurately reflect a doctor's clinical ability: 'I have failed the fellowship three times and I don't consider myself a bad doctor. Because of this I need to leave medicine to do a job which I both enjoy and which will enable me to earn enough money to live on ...'

This linked into the second most common constraint cited by over 10 per cent of both men and women giving other constraints – their own lack of confidence in their abilities or doubts about their medical career. There was evidence of doctors being puzzled by their inability to pass their higher examinations, and, given the undoubted ability of many of them, it was surprising that study opportunities often appeared so limited. There were also a number of doctors who clearly felt themselves to be in the wrong job but found it impossible to get out of medicine.

The third most frequently mentioned constraint was financial, which had hardly been mentioned in the last report. The loss of extra pay for overtime hours was disquieting for some doctors who had left acute specialties in hospital medicine, but one of the most important factors was related to difficulties in selling flats or houses – the new phenomenon noted above.

Other constraints included a number relating to personal lives and relationships, such as planning to get married, planning to have children, wanting to be near a boyfriend or girlfriend, being single, wanting to be near parents, divorce and not wishing to leave their home area. Some 5 per cent mentioned their unconventional personalities as being a constraining factor and a similar proportion cited a particularly negative influence by a senior doctor. A male anaesthetic registrar spoke of his 'informal manner and anti-professional attitude ...' which no doubt endeared him to his seniors. He did not regard himself as a 'conventional person', and neither did an unemployed male research registrar: 'I wouldn't have wanted to be a senior and powerful enough to change the lot of junior doctors and not be able to do it. The predominant attitude is "It never did me any harm" – rose-tinted in retrospect, like National Service. I didn't want to get like that ...'

Other constraints included the perceived inflexibility of the medical career structure in general, being a woman, being too old, their own or a child's illness, lots of small career breaks, lack of manual dexterity or skills, inability to drive a car, the new GP contract, difficulty in finding suitable training posts, cultural or religious discrimination and not following the 'normal' career path in general.

It could be argued that many of these constraints were subject to post-hoc rationalisation on the part of doctors who could not 'make it'. In fact, many of them were put forward by doctors who had had successful careers by most standards. They were important mainly because they showed very clearly the lack of careers support and counselling that the vast majority of these doctors had received. It was clear that many of the problems and constraints which were burning up the lives of some of these doctors could have been ameliorated or removed by discussion and advice from career counsellors. It was quite obvious throughout this research that this was very thin on the ground.

The most important factor imposing career constraints
The last report indicated that the proportion of doctors reporting no constraints on their careers fell from around 40 per cent of the 1966 and 1976 men to one third of the 1981 men, but had increased among women from around 10 per cent of the 1966 and 1976 cohorts to one fifth of the 1981 women. We saw in Table 9.01 that only 24 per cent of the 1986 men and 14 per cent of the 1986 women reported no constraints on their careers.

What was the single most important constraint on the careers of these young doctors? The last study had indicated that it was children or child care among the 1966 and 1976 women, and that it was marriage or children among the 1966 and 1976 men, but to a much lesser extent than among the women. Geographical mobility was mentioned more often by the younger cohorts, and other constraints were mentioned by about one in six of doctors in the sample as a whole. However, the most important constraint among the 1981 qualifiers was undoubtedly the long hours and on-call commitments, mentioned by 24 per cent of the men and 28 per cent of the women. As Table 9.04 shows, the proportion of 1986 qualifiers mentioning this as the most important constraint on their careers was 31 per cent of the men and 40 per cent of the women.

Why was this factor of such crucial importance to these young doctors? After all, previous generations of doctors had worked even longer hours, it was said. We have already mentioned the differences observed by the 1986 qualifiers in the intensity of the work they had to undertake when they were on duty. It often appeared to have ground them down to such an extent that they were incapable of thinking of anything else, like a woman psychiatric registrar – 'It keeps coming back to on-call duties. I could solve the geographical problems, but on call was inescapable ...' – and a former GP trainee, now on maternity leave – 'It was just

Table 9.04   Single most important factor imposing constraints on doctors' careers

column percentages

	Total		Male		Female	
	1981	1986	1981	1986	1981	1986
Marriage	15	13	12	10	17	15
Children/childcare	6	7	4	4	9	10
Care of relative other than child	*	1	0	1	1	2
Break of more than 6 months	1	0	2	0	0	0
Necessity of geographical mobility	11	9	12	13	9	6
On-call/unsocial hours	26	36	24	31	28	40
Any part-time working	0	0	0	0	0	0
Financial problems	*	3	*	3	*	2
Having no higher qualifications	*	3	*	2	*	3
Marriage plans/ relationships	*	3	*	3	*	3
Other factors	14	7	14	9	14	5
No constraints	27	18	33	24	22	14
Base: all qualifiers	*(204)*	*(229)*	*(101)*	*(105)*	*(103)*	*(124)*

intolerable – being chronically tired and never seeing my husband – awful. And the *stress* of actually doing it. I used to be a quivering wreck – the thought of having to do something heroic in the middle of the night was a nightmare ...'

What result did it have? A male registrar said briefly: 'You develop a deep hatred for the whole system that makes you work those hours ...' It was certainly thought to put people off hospital medicine, as a male GP principal explained: 'If you worked a 40-hour week you could put with the fact that it might take 20 years to become a consultant because you're enjoying what you're doing. But when you're working 120 hours a week your main motivation is to get out of it ...'

If more young doctors are not to leave medicine, there clearly needs to be greater attention paid to the hours and conditions of work. The recent cuts in the hours of junior hospital doctors are to be welcomed, but there was plenty of evidence in this study that they were not regarded as being enough. Some of the interviews carried out with the 1986 qualifiers can only be described as heart-breaking in their descriptions of fatigue, stress and depression, and it is this more than anything else which needs to be monitored if British medicine is not to lose some of these glittering young people who had started out on medical school with such high hopes.

10 Interviews, jobs and equal opportunities

In the last study we found many instances of doctors being asked at job interviews or appointments boards very personal questions about their private lives which appeared to them to have no bearing on their ability or capacity to perform the duties expected of them. There was absolutely no doubt that women were much more likely than men to be asked questions about their intention to have children, about the arrangements they would make to look after their children, even if they did not have any children, and other questions related to their domestic arrangements.

We were constantly surprised by the questions that so many women doctors were asked, many of which not only appeared to contravene the legislation against sex discrimination, but were also of a probing and intrusive nature which we had assumed had vanished with the introduction of the legislation so many years before. There were indications that medicine had somehow become caught in a time-warp, with attitudes allowed to be expressed at interviews which had long been controlled in other areas, particularly in public or statutory bodies. The NHS is one of the largest employers in the western world, and yet questions were being asked of women doctors in interviews which were in direct contravention of all equal opportunities legislation and guidelines.

Our research findings and recommendations on interviewing methods and the ensuring of equal opportunities at interviews were taken up by the Department of Health and were incorporated into the Equal Opportunities guidelines issued by the Department (NHSME, 1991). We were particularly interested in seeing to what extent these guidelines, and our recommendations, had been taken into interviewing procedures in the years after the last report was published. Certainly, the matter had been given a good airing in the national and medical press after the publication of the last report, and had been a matter of heated debate at the Department of Health funded seminars which followed the publication of the report in 1988, the papers from which were published in *Discussing Doctors' Careers* (Allen, 1989). The views of some senior doctors who insisted that such questions were either never asked or were quite legitimate were firmly refuted by other senior doctors who said that such questions were still commonplace and had to be controlled by chairs of appointments committees.

In the present study we therefore looked again in detail at the questions asked of both men and women at interviews or appointments boards, with particular reference to those concerned with having children or looking after children. We were interested not only in whether such potentially discriminatory questions were asked at all, but also in whether they were asked more of women than of men, indicating a clear breach of equal opportunities legislation, or, if they were asked of both men and women, whether the intention of the question was thought to be different.

Questions about intentions to have children

We found in the last report that 49 per cent of the women but only 9 per cent of the men in the total sample of doctors had been asked at job interviews whether they intended to have children. There appeared to have been an increasing tendency for women to have been asked this question, with 59 per cent of the 1976 women and 55 per cent of the 1981 women reporting it, compared with only 36 per cent of the 1966 women qualifiers. Among the men too there had been an increase, from only 3 per cent of 1966 men to 13 per cent of the 1981 men.

Table 10.01   **Doctors reporting being asked at any job interview whether they intended to have children**

						column percentages
	Male			Female		
	1976	1981	1986	1976	1981	1986
Yes	10	13	6	59	55	40
No	90	87	94	40	45	60
Base: all qualifiers	*(105)*	*(101)*	*(105)*	*(105)*	*(103)*	*(124)*

Table 10.01 shows that there seemed to have been a fairly marked decline in the proportion of both men and women 1986 qualifiers who had been asked this question. The figures are compared with those of both 1976 and 1981 qualifiers, to give a historical perspective, although the most direct comparison is, of course, with the 1981 qualifiers who had had the same length of career and were of a similar age at the time of interview.

However, although there had been a drop in the prevalence of the question, nevertheless 40 per cent of the 1986 women had been asked at job interviews whether they intended to have children. This in itself is a high proportion, given the length of time since the legislation, but it is of particular importance since only 6 per cent of the 1986 men qualifiers had been asked the question. On this evidence, women were clearly being discriminated against in job interviews by being asked questions which were not being asked of men.

How frequent were such questions? The frequency was naturally related to the number of job interviews the doctors had had. We found in the last study that a third of all women interviewed had been asked this question at one or two interviews, over ten per cent had been asked at three or four interviews and seven per cent reported that they had been asked more frequently, with the younger women being asked more often than the older women.

Among the 1986 women, just over a quarter of all women (two-thirds of those who had been asked the question) said it had happened at one or two interviews, just under a quarter said it had happened at three or four interviews, and a handful said it had happened more frequently. Women with children were more likely to have been asked the question than women without children and were also more likely to have been asked it more often.

When were they asked the question? In the last study we found that 9 per cent of the total sample of women had been asked whether they intended to have children at an interview for medical school. We found this time that the overall incidence had declined, but nevertheless 4 per cent of the 1986 women, but none of the 1986 men, had been asked this question at an interview for medical school. We have remarked before that it seems an astonishing question to ask a 17-year-old girl, particularly at a university entrance interview, and that, in any case, it must be seen as potentially discriminatory, particularly when boys are not asked this question.

Among the 1986 cohort, we found that 6 per cent of all the women, but none of the men, said they had been asked whether they intended to have children at house officer interviews, 16 per cent of the women and one man had been asked at SHO job interviews, and 2 per cent of the women and 1 per cent of the men at registrar job interviews. However, general practice was found to attract a relatively higher proportion of such questions than other jobs, with 13 per cent of all the women and 1 per cent of the men being asked this question at GP trainee interviews, and 12 per cent of all the women and 5 per cent of the men being asked at GP principal interviews. Given the fact that only around one third of the doctors of both sexes were in general practice, it can be seen that it was a frequent question to women. It appeared to have been virtually universal among women at GP principal interviews, since only 10 per cent of the 1986 women were currently working as GP principals. We had noted in the last report that asking such a question appeared to have been common practice at GP principal interviews. Nothing appeared to have changed, and there have been assumptions that such questions do not contravene the Sex Discrimination Act, since GP partnerships are private matters. But this is not so, and any form of sex discrimination is illegal in partnerships of two or more. This includes direct and indirect discrimination and covers questioning at interviews (see literature from Equal Opportunities Commission and *Women in General Practice*, General Medical Services Committee, BMA, 1994).

What did the doctors feel about being asked this question? Of the women who had been asked, nearly 40 per cent said that they had expected it and did not mind, one third said that it had made them annoyed, nearly one third said that they did not see the relevance of the question to their abilities as a doctor, nearly one in ten said they did not think men would be asked such a question, and the rest found it unreasonable or intrusive and upsetting. The few men who had been asked were divided on whether they found it reasonable or unreasonable.

A woman general medical registrar had expected the question: 'In an ideal world I do not think they should be able to ask that or appoint people on that basis. They should appoint on ability and suitability. In an ideal world you've got to try and attain that. But as a woman, if you are going to request special compensation to have children, then you have got to be honest with them about your future plans. It is worrying. The difficulty arises in the interpretation of the information you give them ...'

There was certainly no incentive for women to be honest, it appeared, since their answers were thought to be interpreted in the least favourable way. A woman locum SHO was much more resentful of the question: 'It made me annoyed. I asked if they asked male candidates. I said, "Are *you* married? Do you intend to have children?" It didn't stop me getting jobs ...'

But a number of women thought that it might have stopped them getting jobs and were concerned about the discriminatory nature of the question.

Questions about arrangements for the care of children

We found in our last study that women were being asked at job interviews what arrangements they would make for the care of their children whether they had any or not. The proportion of women overall who said they had been asked this question was 30 per cent, but there were differences among the cohorts, with well over one third of the 1966 and 1976 women having been asked it, compared with only 17 per cent of the 1981 women. This was not particularly surprising, since so few of the 1981 women had children, but on the other hand we found that 10 per cent of the women with no children had been asked this question.

Table 10.02   **Doctors reporting being asked at any job interview what arrangements they would make/had made for the care of their children**

| | Male | | | Female | | *column percentages* |
	1976	1981	1986	1976	1981	1986
Yes	0	0	3	34	17	12
No	100	100	97	66	83	88
Base: all qualifiers	*(105)*	*(101)*	*(105)*	*(105)*	*(103)*	*(124)*

Among the 1986 women, as Table 10.02 shows, we found that 12 per cent said that they had been asked what arrangements they had made or would make for the care of the children. This was a rather lower proportion than found among the 1981 women, although a slightly higher percentage of the 1986 women had children. It was interesting that the 1986 women who had been asked this question divided more or less equally between those who had children and those who did not. Again, it was only asked of 3 per cent of the 1986 men, but this was an increase on the 1976 and 1981 men, none of whom had ever been asked what arrangements they made for the care of their children.

Most of the women had been asked this question at only one or two interviews, although a small number said it had come up more often. Perhaps one of the reasons why it had been asked as much of women without children as of women with children in the 1986 cohort was because it was a question asked mostly at GP trainee or GP principal interviews. Of the 1986 women who had been asked the question, 60 per cent said it was at an interview for a GP principal post, and nearly 30 per cent said it was a GP trainee interview.

In the last study we found that women had been asked the question fairly frequently at senior registrar and consultant job interviews, but, of course, the 1981 and 1986 cohorts had not reached these levels. It is impossible to tell from this study whether or not such questions are still being asked of women at job interviews for such posts.

It was interesting that most of the women and all the men who had been asked the question thought that it was reasonable and did not mind being asked it. However, a small number did not see its relevance to their abilities as a doctor, and one woman found it intrusive. A male GP principal had expected it and did not mind, but reported a rather curious reason for the question: 'In a traineeship interview in Wales, they told me to have a wife to answer the phone and not to be out at work. They said that having children kept wives at home ...' Their enquiries about his child care arrangements could possibly have been interpreted as discriminatory against men with working wives – an odd twist in the complicated ways in which doctors were appointed to jobs.

Other questions at job interviews about domestic lives

We found in the last study that doctors reported a wide variety of other questions about personal lives and domestic arrangements which were sometimes extraordinarily insensitive and inappropriate. These questions appeared to be increasing rather than decreasing, since we found that more than 50 per cent of the 1976 and 1981 men and women reported other questions, compared with only one third of both men and women 1966 qualifiers.

Table 10.03 shows that such questions were still on the increase, with 55 per cent of the 1986 men and 60 per cent of the 1986 women saying that they had been asked other questions about their private lives. Around 70 per cent of both men and women who had children had been asked such questions, compared with rather fewer of their counterparts with no children. Women working part-time or not working were much more likely to have been asked such questions than women working full-time.

What were the questions? The main question, asked of nearly 60 per cent of the men and just over 40 per cent of the women reporting other questions, was whether they were married or planning to marry. It was clear that these questions

Table 10.03   Doctors reporting being asked at any job interview any other questions about their domestic lives or commitments

column percentages

| | Male | | | Female | | |
	1976	1981	1986	1976	1981	1986
Yes	50	52	55	51	58	60
No	50	48	45	49	42	40
Base: all qualifiers	*(105)*	*(101)*	*(105)*	*(105)*	*(103)*	*(124)*

were not just asked as social chit-chat, even if this was acceptable at a job interview, but with a specific purpose. A relatively high proportion of interviews at which other questions were asked were for GP principal or GP trainee posts, and it often appeared that these were thought to be job interviews at which almost anything was acceptable. A male GP principal had mixed feelings about it: 'They asked what relationship I had with my girlfriend, whether we were settled. And I also had to bring her to a later interview. On the practical side I suppose it's a fair question, but I don't know if it should be asked if it's not for practical reasons. "Bring your partner along to the interview ..." I think that's a bit funny ...'

Another male GP did not find such questions odd: 'I was asked whether I was married, how happy I was, where I lived. Reasonable questions, being taken into a partnership. I'd want to know all kinds of things – whether they were gay or not, whether they were HIV positive or not ...' And another male SHO did not object to his wife and children being interviewed when he was applying for posts in general practice: 'It is important to know about the family of the person applying ...' Another male GP noted that GP partnerships preferred to take married men into partnership: 'It prevents scandal in the practice with the patients ...'

On the other hand, women often felt that marriage was a potential bar to their getting a job, as a woman who had left medicine pointed out: 'The implication was that if I was married I'd be less acceptable. They didn't ask any of the men that. It's unfair – a husband has just as much pull to a wife as a wife to a husband ...'

The second most frequent question, asked of over a quarter of both men and women, was their spouse's occupation. It can be seen that this represented a much higher proportion of those who were married. The question was often clearly related to whether the doctors were married to other doctors or to people who might find it difficult to move to the same place. It was a question often linked to the third most frequently mentioned question which was whether a spouse's job would affect geographical mobility. This question was asked more often of women than men, but a male registrar in psychiatry had been asked about his wife's career and the effect moving might have on her: 'I thought it was irrelevant.'

I'd applied for the job which meant I was willing to take it ...' Women often replied in the same way.

The intense interest in the wives and husbands of doctors was more marked in general practice posts, and it was perhaps rather depressing to find that one in ten of the men and one in twenty of the women reporting other questions at job interviews said that they had been asked whether anyone would be available to answer the telephone or to perform clerical duties for them – another question asked almost exclusively at GP principal or trainee interviews.

Other frequent questions were whether the doctors had a boyfriend or a girlfriend and whether they had any children. Other questions ranged far and wide and included enquiries about whether doctors were prepared to move, why they had moved around so much, whether they were prepared to live away from their spouses, how their spouses felt about their work, whether they were prepared to do night duty, and whether they were intending to stay in the UK. Women were asked exclusively whether as a woman they could cope with the demands of the job, whether they were career-minded, and if they were working in the same hospital as their spouses whether it would affect their work. Other doctors reported being asked about their religious beliefs, whether they might be too old for the job, their social interests and detailed questions about their personal habits.

On the whole men were much more tolerant of such questions than women were, with nearly two thirds of the men who had been asked other questions saying that they had expected them and did not mind, compared with less than half the women. However, around a quarter of the men but only one in six of the women said that they did not see the relevance of the question to their abilities. Women, on the other hand were more likely than the men to say that they found the questions unreasonable, intrusive or ridiculous, and that they had made them annoyed or cross. One in ten of them said they did not think that men would have been asked the same question.

The questions were most often asked at SHO posts (reported by nearly 40 per cent of doctors asked other questions), at registrar jobs, reported by one fifth of the men but less than 10 per cent of the women, and at posts in general practice. Again we found that of those who had been asked other questions about their domestic or private lives, nearly one third of the women but less than one fifth of the men had been asked at GP trainee or vocational training scheme interviews, but over one third of the men and a quarter of the women had been asked at a GP principal post interview. There can be little doubt that GP principals take a keen interest in the private lives and habits of their potential partners. Some of their questions could well be discriminatory under the legislation. Doctors seeking partnerships know that bringing a case against GP practices could well spell the effective end of their careers, and few, if any, appear willing to take the risk.

Discrimination on the grounds of sex

In the last study we asked women doctors whether they thought they had ever failed to get a job because they were women. This was the only question in the interview which was asked of one sex and not the other. We realised that this could be construed as potentially discriminatory, and in this study we decided to ask both men and women whether they thought that they had ever failed to get a job because of their sex.

We had found last time that a quarter of the 1976 women thought they had failed to get a job because of their sex, compared with 15 per cent of the 1966 women but only 7 per cent of the 1981 women. We suspected that this was more a reflection of the career stage and relative lack of domestic commitments of the 1981 qualifiers rather than an indication of a big shift in attitudes in the five years separating the two cohorts. This was confirmed to some extent by the fact that the jobs which women felt they had not got were mainly registrar or GP principal posts, rather than SHO or house officer posts. However, discrimination was felt to operate at all levels, and one of the main reasons general practice was mentioned more than other specialties was that more women were found in general practice than elsewhere.

Table 10.04   Whether doctors think they have ever failed to get a job because of their sex

column percentages

| | Male | | | Female | | |
	1976	1981	1986	1976	1981	1986
Yes	n.a	n.a	13	23	7	14
No	n.a	n.a	86	69	88	81
Don't know	n.a	n.a	1	9	5	5
Base: all qualifiers	*(n.a.)*	*(n.a.)*	*(105)*	*(105)*	*(103)*	*(124)*

In the present study we found that the proportion of 1986 women qualifiers who thought that they had failed to get a job because of their sex had doubled from the 1981 proportion to 14 per cent, but that this experience was almost exactly mirrored by their male counterparts, 13 per cent of whom thought they had failed to get a job because of their sex.

What were the jobs? They were mainly GP principal posts, but interestingly they were mentioned by nearly three-quarters of the men citing discrimination compared with only just over half the women. A quarter of the women but only just over one in ten of the men mentioned SHO posts, one in ten women mentioned house officer posts, one woman mentioned a lecturer post and one man mentioned a GP trainee post. Apart from general practice there was no one specialty which appeared to have been more discriminatory than another.

What had happened to cause this alleged discrimination against potential male GP principals. The main reason given by the men was that the practice had wanted a woman doctor, often because of patient demand: 'There were two male partners already and they were under pressure to get a female partner. It was necessary to have women GPs, especially for female Asian patients ...'

Given the fact that over a quarter of practices in this country have no female partners (Allen, 1992; Electoral Reform Ballot Services, 1992)), it was perhaps almost refreshing to find that some practices were attempting to redress the balance, although it was disturbing to find that young men considered themselves discriminated against. The young women had much longer experience of such perceived discrimination, and often reported detailed accounts of how they had been asked what they regarded as impertinent questions about their domestic lives and intentions only to be rejected with no reason given.

Some women reported that discrimination was often covert – 'My first house job was given to a rugby player. The Hospital Cup is a very big event ...' – while others found they were asked questions that were potentially discriminatory in their interpretation – 'I was asked in one interview what is the role of women in hospital medicine. I'm sure that men don't get asked what role men have to play in hospital medicine ...'

A women from an ethnic minority background reported an unfortunate experience, in which she felt discriminated against for her sex rather than her ethnic minority origin. Her first name was an Asian name which had clearly not been identified by the panel short-listing for a registrar post in cardiology: 'In one interview there was this silence – and then a giggle. They said they didn't realise that .... was a female name. I almost walked out. There were eight of us, and the other seven were men. Someone obviously had made a mistake – including me ...'

What did these doctors feel about being turned down on the grounds of their sex? Over three-quarters of the women were angry, frustrated or upset, a view shared by just over half the men. On the other hand, nearly half the men found it reasonable and did not mind, compared with only one woman. Other women had expected it but found it unreasonable and annoying.

There were one or two examples of both men and women saying that they thought they had actually got jobs because of their sex. One woman surgical SHO said: 'I think I might have had some positive discrimination. The surgeon I'm working for likes having presentable females around, but I don't know if that will continue past SHO level ...' And a male surgical registrar thought that 'being male helps – it certainly helped me. As a junior doctor it's advantageous to be male ...'

Discrimination on grounds of ethnic origin
We asked a new question in this study on whether doctors thought that they had ever failed to get a job because of their ethnic origin. In the last study this had hardly arisen, since such a tiny number of the UK qualifiers from whom the

Table 10.05 **Whether doctors think they have ever failed to get a job because of their ethnic origin (1986 qualifiers only)**

column percentages

	Total	Male	Female
Yes	3	5	2
No	95	91	98
Don't know	2	4	1
Base: all qualifiers	*(229)*	*(105)*	*(124)*

sample was drawn were of anything other than white British origin. As we have noted, we were aware that members of minority ethnic groups were increasingly likely to be entering UK medical schools and we wished to investigate their experience, particularly in the light of recent reports of racial discrimination in the medical profession (Esmail and Everington, BMJ, 1993)

Table 10.05 shows that 5 per cent of the 1986 men and 2 per cent of the 1986 women felt that they had failed to get a job because of their ethnic origin. We reported in Chapter 2 that 90 per cent of the men and 93 per cent of the women had said they were of white ethnic origin, that 8 per cent of the men were of Indian ethnic origin, 2 per cent of the women of Pakistani ethnic origin, 3 per cent of the women of Chinese ethnic origin, one man of Black-Caribbean origin and 2 per cent of both men and women of mixed ethnic origin.

We found that among the 7 doctors who felt that they had failed to get a job because of their ethnic origin, three were Indian men, one was a Chinese woman, while two men and one woman were of white ethnic origin. These three doctors, however, were of non-British origin, and, perhaps more important, their names sounded non-British.

The perceived discrimination had mainly taken place among the men at SHO level, although two men reported it at registrar level, while the women reported it at GP trainee or GP principal posts. No one specialty was mentioned more than any other. The discrimination was often felt impossible to prove, although some of the doctors might have been forgiven for becoming rather suspicious, like a male registrar in public health with a typical Indian-sounding name who found it difficult to get to the interview stage: 'I made twenty applications but only five replied. There was no actual proof that it was racism, but I felt it was. Others at least got a rejection slip. In 90-95 per cent of interviews I got the job, so maybe once you're at the interview stage overt racism has gone ...'

It was rather depressing to find that five of the seven doctors who felt they had been discriminated against said that they had expected it, but their reactions were mixed. Only two of the seven said that they were angry or upset by the perceived discrimination.

Discrimination on the grounds of age

We had repeatedly found in the last study indications that career advancement in medicine appeared to be closely linked to age, and that doctors with 'sound' careers were expected to have reached a certain stage or grade by a certain age. As we saw in Chapter 6, this expectation was thought to militate against women or others who might have taken longer than average to reach certain stages, as well as those who started later than others, for example, mature students or overseas qualifiers.

We therefore asked doctors whether they thought they had ever failed to get a job because of their age. We were aware that among the 1986 qualifiers, who were only five years into their medical career, we were not likely to find many who would be too far out of alignment, if only because of the shortness of their careers in general and the extent to which they were clustered around the ages of 28-29 (see Chapter 2).

Table 10.06   **Whether doctors think they have ever failed to get a job because of their age (1986 qualifiers only)**

			column percentages
	Total	Male	Female
Yes (too young)	4	5	4
Yes (too old)	1	2	0
No	94	92	95
Don't know	1	1	1
Base: all qualifiers	*(229)*	*(105)*	*(124)*

In fact, as Table 10.06 shows, only two doctors (both men) thought they had ever failed to get a job because they were too old, but 10 doctors (5 men and 5 women) thought they had failed to get a job because they were too young. The jobs were scattered throughout the structure at house officer, SHO, registrar, senior registrar and GP principal level and covered a number of specialties.

On the whole those who thought they had been regarded as too young had expected it, although both men and women were annoyed by it. The two men who had been regarded as too old were both angry. One had started medicine late because he had had to do national service in his country of origin. He was now a general medical registrar: 'It's the rigid attitude they have – fixed ideas on which age you should reach each stage. If you're not a consultant by the time you're 40 you're finished ...' His anger was shared by a male senior registrar who had found difficulty earlier on: 'I was furious! I'd gone five years through medical school, working nights to support myself and pay my way, and then was told I was too old at 31 ...'

It is clearly impossible to generalise from the experience of these two doctors, but it is indicative of a certain type of thinking which brands two doctors who, on any objective basis, were potential high-flyers, as too old without even looking at the reasons. There must be some unease about a system which allows for such practices, which many women felt were bound to discriminate against them in the future, particularly if they were to spend any time in part-time training. One of the most important factors affecting the willingness of women (or men) to train part-time in medicine is the fear that it will count against them in being considered for 'good' consultant posts. This is often combined with a fear of being 'too old' to be appointed a senior registrar or consultant. The received wisdom that 'good' doctors reach certain grades at certain ages is firmly entrenched in the medical career structure. The following chapters look closely at less than full-time working in medicine and examine its perceived advantages and disadvantages.

This chapter has shown that practices which are less than equitable still appear to be prevalent in job interviews and at appointments boards. The incidence of directly discriminatory questions appears to have diminished slightly, but women are still being asked questions which are not asked of men, and, indeed, both sexes are being asked questions which could be interpreted as directly or indirectly discriminatory. The freedom to ask any kind of personal question which has traditionally been accepted as completely reasonable in interviews for partners in general practice requires very close scrutiny, and will be discussed at greater length in the final chapter.

11 Part-time training posts

One of the main aims of the last study was to explore the extent to which women considered that part-time postgraduate training in medicine was useful in helping them to continue in hospital medicine, and to examine any constraints on women's careers which might have been imposed by the ways in which part-time or less than full-time training was organised.

It had been accepted for some years that there was a need to institute some way of allowing women to train part-time, since full-time training in medicine was undoubtedly difficult to combine with domestic or family commitments and it was recognised that most postgraduate training came at a time when many young women doctors would have such commitments. This had led to the introduction of schemes designed to allow doctors with domestic commitments to train part-time – HM(69)6 (DHSS, 1969), which was replaced in 1979 by the PM(79)3 scheme (DHSS, 1979) which has now been replaced by a scheme in which appointments procedures are devolved to regional level, although the manpower approvals for senior registrars and registrars are still held centrally and applications for senior registrars are only considered once a year. The new arrangements are set out in the Annex and Appendix to EL(93)49 (NHSME, 1993) and the revised scheme is known as *Flexible Training: Senior Registrars.*

Part-time training in medicine has been beset with difficulties, and is by no means regarded as the answer to all the problems of women striving to make a successful career in hospital medicine. Nevertheless it has undoubtedly enabled many women to continue in hospital medicine and reach consultant status who would otherwise have had to train full-time or abandon hopes of becoming a consultant.

Part-time training has recently been reassessed and relabelled 'flexible training' (NHSME, 1993), which, as we have noted before in this report, does not fully capture the notion of less than full-time working. However, the report's recommendations are to be welcomed as further steps in the direction of ensuring opportunities for doctors who may not be able to pursue the 'straight', uninterrupted, full-time career path which so many find difficult to follow.

This chapter is concerned with part-time training only. In the last report we started by giving a composite picture of the full-time or part-time working status of women doctors from all three cohorts by grade and broad area of medicine (Allen, 1988, Table 11.01). We will return to the proportions of those in non-training posts in the next chapter, but we found that in the last survey 11 per cent of women GP trainees, 33 per cent of women senior registrars, 6 per cent of women registrars and no women SHOs were working part-time. The majority of the part-time GP trainees and registrars were in the 1981 cohort.

In the present research, we found that among the 124 1986 women qualifiers, 3 (25 per cent) of the women GP trainees, none of the women senior registrars, none of the women registrars, and 1 (4 per cent) of the women SHOs were part-time. Of the 63 women (51 per cent of the total women) in training posts, 4 (6 per cent) were working part-time, meaning that only 3 per cent of the total sample of 1986 women qualifiers, five years after qualification, were actually in part-time training posts.

It should perhaps be noted here that of the 23 (19 per cent of the total) 1986 women doctors working part-time at all, both in training and non-training posts, 18 (78 per cent) were in general practice.

Part-time training in medicine
We had found in the last study that, although many doctors might accept the desirability of part-time training opportunities, it was thought that there were certain specialties which were unsuitable for part-time training, not least because senior doctors in those specialties considered it to be completely out of the question.

We found that 60 per cent of the total sample of doctors in the last study thought that there were specialties which were particularly unsuitable for part-time training, representing 66 per cent of the men and 54 per cent of the women. The 1981 women were less likely to think that there were specialties unsuitable for part-time training than any of their older counterparts.

In the present study, we found a big drop in the proportion of both men and women taking this view. 44 per cent of the 1986 men but only 27 per cent of the 1986 women thought there were any specialties which were unsuitable for part-time training. The 1986 doctors clearly took a much more robust view of what was possible or not possible than the earlier cohorts.

We had found last time that surgical specialties were generally regarded as unsuitable for part-time training by those who mentioned particular specialties, followed at some distance by general medicine, obstetrics and gynaecology and all major or acute specialties. Paediatrics, orthopaedics, anaesthetics and general practice were mentioned by relatively small numbers of doctors. These findings were replicated in the present study among those who thought there were specialties particularly unsuitable for part-time training. Surgical specialties were mentioned even more often – by two-thirds of those citing particular specialties. However, obstetrics and gynaecology had crept up to second place, and was, in fact, mentioned far more frequently by women than men, perhaps reflecting the difficulties some were finding in carving out a career in obstetrics and gynaecology. General medicine came next, with acute and other hospital specialties following in a similar pattern to that found in the last study.

The main reason given in the last study for considering certain specialties particularly unsuitable for part-time training was that acute specialties needed continuity of care. Over a fifth of doctors thought that acute specialties needed doctors to be on-call and a further fifth thought that training posts demanded the full range of experience, including weekend and night duties. Other reasons included the need for a full-time commitment in any case, the need to keep in practice with surgical skills and the feeling that it would take too long to complete training on a part-time basis. Many other factors were cited, many of which were related to part-time training in general rather than to particular specialties.

In this study, we found the reasons stated by those considering certain specialties unsuitable for part-time training to be broadly similar to those cited above, with one interesting exception which was the high proportion of 1986 qualifiers who felt that surgical specialties needed a full-time commitment and constant exposure in order to keep up with practising surgical skills. Nearly 40 per cent of the men felt this – a much higher proportion than recorded for any reason in the last study. It was a firmly held view among some, like a male doctor taking time out to study: 'If you want to get on you have to have hands-on experience all the time, just to keep your level of competence up. It's so easy, after a break of only a few weeks, to forget minor things. It's something you need to keep doing to do well ...'

As we found last time, although doctors might have thought that there were specialties which were particularly unsuitable for part-time training, they did not necessarily agree that this was a desirable situation. A male psychiatric registrar summarised this point: 'As things stand, they're probably unsuitable, but there's no reason why they can't be made suitable ...'

Many of the women were vociferous in their condemnation of a system which they thought was perpetuated at the expense of juniors. A woman SHO in paediatrics summarised the views of many who thought there were a few hidden agendas around: 'It's an infuriating argument put forward by senior hospital staff to say it's impossible to achieve appropriate experience unless you're working the hours we do – ie 90 hours a week. Consultants are very traditional in their views about training and aren't prepared to look at other systems, for example those in operation in Australia and New Zealand where they have a shift system and a structured career system ...'

Another woman GP trainee agreed: 'The authorities would argue that it's not possible if you're not on call at least one in three to get enough training. But I don't go for that at all – it's a lot of nonsense ...' And a woman psychiatric registrar thought that deep-rooted attitudes needed to be changed at a senior level to allow for a change in the system: 'You should be able to train part-time in any specialty, but the set-up is not appropriate. Consultants aren't prepared to have someone who's only part-time. They don't like the job shared or part-timers ...'

But as we have seen, the majority of doctors thought there were no specialties unsuitable for part-time training. The main reason they put forward was that it only needed proper organisation to make it possible. A woman on maternity leave said: 'There is no reason why. Nights are an important part of training, but you do not need to work the next day as well. Also patients are in and out in such a short time these days, I doubt if it matters to them who deals with them. They're probably more worried about over-tired doctors than strange faces ...'

And many doctors agreed that there was no reason why it could not be organised better, like a woman who had left medicine: 'You could have continual content and good handovers if you arrange it properly, just like you do at weekends ...'

As we found in the last study, there was general agreement that nothing would change unless senior members of the profession made it happen. The important role of individual consultants in making part-time training possible and acceptable was reiterated time and again in the last study, particularly by women who saw little prospect for change until attitudes changed. Five years later, the pressure appeared even greater, but there was little evidence that many doctors perceived much evidence of changing attitudes among consultants.

Personal experience of part-time training

We asked the doctors in both studies whether they themselves had ever considered part-time training or whether they had actually had part-time training at any stage. In addition, we asked the 1986 qualifiers whether they might or would consider part-time training in future.

We compared the 1986 qualifiers both with the 1981 qualifiers, who had been at the same career stage at the time of the last study, and with the 1976 qualifiers, who had been five years further into their careers, just to give some indication of the potential incidence of part-time training. We knew that five years into a career would not necessarily produce a high proportion of people taking part-time training opportunities, even if they were in their late twenties.

Table 11.01   Doctors considering or experienced part-time training

	Male			Female		
	1976	1981	1986	1976	1981	1986
Has considered part-time training	4	3	2	21	16	9
Has had part-time training	0	0	0	8	2	5
Not had/considered part-time training to date	96	97	98	71	83	86
Might/will consider part-time training	n.a	n.a	8	n.a	n.a	32
Base: all qualifiers	*(105)*	*(101)*	*(105)*	*(105)*	*(103)*	*(124)*

column percentages

Table 11.01 shows that none of the male qualifiers from 1976, 1981 or 1986 had had part-time training posts, and that the relative proportions were 8 per cent of the 1976 women, 2 per cent of the 1981 women and 5 per cent of the 1986 women. These figures were considerably lower than for the 1966 women, 29 per cent of whom had had part-time training when we interviewed them in 1986.

Clearly the 1966 women we interviewed had had a career of 20 years compared with the 10-year career of the 1976 women, but the difference was quite marked, even allowing for this. This general decline in the proportion of women working part-time at registrar and senior registrar level is reflected in the graphs in *Flexible Training: Report of the Joint Working Party* (see pp 7 and 8, NHSME, 1993), which indicate that the numbers in such posts have been gradually falling over the past ten years or so.

There are many reasons why the numbers in part-time training posts might be falling. The most obvious reason would be a fall-off in demand. It could be argued that people are not taking part-time training because they do not want or need these jobs. But all the evidence has been, and still is, to the contrary. The picture is clearly complicated and we consider it in detail at the end of this chapter, having established all the factors which go to make it up.

Table 11.01 shows that, although rather more 1986 women (5 per cent) had had part-time training than their 1981 counterparts (2 per cent), rather fewer of them (9 per cent compared with 16 per cent of the 1981 women and 21 per cent of the 1976 women) had considered it. However, we found that 32 per cent of the 1986 women and 8 per cent of the men said that they might or would consider it in the future.

At what level had the doctors considered or had part-time training? Six women doctors (5 per cent of the 1986 women) had had part-time training – 5 as GP trainees and 1 as an SHO. (3 of the GP trainees and the SHO were still in these part-time training posts.) Of the 11 women (9 per cent of the 1986 women) who had considered part-time training, 3 had considered it at SHO level, 4 at registrar level, 1 at senior registrar level, 2 at GP trainee level and 1 did not give a grade. Of the two 1986 men who had considered part-time training, one had considered it at registrar and the other at GP trainee level. The majority of the 1986 women doctors who had had part-time training or had considered it had already done some full-time training at that level, but a quarter of them had not. One man had and the other had not.

It should be noted that all these doctors were in training posts at the time of considering part-time training. In the last study we found that over a third of the men and 10 per cent of the women who had considered part-time training had already been in a career post, but were considering part-time training in another specialty while continuing to work in their original specialty, in order to change specialty at a later stage.

We had found in our study of *Part-time Working in General Practice* that many women doctors had been reluctant to seek careers advice on part-time working until they were absolutely certain that there was no alternative. There were many perceptions that even seeking advice on part-time working could adversely affect doctors' careers, in that they might be seen as 'less than serious' or 'unsound'. We asked the 1986 doctors the same question we had asked in the last study, where we had found that only two-thirds of the women considering part-time training, but over three-quarters of those who had had part-time training, had sought advice first.

In the present study we found that two-thirds of the women who had considered or had part-time training had sought advice, but neither of the men had done so. Just over a quarter of the women had spoken to an officer at the Regional Health Authority, a quarter had spoken to a consultant, one fifth to the regional postgraduate dean, two had spoken to their GP trainers, two to other colleagues and one to the Regional Medical Officer.

The advice had been fairly mixed, with about half of the women saying they had been encouraged to proceed, but others saying they had been discouraged by advice that it would take too long, would spoil their job prospects, that there was no point in even applying, or that job-sharing would be a better option than part-time training.

What happened to the women? Six went ahead and took part-time training posts. Of those who had considered it, 4 decided against it, 3 postponed their decision, 1 intended to apply for part-time training on the PM(79)3 scheme, 1 decided to continue with full-time training and the others were undecided. Both men decided against it.

Looking at the six women doctors who had had part-time training, (four of whom were still in these posts), the average length of time in post was 11 months, but, of course, this would no doubt be longer by the time they had all finished. However, it was clear that none of them would be in part-time training posts for very long since all but one were GP trainees. All but one had taken part-time training to fit in with domestic commitments, while the other had done so because of illness. All but one, who thought it was too soon to say, thought it had not had an adverse effect on their careers.

We asked all those who had considered or might consider part-time training for what reason they would want it. Of the 51 women and 10 men who replied, 90 per cent of the women and 40 per cent of the men said it would be to fit in with family or domestic commitments; one fifth of the men and one in ten of the women said they would like to gain experience in another specialty; one in ten of the men and a small number of women said they would like it while studying; one third of the men and one in ten of the women thought it would allow them time to develop other interests, and one or two men and women said it would give them time to sort out their affairs.

The majority of both men and women considering part-time training either now or in future wanted it at registrar or senior registrar level, although a third of both men and women wanted it at SHO level, and 10 per cent of the women wanted it at GP trainee level.

The average length of time they wanted to train part-time was 32 months for the women and 25 months for the men, with a median time of just under two years for both sexes. It should be noted that half the men and a quarter of the women could not answer the question since they felt that so much would depend on their circumstances at the time.

Finally we asked those who had considered part-time training in the past but were no longer thinking of it why they had not proceeded with it. The reasons reflected the general criticisms of part-time training – that it would take too long, that jobs were too difficult to find, that they had been discouraged by others and that it would slow down their career progress. The few men in this category had been told that they were not eligible since they were men or had found it difficult to find any posts. There were several sharp comments about the present schemes, like this from a woman anaesthetic registrar: 'Not the way it's structured at the moment – seven years instead of four, and being paid a pittance ...'

Part-time training opportunities

We were particularly interested in the views of doctors about the various schemes available, either locally and centrally, designed to facilitate part-time training opportunities. The longest-established scheme at the time of the present research was the PM(79)3 scheme which was set up in 1979 with the specific purpose of enabling doctors with domestic commitments, physical disability or ill-health to train part-time. It was nationally organised at senior registrar level. Health authorities were encouraged to set up part-time training in other grades, for example, registrar, SHO and GP trainee grades and for training grades in public health medicine. All these arrangements used to come under the main umbrella of the PM(79)3 scheme but new regional arrangements for part-time registrar training were introduced in 1991 (Department of Health, 1991).

The PM(79)3 scheme, which was mainly used for part-time senior registrar training, has been criticised over the years on a number of counts, not least the fact that applications were accepted only once a year, and that manpower approval was given centrally but that the doctors then had to find their own jobs, funding, and training approval for the posts from the relevant Royal College or Faculty or Joint Committee on Higher Training. The posts were supernumerary, which meant that they were not always thought to have comparable status to full-time jobs, and some women have criticised the lack of monitoring and interest taken in their progress once manpower approval has been granted. The scheme has also been criticised for adhering very rigidly to the view that doctors have to demonstrate that domestic commitments are the reason preventing them from training full-time. This was thought effectively to preclude men from being considered from an opportunity in which increasing numbers were interested.

We found in the last study that only fifteen women and one man in the whole sample of 640 had applied to the Department of Health for manpower approval for part-time senior registrar posts under the PM(79)3 scheme, and that only eleven had been successful. We knew that it was unlikely that many of the 1986 qualifiers would have been at the stage in their career when they would have reached senior registrar level and even less likely that they would have applied for the PM(79)3 scheme. As expected, we found that none of them had.

However, we were interested in establishing how much the 1986 qualifiers knew about schemes which facilitated part-time training in medicine. In the last study, in spite of the fact that high proportions of doctors thought that there ought to be more part-time training opportunities, we found that 81 per cent of the men and 68 per cent of the women interviewed had never heard of the PM(79)3 scheme, even when described in detail, rising from 62 per cent of the 1966 women to 65 per cent of the 1976 women to as many as 80 per cent of the 1981 women qualifiers. We remarked that these were very high proportions of women not knowing about a scheme which was designed specifically to help women train part-time. It reinforced the views expressed by many women, both in the last study and elsewhere, that it was very difficult to find out about part-time training opportunities and that the PM(79)3 scheme was not well enough publicised.

What had happened by the time we interviewed the 1986 cohort? We found, interestingly, that the 1986 men appeared to be better informed than the women about the PM(79)3 scheme – 62 per cent of the men said they had never heard of it, compared with 68 per cent of the women, which, although it was better than the 80 per cent of 1981 women qualifiers, was still not a very reassuring proportion.

We asked those who had heard of it from which source they had their information, since it was clearly important to see how the information was filtering through. One third of both men and women said they had seen an advertisement in the medical press, and exactly the same proportion said they knew about it through friends or colleagues having applied for it or having a post through it. Around one in six knew about it through other colleagues, and one in ten of the women said they had heard of it through a consultant. Only one woman had heard of it through a regional postgraduate dean, one through a women's medical organisation, and only one woman through a clinical tutor. Others had read articles or had learnt about it through professional bodies.

Even among those who had heard of the scheme, knowledge was very sketchy, and a substantial proportion found it difficult to make any comment on it. However, the majority of both men and women thought that it was a very good idea in principle. There were familiar criticisms of the scheme, such as the length of time it took to get manpower approval and set up posts, that it was too inflexible, considered of lower status than full-time training, not well enough publicised, and was generally administratively cumbersome with no guarantee of funding or jobs. On the other hand, some doctors were particularly enthusiastic about it, like a male paediatric registrar: 'I think it's wonderful. I think medicine will cut its own throat if highly trained people leave at a late stage of their career because the system won't accommodate them ...'

We asked doctors if they had heard of the new regional arrangements for part-time training for registrars which had recently been introduced (Department of Health, 1991) and the regional arrangements for part-time training for SHOs. We found that they were less well-known than the PM(79)3 scheme, even though the part-time registrar arrangements had been announced and discussed in the medical press not long before the interviewing took place. Only 20 per cent of the men and 27 per cent of the women said that they had heard of the part-time training for registrar arrangements, and 18 per cent of the men and 23 per cent of the women said they had heard of the regional arrangements for part-time training for SHOs. In both cases, those who said they had heard of the schemes usually thought they were a good idea. Others thought there should be more such opportunities, but it was noted that posts were difficult to set up. In fact, the interviews indicated that most of those saying that they had heard of the schemes had little idea of what they were, how they worked or how they could gain access to them.

The main message which emerged from the questions about the various schemes designed to facilitate part-time training in medicine was how difficult doctors found it to find out about them initially, and, having found out about them, to find someone who would help them go through the necessary administrative processes to actually get a part-time training post.

Greater availability of part-time training

We noted earlier in this chapter that the numbers of part-time training posts appeared to be declining rather than increasing, which did not seem to coincide with the generally held view, supported by our previous research among other studies, that there was unmet demand for part-time training opportunities. It is clearly very difficult to quantify demand of this nature. Many of the questions to be asked are necessarily hypothetical if the supply is not actually there. It should be noted that even if the supply is there, the reasons for a low take-up may have a great deal to do with factors other than lack of demand.

If part-time training posts are not seen to provide what doctors want or need from their careers they will not be taken up in large numbers. If few people know that they exist they will not be taken up. If they are perceived as having second class status, as being held by second-rate doctors or as offering inadequate training, they will not be taken up. There are many other reasons why part-time training opportunities will not be taken up. Before it is assumed that there is little demand, a close examination should be taken of the way in which the opportunities are offered and the various schemes are implemented.

But what did the doctors themselves feel about part-time training? In the last study we found overwhelming support for greater availability of part-time training opportunities among the women, rising from 84 per cent of the 1966 cohort to 88 per cent of the 1981 cohort. The enthusiasm among the men was rather more muted, but nevertheless two-thirds of all three cohorts were favour of it. Table 11.02 indicates a big increase among both men and women in support for more part-time training opportunities – 87 per cent of the 1986 men and an almost universal 98 per cent of the 1986 women.

Table 11.02   Doctors' views on whether there should be greater availability of part-time training posts

column percentages

	Male			Female		
	1976	1981	1986	1976	1981	1986
Yes	67	64	87	83	88	98
No	20	21	7	14	6	1
Don't know	13	15	7	3	6	2
Base: all qualifiers	*(105)*	*(101)*	*(105)*	*(105)*	*(103)*	*(124)*

How did they think that part-time training should be organised? Among those who thought there should be greater part-time training opportunities, two-thirds of the women and half the men thought there should be more job-sharing and split jobs. This response dominated the answers in the last study, and was clearly put forward by people who not only recognised many of the disadvantages of the PM(79)3 scheme, with its supernumerary element, but also recognised the criticism of part-time training as not providing sufficient continuity of care. It was obviously hoped that proper job-sharing posts would avoid both types of criticism.

The second most frequent recommendation, by 40 per cent of the 1986 men and half the women, was that part-time training posts should be part of the establishment and not supernumerary. This was a considerably higher proportion than we found in the last study, and perhaps reinforces the observation that supernumerary posts were in some way not regarded as 'serious' or 'proper' posts.

As in the last study, these two recommendations accounted for most of the answers, but there was one interesting change, which was the fact that one fifth of both men and women advocating more part-time training opportunities said that these opportunities should be more available to men. The Department of Health has held out steadfastly against extending schemes like the PM(79)3 to either men or women unless they can prove domestic commitments which prevent them from training full-time. The Royal College of Physicians Working Party on Part-time Work in Specialist Medicine (Royal College of Physicians, 1994) debated the issue at some length and recommended relaxing the criteria for part-time working opportunities. There really can be little doubt that rigid adherence to the need for domestic commitments may well be discriminatory, as well as providing too little flexibility in the careers of both men and women. It is, after all, only in medicine that full-time working entails such long hours for such a long period of time.

In addition, there were a variety of other recommendations on how part-time training opportunities could be organised, including central/local liaison so that jobs and money were available; that it should be organised centrally, regionally, at district level, by the Royal Colleges, on a shift system, on a sessional basis; that it should cover all aspects of training, should be recognised for accreditation, should take into account specialty needs, should be tailored to individual requirements, should be built into the career structure, and should be encouraged by health authorities. There was absolutely no shortage of good ideas from individual doctors, both male and female, although some 10 per cent said it was a very good idea but they would not know how best to organise it.

The demand for job-sharing or established posts was often related to concern about the status of people holding supernumerary posts at present, as a male general surgical registrar pointed out: 'I've seen supernumerary people not get a fair crack of the whip – ignored for teaching opportunities because they have had no responsibilities for patient care ...' And a woman registrar in psychiatry confirmed his view from another specialty: 'They're called YTS here ...'

Some doctors felt that the impetus had to come from the doctors themselves, like a woman who had just returned from overseas: 'Only women can push for this. They should propose a scheme, do it well and impress the consultant in each case. It will not be organised for us, will it?' But some women were concerned that part-time training should not be seen only as an issue for women, like a part-time GP principal: 'It should be available to both men and women. They must accept that doctors don't have to work hundreds of hours, and men must be involved as well so that it doesn't become a women's ghetto ...'

A male psychiatric registrar was all in favour of part-time training and even had good words to say for the PM(79)3 scheme: 'One of my friends applied. He wants to help look after the children. His wife is a doctor too and they both applied so they can share bringing up the children ...' It remains to be seen how many male doctors can achieve part-time training status, but there was certainly great support for it.

Many doctors thought that part-time training opportunities did not meet the demand, as this woman SHO explained: 'There's not enough availability for the number of people who want it. It's necessary and feasible. It's ridiculous to put 50 per cent women into medical school and then not provide jobs. It's money down the drain ...' Even doctors who saw problems in organising part-time training thought it worth the effort,like a male GP principal: 'The problem would be on-call. But it needn't take double the time because much of it is service commitment. You could make more use of your experience if you had time to reflect ...'

In the last study we found much interest in part-time training but relatively few concrete suggestions on how best to organise it other than job-sharing. In this study, there were many examples of well-thought out plans by doctors, and, indeed, a much more realistic appraisal of the need for more part-time training and how best to meet it.

How part-time training helps doctors' careers

We explored the ways in which part-time training had or might help the careers of doctors. We have seen that only 6 of the 229 1986 qualifiers had had part-time training, and their reasons were not unexpected. They mainly said that working part-time had helped them to combine a family and training, while one, who had been ill, said that it enabled her to stay in her chosen specialty.

Looking at the doctors who had not had part-time training, it was interesting that over three-quarters of both the men and the women said that part-time training would not have helped or would not help their careers in future. Some, of course, were already in career grade posts. The finding was interesting put against the overwhelming recommendation for more part-time training opportunities. Doctors were not only thinking of themselves it appears, but both men and women were interested in providing opportunities for others.

Among the women, 15 per cent said it would have helped them to combine family and career, but this was mentioned by only one man. Other reasons were spread fairly equally between men and women. Eight doctors said that it would give them better opportunities to study, and others thought it would give them a chance to a lead a normal social life or to increase their knowledge in a particular area. Four doctors said it would have enabled them to continue in medicine, two said it would have meant that they would not have been pushed into full-time training or nothing, and three said it would have helped them avoid the 'clinical assistant dead-end'. Three women said it would have enabled them to stay in hospital medicine.

It was of interest that half the doctors who were not working at the time of the interview gave specific reasons why part-time training would have helped their careers.

Many of the doctors who were in favour of more part-time training gave detailed reasons why it would not help their careers. A male registrar said: 'Had I trained part-time as a gastro-enterologist at the current rate it would have been 28 years to reach consultant – I would have been 52! My feeling is that I wouldn't have been taken seriously if I'd trained part-time. It's quite a high profile career and I would have been regarded as not being able to hack the pace ...'

The notion that 'serious' doctors did not have part-time training clearly ran deep, as a male paediatric SHO reaffirmed: 'Medicine is too demanding. They won't take you seriously if you've trained part-time. People would ask, "Don't you love medicine with all your heart, life and soul?" You've got to keep up – medical information doubles every year. It's a wife and a job ...'

It was also apparent that many doctors, particularly men, felt that part-time training was necessarily half-time and would cover the full length of training, thus taking double the length of full-time training, as a male orthopaedic registrar noted: 'It takes ten years to train in surgery. Part-time training would go on too long. I wouldn't have got the experience ...'

The fact that few women who have trained part-time have done so for any length of time or that they normally work far more than half time often appears to have escaped the notice of commentators who ought to be better informed. Perhaps it is not surprising that so many doctors think it would be the kiss of death to their careers. There were many worries among women as well as men that part-time training was a last resort, as a woman psychiatric registrar explained: 'I hope it would be a viable option in future. I have a lot of reservations. I think it could discredit me in becoming a consultant. I feel it's harder to get subsequent posts if you've worked part-time because people feel you're not 100 per cent committed ...'

Assessment of part-time training

The present study has shown that almost 100 per cent of the 1986 women and nearly 90 per cent of the 1986 men thought that there ought to be greater availability of part-time training posts. In the study on *Part-time Working in General Practice* (Allen, 1992), some three-quarters of the men and over 90 per cent of the women GPs shared this view. And, as the parallel follow-up study shows, the proportion of 1976 and 1981 women qualifiers who agreed had increased considerably in the five years since the last study.

12 Part-time working and other career posts

The last chapter confirmed earlier findings that part-time training opportunities in medicine are considered inadequate by the majority of doctors. The feeling was almost universal among the 1986 women and was a view held by nearly 90 per cent of the 1986 men. We have seen that their views were supported by increasing numbers of the respondents from earlier cohorts in the follow-up study of *Doctors and their Careers* (Allen, 1994) and by their colleagues in general practice (Allen, 1992).

What did they think about part-time working in other posts in medicine, particularly in career posts, such as GP principal and consultant posts? After all, the interest of many women in less than full-time working does not cease when they reach career grade – if they reach career grade. This is particularly true in general practice, where doctors can reach career grade in their late twenties, a time at which many women may then wish to work less than full-time for some time. The difficulties encountered by women in securing part-time GP principal posts has been fully documented in *Part-time Working in General Practice* (Allen, 1992) and discussed in other recent literature, including *Women in General Practice* (General Medical Services Committee, British Medical Association, 1994).

The relative lack of part-time training opportunities has led to a number of consequences. One is clearly that women abandon the idea of continuing in hospital medicine with the aim of becoming consultants. In the study of young GPs (Allen, 1992), we found that 25 per cent of the women from all three cohorts studied said that they would have stayed in hospital medicine if part-time training opportunities had been more readily available. The second consequence is that women may not leave hospital medicine but take clinical assistant posts. The third consequence is that women may not find themselves able to complete GP vocational training or hospital training and instead opt for a series of community health and other medical officer jobs, which may carry clinical autonomy without being career grade jobs. The fourth consequence has been one that some women have found more satisfying, which is that they have reached associate specialist status – a personal grade of consultant equivalent without the departmental and other duties of consultants. A fifth consequence, which has been available only since the last research was conducted, is that women take staff grade jobs – a new grade introduced in 1988, which is a non-training intermediate-level service grade designed for doctors who do not wish or are unable to train for consultant grade (Department of Health, HC(88)90, 1988).

There is little doubt that there are more part-time or less than full-time opportunities in all these jobs than in consultant or, to a lesser extent, in GP principal posts. In this chapter, we first look at the experience of the 1986 women in part-time posts other than in the training posts which we discussed in the last chapter. We found that of the 12 women GP principals, one third (4) were working part-time, of the 15 women GP locums, just over half (8) were working part-time, as were all three women on the GP retainer scheme. In addition, 3 of the 4 clinical assistants and one medical officer were working part-time. The five women in academic medicine and the two clinical medical officers were all working full-time, as were the two women working outside medicine or in medically related occupations.

To summarise the picture, of the 23 1986 women doctors working part-time, 4 were GP principals, 3 were GP trainees, 8 were GP locums and 3 were on the GP retainer scheme, giving a total of 18 working part-time in general practice. In addition, 1 woman was an SHO, 3 were clinical assistants and 1 was a medical officer doing a variety of work.

It should be noted that of the 23 women working part-time at the time of the interview, less than one third (7) had children, while the rest had no children. There are clearly many reasons for working part-time.

At the time of the research, only 4 women (the GP principals) were in part-time career posts in medicine. The last report (Allen, 1988) showed clearly that the majority of women working part-time in medicine were not in training posts and were certainly not in career posts in the hospital sector. Over half the women GP principals (taking all three cohorts together) were, however, working part-time. These were early days for the 1986 cohort, but it looks as though this is the pattern which is going to emerge for them too, unless major changes are quickly introduced.

Greater availability of part-time career posts

In the last report we had found that our respondents were rather more enthusiastic about an increase in part-time career posts than in an increase in part-time training posts, with over 90 per cent of the 1976 and 1981 women holding this view, compared with over 70 per cent of their male counterparts. Again, the 1986 cohort were more likely than previous generations to think there should be greater availability of part-time career posts – 97 per cent of the women and 79 per cent of the men, as Table 12.01 shows.

We asked the doctors how more part-time career posts should be organised. Again, the main recommendation was that there should be more job-sharing or split posts, a view held by two thirds of both men and women thinking there should be greater availability of part-time career posts. One fifth of the women but less than 10 per cent of the men said that recognised part-time posts should be established. Over 10 per cent of the men, but fewer women, said that there

Table 12.01   Doctors' views on whether there should be greater availability of
part-time career posts

column percentages

	Male 1976	Male 1981	Male 1986	Female 1976	Female 1981	Female 1986
Yes	75	69	79	90	92	97
No	15	18	9	6	5	2
Don't know	10	13	12	5	3	2
Base: all qualifiers	*(105)*	*(101)*	*(105)*	*(105)*	*(103)*	*(124)*

should be different levels of consultant grade, while 10 per cent of the men and rather fewer women said that more consultants should be employed to look after fewer patients each.

Other suggestions, each made by less than 10 per cent of the respondents, included making it easier to work part-time as a GP principal, working on a sessional basis, giving part-timers equal status and power to full-timers in equivalent posts, organisation on a team or departmental basis to ensure continuity of care, organisation of part-time posts through a committee structure, or through a central or regional structure. Other comments related to particular specialties in which it was thought to be easier or more difficult to organise part-time career posts. Some 6 per cent of men commented darkly that most consultants worked part-time in any case, while around one fifth of both sexes thought it a very good idea but did not know how it could be organised.

It was thought to be useful for both sexes, and there was little doubt that domestic or family commitments were not the only reasons for thinking there ought to be more part-time opportunities in career posts. A male paediatric registrar spoke for a number of his colleagues: 'I have 100 per cent commitment to the NHS, but I think you occasionally burn out and need to have time out to do other things – reading, studying – and know that the NHS isn't going to suffer or someone else has to cover for your absence ...'

This reflected the interest we found among both male and female GPs in the study *Part-time Working in General Practice*, where there were many indications of stress, burn-out and boredom which had led doctors to think that at least some period working less than full-time might be beneficial, not only to them but also to their patients.

The notion of full-time commitment only being possible through full-time – or more than full-time – working runs very deep in the medical profession, even if so many doctors interviewed thought that there ought to be more part-time career posts. The main reason given by the few doctors who disagreed with the idea was that acute specialties needed continuity of care. Other objections were concerned with difficulties in general practice in coping with part-timers, the need for more full-time consultants rather than part-timers, the thought that it might be a way of getting cheap labour, and the view that consultants needed a full-time commitment.

We asked whether there were any specialties which were particularly unsuitable for part-time career posts. 34 per cent of the 1986 qualifiers thought there were (39 per cent of men and 31 per cent of women). This represented rather fewer men but rather more women than we found when we asked about specialties unsuitable for part-time training posts (see Chapter 11). As we found in the case of part-time training posts, surgery was the specialty most frequently mentioned – by two thirds of those citing particular specialties. It was again followed by general medicine and obstetrics and gynaecology, with paediatrics some way behind. Over a quarter of those thinking there were specialties unsuitable for part-time career posts said that all major or acute specialties fell into this category.

Continuity of care or on-call responsibilities were again given as the overwhelming reasons for thinking that certain specialties were unsuitable for part-time career posts, with the added comment that surgical skills needed full-time exposure to keep them in trim. Some 10 per cent of those who thought that part-time career posts should not be made more available said that consultants needed a full-time commitment. Some of the views were very strongly held, like those of a male GP principal: 'Patients die if service is not 100 per cent. You can't mess about. Acute specialties need on-call and continuity of care. You just need to be available all the time ...'

But others held the view for rather different reasons, like a male anaesthetic SHO: 'Surgery – because you often find that two consultant surgeons can have different ideas on pre-op. treatment, definitive treatment, post-op. care etc ... And surgeons being the beasts they are, it could lead to friction because they all think they are right ...'

Some doctors who thought there were no specialties unsuitable for part-time career posts commented that it was all a matter of organisation, but a woman former trainee GP said: 'The problem may be continuity of care. But people go on holiday. The problem is the commitment of the full-time people to the idea. If it were more common it would be easier ...'

And this observation was repeated time and again in these interviews. If part-time or less than full-time working, whether in training or in career posts, were more common, there would be fewer obstacles put in its way. But the argument was often felt to be circular. In the absence of sufficient part-time posts, many doctors felt inhibited from agitating for more, in case they were seen as doctors without the magical 100 per cent commitment.

How part-time career posts help doctors' careers

We were aware that few of the 1986 qualifiers would have reached career grade in medicine, and that these were all likely to be GP principals, as indeed they were. We saw in Chapter 2 that 23 per cent of the men and 10 per cent of the

Table 12.02 Whether doctors had ever worked part-time or less than full-time in medicine other than in a training post (1986 qualifiers only)

column percentages

	Total	Male	Female
Yes (at present)	9	3	14
Yes (in the past but no longer)	2	1	3
Yes (in the past and at present - different jobs)	*	0	1
No	36	33	38
Not applicable - still in training grade	53	63	44
Base: all qualifiers	*(229)*	*(105)*	*(124)*

women were GP principals. (In the last study we noted that not all doctors who had reached career grade were necessarily still working in those posts. In this study this did not appear to be the case, since most had only just arrived in the grade.)

We found in the last study that many doctors were unaware of the distinctions between career grade posts and non-training posts, even if they knew that training posts were different. We therefore asked doctors in the follow-up study whether they had ever worked part-time or less than full-time in medicine other than in a training post, and then asked them to specify the post, so that we could make the distinction for them.

We found that 15 per cent of the women and 3 per cent of the men were working part-time in non-training posts at present (one woman had had a different post in the past as well), while 3 per cent of the women and 1 per cent had done so in the past, but were now working full-time.

We saw earlier in the chapter the jobs in which women were working part-time. We found that, in addition to the 4 women who were currently working as part-time GP principals, 2 others had previously done so. Of the four men who had previously worked part-time, mainly as clinical assistants, all but one – a GP locum – were working full-time at present.

The numbers of women who had worked part-time in career posts was clearly tiny, so we combined them with those who had worked part-time in other non-training posts and asked them how working part-time had helped their career. As expected, over 40 per cent said that it had enabled them to continue working, while one third said that it had given them more time for domestic or family life. It was perhaps interesting that these reasons were given as frequently by women without children as by those with children.

Around one in six of the women said that working part-time had given them more time for interests other than medicine, two men and one woman said it had given them the chance to combine two specialties, each part-time. However, three women and one man said that working part-time had not helped their careers but was the only job that they could get.

We asked those who had not had part-time posts in non-training grades in medicine how these would help their careers now or in future. Over 80 per cent of the men, but less than half the women said that it would not help their careers. However, nearly one third of the women, but only four men, said that it would give them more time for family or domestic life. 14 per cent of the women and 3 per cent of the men said that it was too soon to say, but it might help in future. Otherwise, reasons were given by small numbers of doctors of both sexes, covering more time for other interests, private work and study.

Career posts in hospital other than consultant grade

At the time of the last study, there had been much discussion of the question of whether there should be posts in hospital of career grade status, which would have full clinical autonomy but without the full departmental responsibilities of the consultant grade. The Department of Health issued a consultative document *Hospital Medical Staffing: Achieving a Balance* (DHSS, 1986) followed a year later by *Hospital Medical Staffing: Achieving a Balance – Plan for Action* (DHSS, 1987). As a result the staff grade was introduced in 1988 which, as we saw earlier, is a non-training intermediate-level service grade designed for doctors who do not wish or are unable to train for consultant grade (Department of Health, HC(88)90, 1988).

The battle has raged for many years about whether a 'sub-consultant' grade should be introduced, and has been fiercely resisted by many for a variety of reasons. Some have seen it as a way of creating a cadre of second-rate doctors, others have seen it as a way of restricting the number of consultants, while others have been concerned that it might be a way of getting cheap labour, particularly in the form of women and overseas qualifiers.

In the last study, we asked doctors if they thought there should be career posts in hospital other than consultant grade, and surprised the Department of Health with the finding that there was overall support for such a grade, with 56 per cent of the men and 59 per cent of the women in the sample as a whole thinking that there should, reflecting broad agreement through all three cohorts.

Clinical assistants, many of whom thought they were already doing work of this nature, were not surprisingly more in favour than most, although it was interesting to see the relatively high proportion of GP principals, particularly women, who were also in favour.

We were interested in this study to see what doctors thought of the introduction of the staff grade, and, in addition, to see how useful they thought the associate specialist grade was. (Since the fieldwork for this study was completed we have conducted a study of staff grade doctors in which we asked the same questions, among others (Allen and Rolfe, 1994; SCOPME, 1994). We went on to ask the 1986 qualifiers whether they themselves would like a career grade post without the full range of consultant responsibilities.

Table 12.03   Doctors' assessment of whether staff grade a useful grade (1986 qualifiers only)

		column percentages	
	Total	Male	Female
Yes	52	54	51
No	34	33	34
Don't know	11	12	10
Yes and no	3	0	6
Base: all qualifiers	*(229)*	*(105)*	*(124)*

We found that enthusiasm for staff grade was mixed, with 54 per cent of the 1986 men and 51 per cent of the women considering it to be a useful grade. One third of both sexes did not consider it useful, while just over 10 per cent did not know, and 6 per cent of women had mixed views.

Why was it thought to be useful? Just over a third of both men and women thought that it helped experienced doctors or good doctors get to the top who might not otherwise be able to do so, while a further third of both sexes thought that it suited those who wanted less responsibility than a full consultant grade post. In addition, one fifth thought that it helped to keep good experienced doctors in hospital medicine, rather than losing them to general practice, and one fifth of women, but less than 10 per cent of men, thought that it suited people with family commitments. Other reasons for finding staff grade useful included the view that it unblocked the 'bottleneck' at senior registrar level, that it created 'middle' management, that it took the pressure off junior doctors, gave job security and was good for those who wanted more clinical work and less administration and management.

Those who found staff grade a useful grade were often sympathetic to those who did 'an excellent job' but found it difficult to get consultant posts for a variety of reasons. A male senior registrar spoke of the stress he had observed in others: 'If you don't have something like that you have to go up relentlessly. There's a great deal of pressure to go up. It's detrimental to your career to stay in a grade too long – and too long can be only two years. To have the option not to go on to consultancy is good ...'

A male general medical registrar agreed: 'I think it'll help: a) because there's a need for a position for people who don't want to do general practice but want to continue in hospital medicine; b) having staff grade doctors around would help take the pressure off junior doctors in training who are meant to be doing everything; and c) in medicine I don't know why there is no system of middle management ...'

Others agreed that it provided a useful intermediate grade, like a woman GP principal: '... because you have a well-qualified and experienced person who's at a level where they can teach junior staff, ie not a registrar who has only just learnt what they're doing. It's less load for the registrars and it's not all-or-nothing. It gives an intermediate career ...'

A woman registrar in obstetrics and gynaecology reflected the views of many who thought it was useful for 'stuck' doctors: 'It suits foreign doctors, long-term locums. They're never going to get a consultant post because they can't compete, but they do an excellent job. Maybe they can't get the exams, but they can use their abilities ...' There was a clear view, even among those who felt that staff grade was a good idea, that it was only suitable for doctors who could not reach consultant grade, as a male GP principal noted: 'Only people who can't go home to their own country fill these posts. It's a second class consultant grade. They have no choice ...'

In the PSI study of *Staff Grade Doctors: a Structured Enquiry into their Educational Needs* (Allen and Rolfe, 1994), conducted for SCOPME, we found that many staff grade doctors thought that junior doctors were much less likely than consultants to recognise their worth or to hold the staff grade in any esteem. Their concerns were confirmed by many of the comments made by 1986 qualifiers in the present study who did not think that staff grade was a useful grade, certainly not for people like them, as a male doctor studying for his fellowship said: 'Some people will benefit from it, but those wanting a career won't apply. I can't see many British graduates who want a career being happy in those posts, and it doesn't help the structure for anyone who's dead set on a consultant post ...'

We have seen that one third of both men and women did not think staff grade a useful grade. Of these, nearly half the women and one third of the men thought it a dead-end job in which no career progress was possible, and over 40 per cent of the men and under one third of the women thought that staff grade was perceived as second class and not taken seriously. Around one fifth of both sexes thought that people in staff grade posts had no power and no status, and nearly one fifth thought that staff grade just provided 'cheap labour' and that more consultant posts should be created. Around one in six of the men thought that it exploited doctors from overseas, and two women thought that it exploited women.

A woman senior registrar was concerned about the status and prospects of people in staff grade posts: 'It's a dead-end job really – a one-way ticket. You can't get back into training ...' And her view was reiterated by others, including a woman registrar: 'It's not useful because of the stigma of not being able to return to the continuing career structure ...' (This factor was of great concern to many doctors in our study of staff grade doctors (Allen and Rolfe, 1994).)

A male GP locum was worried about exploitation: 'It's a cop-out. They've created the grade to get people to do the work without paying them as consultants. It's for people who can't cut it. Around here, most of them are foreign doctors who do most of the work ...' A woman paediatric registrar returned to the theme of the danger of dropping off the career ladder: 'Medicine has a definite career path and if you deviate off it you may be ignored as a failure ...'

**Table 12.04   Doctors' assessment of whether associate specialist a useful grade
(1986 qualifiers only)**

column percentages

	Total	Male	Female
Yes	58	61	56
No	24	27	23
Don't know	15	11	18
Yes and no	3	1	4
Base: all qualifiers	*(229)*	*(105)*	*(124)*

Although more than half the 1986 doctors thought staff grade a useful grade, many of their comments reflected their feelings that it might be useful in general but was not an option that career-minded doctors would consider. It was interesting that, although the two main groups of doctors in staff grade are male overseas qualifiers and female UK qualifiers, the usefulness of staff grade to women doctors was hardly mentioned. What did they feel about the associate specialist grade?

We found that rather more 1986 doctors thought that associate specialist was a useful grade – 61 per cent of the men and 56 per cent of the women. The rather high proportion of 'don't know' responses indicated a genuine lack of knowledge about the associate specialist grade, and, indeed, given the numbers of such posts, it is quite possible that doctors might not have had much experience of meeting associate specialists.

Those thinking it a useful grade often gave similar reasons for thinking staff grade a useful grade, for example nearly one third thought it helped experienced or good doctors get to the top who would not otherwise be able to and a similar proportion thought that it suited those who wanted less responsibility than a full consultant post. Some one in six said that it kept good and experienced doctors in hospital medicine rather than in general practice, and just over 10 per cent of both sexes thought that it suited people with domestic or family commitments. Again, other reasons similar to those cited for staff grade posts were given, like unblocking the bottleneck at senior registrar level, creating middle management, taking pressure off junior doctors and good for those wanting more clinical work. There was a clear misunderstanding among a number of doctors, in spite of the explanation of the grade given by interviewers, who thought that associate specialists were GPs working in hospitals. They thought that was a good idea.

Among those who did not think the associate specialist grade was useful, the reasons given were very similar to those given for staff grade, suggesting a blurring of the two grades in the minds of many of these young doctors. One third thought that associate specialist was a dead-end grade, a quarter thought it had no power or status, a fifth thought it was perceived as second class, and over a quarter thought that it was cheap labour and that the answer was to create more consultant posts. Four doctors thought it exploited doctors from overseas and three thought it exploited women.

A male student thought it was useful for some people: '... but I cannot see how it would appeal to strong-minded career people, I'm not doing all this training to end up in a second-best post, which is how a lot of people view it ...' A male psychiatric registrar agreed: 'I suppose it is useful for women with children or demanding husbands – but it is a pity ...'

Given the level of misunderstanding of the grade, it was refreshing to find a woman surgical SHO who could see its usefulness: 'It provides a post where there's not quite the breadth of commitment that's required of a consultant post but provides similar patient responsibilities ...'

But a male SHO thought that there were problems which made the grade less than useful: 'The medical structure is based on boss and slaves. You'd still be a slave – the structure is so hierarchical ...' And a woman SHO agreed that it was not particularly useful: 'People get disenchanted stuck in mid-grade. It affects performance ...'

We asked the doctors whether they themselves would like a career grade post without the full range of consultant responsibilities. We worded the question in this rather open way, since we did not want to imply that staff grade and associate specialist grades were the only grades possible in this category, partly because we knew that they might be misunderstood and partly because we wanted a more general answer if possible.

Table 12.05   Whether doctors would like a career grade post without the full range of consultant responsibilities (1986 qualifiers only)

column percentages

	Total	Male	Female
Yes	18	10	25
No	77	88	69
Don't know	4	2	6
Base: all qualifiers	*(229)*	*(105)*	*(124)*

Table 12.05 shows that 18 per cent of the 1986 qualifiers would like a career grade post without the full range of consultant responsibilities, but that this represented only 10 per cent of the men compared with 25 per cent of the women. Interestingly, there was little difference between those with or without children, or between those working full-time or part-time.

We then asked the doctors who would like such a career post how the present staff grade fitted their requirements. Over half the men and a quarter of the women said it did not. A quarter of the women but none of the men said it did because there was no on-call and the hours were generally good. One fifth of the women and one man said that it provided more time to do things outside medicine. One in six of the women and one man said it gave more career options. One in ten of both sexes liked the idea of autonomy without too much responsibility, and one in ten of the women thought that it would provide them with stability.

A woman surgical SHO thought that it was a possible option: 'My ambition is to be a consultant, but, if I can't, staff grade would give me a chance to use my skills. General surgery isn't well sorted out and not everyone will get a consultant's job. I think staff grade doctors tend to be more involved in ward work – more continuing care – and I like patients, unlike some of my colleagues ...'

A male SHO said: 'The trouble with the present staff grade is the rather restricted fields in which the posts are available. It tends to be staffing a geriatric day hospital or mundane posts. Hopefully as the system gets used to availability of staff grade posts, the scope will be expanded. I'd fancy general medicine – maybe rehabilitation medicine ...'

A woman with a young child who was not working at the time of the interview did not want such a grade : '... not in the long-term. Temporarily yes – but it would be a compromise. When my domestic commitments change then I would feel I hadn't quite made the grade ...'

Doctors who would like a career grade post without the full range of consultant responsibilities were rather more likely to think that the associate specialist grade would fit their requirements. Only a quarter of men and one in six of the women said that it definitely would not suit them, but around one fifth could not comment at all. Like the staff grade it was thought useful by women because of the hours and lack of on-call commitments, and others liked the idea of clinical autonomy without too much responsibility, more career options and stability. However, it was apparent that many doctors were really unaware of what an associate specialist was. The term 'specialist' was found attractive to staff grade doctors in our study on their educational needs, and it is possible that it appeared more suitable to some of those interviewed in the present study because of the connotations of specialism in the title.

The findings are somewhat inconclusive, given the level of knowledge about the staff grade and associate specialist grade. There was undoubtedly a strong undercurrent of demand for career grade posts in hospital without the full range of consultant responsibilities, particularly among the women. It should be remembered that some 40 per cent of the doctors were in general practice, and, although some of these might have stayed in hospital medicine if more career posts of this nature were available, it is likely that many of those saying that they would like such posts were thinking of working in hospital medicine. We have explored the comments of the doctors about staff grade and associate specialist grade in some depth. Neither appears to present the ideal grade for relatively young UK qualifiers seeking hospital career posts other than consultant posts, indicating that some further refinement and thought about the nature of such posts might be desirable.

13 Women doctors

In the last study we asked the doctors a series of questions about the opportunities for women in medicine and whether they thought that more could be done to help women doctors achieve their full potential. We started by asking the doctors the same question we had asked the women managers in industry and the BBC in *Women in Top Jobs 1968-79* (Fogarty, Allen, Walters, 1981) – whether the employer, in this case the NHS, or the medical profession itself, should do more than at present to help women doctors a) continue working while they had small children and b) return to medicine when their children were older with the opportunity of rising to senior positions.

It is interesting, of course, that we asked the second question on the assumption, encouraged by commentators at the time of our first study, that there would be a pool of women who would have opted out of medicine while they had small children but who would wish to return. We found, in fact, that the vast majority of women doctors do not stop working, but either continue in full-time work or find some kind of part-time or less than full-time work while they have small children. The concept of 'women returners' is far less applicable to the medical profession than virtually any other field of employment. Nevertheless, the result may be similar, in that part-time working in medicine, as we have observed in all our studies on medical careers, may well have a lower status than full-time working and may be seen as similar to not working in terms of career progression. The women may not be returning to medicine, in that they have not 'dropped out', but those who wish to return to full-time work from part-time work with the aim of rising to senior positions may find themselves in more or less the same position as those who have dropped out altogether.

We were interested to see whether the 1986 qualifiers differed from the earlier cohorts in their response to these questions. We had thought it likely that they might be relatively more concerned about the prospects for women doctors than older generations, but we were surprised by the extent of the shift in attitudes among both men and women.

We found in the last study that 69 per cent of the men and 84 per cent of the women from all three cohorts thought that the medical profession or NHS should do more to help women doctors continue working while they have small children, with greater support for this among the 1976 and 1981 cohorts than among the 1966 cohort. Table 13.01 indicates the considerable increase in the proportion of 1986 men and women taking this view compared with the 1976 and 1981 cohorts.

Table 13.01 **Doctors' views on whether medical profession/NHS should do more than at present to help women doctors continue working while they have small children**

column percentages

	Male 1976	Male 1981	Male 1986	Female 1976	Female 1981	Female 1986
Yes	71	72	92	86	84	98
No	21	19	5	11	11	1
Don't know	8	9	3	3	5	1
Base: all qualifiers	*(105)*	*(101)*	*(105)*	*(105)*	*(103)*	*(124)*

As many as 92 per cent of 1986 men and 98 per cent of 1986 women thought that more should be done to help women doctors continue working while they had small children, compared with just over 70 per cent of men and 85 per cent of women from the earlier two cohorts.

This near universal support by both men and women for increased action on the part of the NHS and medical profession was rather unexpected, but does reinforce other evidence in the present research that the issue of equal opportunities for women doctors is seen increasingly as an issue in its own right rather than an issue only for women. What did the doctors think should be done? Among those who recommended action by the NHS/medical profession, the main suggestion, by 80 per cent of respondents (74 per cent of the men and 84 per cent of the women), was increased creche facilities. This proportion was considerably greater than that found in the last study, even among the 1981 qualifiers, where it was supported more by men than by women, but still only accounted for around 60 per cent of both sexes.

The second most common suggestion (by two-thirds of the 1986 women and over 40 per cent of the men) was for more part-time training posts, closely followed by more part-time career posts supported by similar proportions of men and women. 40 per cent of women and 29 per cent of men advocated more job-sharing, again an increase on the proportions found among the 1981 qualifiers in the last study. Over one fifth of the women and more than one in ten of the men advocated increased tax relief, more than doubling the proportions found among 1981 qualifiers five years earlier.

Other suggestions, from more than 10 per cent of respondents, included better organisation of part-time training schemes, more flexible hours of working and a general change in attitudes among male doctors towards women doctors with children. (The men were more likely to hold the latter view than women.) There was no shortage of other suggestions, which included other financial incentives, an extension of maternity and/or paternity leave, standardised or mandatory maternity leave particularly in general practice, decrease in hours, increase in length of contracts of junior doctors, revamping of the doctors' retainer scheme and more information about opportunities for doctors with family responsibilities.

Many of these suggestions had been put forward by respondents in the last study, but little appeared to have changed. A woman anaesthetics registrar outlined the problems as she saw them: 'Nursery facilities, as they exist, are only suitable for day-workers – part-time nurses, radiographers, physiotherapists. The maternity leave system is diabolical – one month's full pay, then half pay, then nothing. And very little job security. It depends where you are in the contract and how long you've worked in the health authority. They don't carry on maternity pay from one health authority to another, so if your contract is only for three months, then you've had it ...'

The shortness of the contracts only seemed to exacerbate problems with maternity leave and pay, as a woman GP locum complained: 'Maternity provision should be mandatory. If you're doing six-month sessions in GP vocational training and you become pregnant in the middle, you lose all that time ...'

A woman who had temporarily given up work recommended: 'Longer maternity leave so that women would return. Look at other countries – say like Sweden, where you can take one year off on nine-tenths pay or two years at half pay (and have the guarantee of your job back) split between the mother and father. I personally, as a tax-payer, would be prepared to pay the extra for all workers ...'

Creches were often seen as the answer to the problem, although few doctors had used them. There were clearly problems with the hours that junior doctors worked, as pointed out above, but there were also thought to be financial difficulties, as a woman locum GP explained: 'The NHS creche in a London teaching hospital costs £400 a month ...'

Although many doctors put forward practical ideas for helping women doctors continue working with small children, there was a strong underlying feeling that little would change unless attitudes of senior doctors changed, as a woman on the GP retainer scheme noted: 'Change attitudes to part-time doctors. Two hours by a good part-time GP is worth eight by a mediocre GP ...'

However, in spite of the overwhelming support for greater help for women doctors with children, there were one or two dissenting voices, like a male research fellow: 'Women colleagues of mine who are committed have no problems getting on. I admit there is an enormous sacrifice, but it is one women have to make. I see no way around that without lowering standards ...' And a male locum registrar was even more forthright: 'Only if there is a shortage of doctors. The policy of medical schools is wrong. These women should be directed towards nursing ...'

The difficulty of returning to medicine after a break with the hope of rising on the career ladder was thought to be considerable, not without reason, as we have seen. This was one of the main reasons that so many women doctors continued to try and work part-time, since it was recognised how difficult it was to return. Again we found that the 1986 qualifiers were much more likely than

Table 13.02   Doctors' views on whether medical profession/NHS should do more than at present to help women doctors return to medicine with opportunities for rising to senior positions

column percentages

	Male			Female		
	1976	1981	1986	1976	1981	1986
Yes	71	69	82	80	81	91
No	22	17	7	10	11	2
Don't know	7	14	11	10	9	7
Base: all qualifiers	*(105)*	*(101)*	*(105)*	*(105)*	*(103)*	*(124)*

their predecessors to say that the NHS/medical profession should do more than at present to help women doctors return to medicine with opportunities for rising to senior positions.

As Table 13.02 shows, 82 per cent of the 1986 men and 91 per cent of the women thought that more should be done to help women returners, compared with around 70 per cent of the 1976 and 1981 men and 80 per cent of the women from these two cohorts. It was perhaps not surprising that all the women with children thought that more should be done to help women returners.

The main suggestion, by nearly 70 per cent of the women and half the men, was that more refresher courses should be provided. Nearly 40 per cent of both sexes thought there should be more part-time training posts and the same proportion thought there should be more part-time career posts. One fifth thought there should be greater recognition of part-time training and a quarter advocated more job-sharing.

Over a quarter of the women and nearly one fifth of the men thought there should be less linking of age to career status, which was thought to inhibit the development of careers when people were rather older than average at a certain stage or grade, as women returners were likely to be. This was often linked to the general observation that attitudes among senior doctors towards women with children should change.

In addition, doctors advocated more retraining schemes, properly organised re-entry schemes, continuing up-dating schemes while women were not working, an improvement or revamping of the retainer scheme, better careers advice and information, greater recognition of previous training, more flexibility of hours, the creation of posts for women, and extension of maternity leave with guaranteed return to post, the creation of limited responsibility posts to ease women back into work, and greater financial incentives to return, for example, the payment of examination fees. It can be seen that there was no shortage of ideas among the 1986 qualifiers.

However, there were many indications that women were well aware that they would be foolish to take time out if they wanted to rise in the hierarchy. A woman registrar in general medicine thought there should be facilities for up-dating skills, but was sceptical about whether the medical profession would change: 'If you take years out now you never get back in. There's so much competition and no-one will employ a woman of 40 when they've got someone of 25, fresh, to fill the part, although there's a lot that stable older women can offer ...'

Some men doubted that, like a male GP locum: 'If you've missed ten years, you cannot really expect to rise to senior positions. You're just too old. It's a waste of resources to train older women. It's a waste of money. It's not feasible to keep up while you're bringing up a family ...'

Opportunities for women doctors

We were interested to see whether the various cohorts thought that opportunities for women doctors had changed since they had qualified. After all, at the time that the 1966 qualifiers had been at medical school, women accounted for only 25 per cent of medical school entrants, while by the time the 1986 qualifiers had graduated, the proportion was nearly 50 per cent. We found in the last study that the proportions of 1966 and 1976 qualifiers thinking that opportunities for women doctors had improved since they had qualified were much higher than for the 1981 qualifiers. This was not surprising, considering that the older qualifiers had been out of medical school for twenty years and ten years respectively. Comparing the 1986 qualifiers with the 1981 qualifiers, five years after qualification, we found that almost exactly the same overall proportion, 40 per cent, thought that opportunities for women doctors had improved since they qualified. However, as Table 13.03 shows, the proportion of 1986 men (45 per cent) thinking this was much higher than the proportion of women (35 per cent).

Table 13.03   Views of doctors on whether opportunities for women doctors had changed since they qualified

column percentages

	Total		Male		Female	
	1981	1986	1981	1986	1981	1986
Yes	38	40	39	45	37	35
No	50	49	50	42	50	55
Don't know	12	11	12	13	13	10
Base: all qualifiers	*(204)*	*(229)*	*(101)*	*(105)*	*(103)*	*(124)*

We recognised that the change might not always be for the better, but, as we found in the last study, in fact if a change was acknowledged it was usually thought to be for the better. The main change noted – by nearly half the men and over 40 per cent of the women by those who had noticed any change – was less prejudice and more acceptance of women. This was reassuring news for women. The second most frequently mentioned change was more part-time opportunities, mentioned by over a third of the women and over a quarter of the men. It was thought by a quarter of the men and a fifth of the women that more women in medicine had led to more opportunities for them. It was interesting that in all four cohorts this view was put forward by more men than women. Sheer weight of numbers was thought to have improved the situation, but women were rather more doubtful about that.

Other improvements noted were more opportunities in general practice, more job-sharing opportunities and more demand for women doctors from patients. Among the adverse changes noted, only by a few doctors, were tighter competition for jobs, less part-time training because of cuts in funding and adverse effects from the GP contract.

A male registrar thought that there was less prejudice: 'There has been an easing of attitudes among older men, though women consultants can be tricky, I suspect ...' A woman on maternity leave agreed that there was more acceptance of women doctors: 'But maybe that's because we compete on equal terms as juniors when we have no domestic commitments. Those who cannot compete probably have to change specialty. In some hospitals it depends on what is available and what has been organised ...'

It must be remembered that around half the 1986 qualifiers thought that there had been no change in opportunities for women doctors since they had qualified. They mainly said that they had not noticed any change, but one fifth of women said that there was still a lot of prejudice against women. Others said that it was too soon to say. Some doctors were doubtful about whether any change had happened, in spite of assertions to the contrary, like a registrar in gastroenterology: 'I think there's been a lot of talk about increasing part-time jobs, but actually not much has happened. Part-time work is very poorly publicised and the woman has to really push and use her own initiative to get there. If she's got a family she may lack confidence and/or the energy to do this. The funding takes ages to come through ...'

It is perhaps interesting that men and women in general practice were more likely than others to think that there had been a change in the opportunities for women doctors since they qualified. These changes were usually thought to be for the better, although some women GPs were beginning to be concerned about the effects on women of the new GP contract, while others thought it was becoming more difficult to get partnerships.

Future career prospects for women doctors

The present study repeated the finding of the last study that women were generally thought to encounter greater difficulties than men in pursuing a successful career in medicine. In the last study we found that there was a feeling among the younger doctors in particular that it was becoming increasingly difficult for doctors of both sexes to pursue a successful career in medicine. We look at this in the next chapter, but first we wanted to establish whether our respondents thought that more should be done to enhance the future career prospects for women doctors in general.

Table 13.04 compares the views of the 1986 qualifiers with those of the 1981 qualifiers at the same stage of their careers. The proportion of men who thought more should be done for women increased from 70 per cent of the 1981 men to 74 per cent of the 1986 men, while among the women, the proportion increased from 81 per cent of the 1981 women to 91 per cent of the 1986 women.

Table 13.04 Doctors' views on whether more could be done to enhance the future career prospects for women doctors in general

column percentages

	Total 1981	Total 1986	Male 1981	Male 1986	Female 1981	Female 1986
Yes	75	83	70	74	81	91
No	24	16	28	26	19	8
Don't know	1	*	2	0	0	1
Base: all qualifiers	(204)	(229)	(101)	(105)	(103)	(124)

Why did they think more should be done to increase the career prospects for women doctors? One third of the men and over a quarter of the women thought that women had special needs which needed special attention, while nearly one third of the women but only just over one in ten of the men thought that it was necessary to prevent a waste in human resources, and rather fewer thought it would prevent a waste of financial resources. Just under a quarter of men and nearly one fifth of the women said it was necessary to redress the imbalance or prejudice in certain specialties, like surgery.

One fifth of the women but few men said that more should be done because women brought special qualities to medicine, while one fifth of men and one in ten of the women said that it was a matter of equity that women should be allowed to compete on equal terms with men. It was also thought that women should be enabled to maximise their career potential, that there was an increasing demand for women doctors and that their contribution should be enhanced because half the doctors qualifying were women. A few doctors thought that improvements for women could also help men, and that in any case the whole medical careers structure needed a shake-up.

There was a general feeling among both men and women that it was a waste of resources to ignore the fact that women had special needs. A woman who was not working at the time of the interview thought attitudes had to change: 'The profession as a whole must accept it and make it normal. At the moment, consultants still think they're doing you a favour if they let you go on maternity leave or do a part-time job ...' A woman GP trainee agreed: 'Women are a great resource in medicine. We spend a lot of money training them, they have a lot to offer – their attitude to life – so you lose a lot if you exclude them from top jobs ...' And a woman SHO said: 'In the end, it's the consultants who have the big say on who climbs the ladder. A change in attitude from them would be a good start ...'

Men and women were concerned at the lack of interest at a senior level in trying to help women, as a male GP locum noted: 'I've seen friends – girls – who've dropped out to an extent, when they could have been well used and could have had a post which fitted in with their commitments – especially in hospital medicine. A lot of girls drift into general practice, possibly because they don't know of part-time training schemes which are available but under-utilised. Basically we could do with more women in hospital medicine ...'

Relatively few doctors, as we have seen, thought that it was unnecessary for more to be done to enhance the careers of women doctors. The majority of these thought that women should be treated like men or that doctors should be assessed only on merit. Others thought that women should make changes for themselves since opportunities were already good enough for women, and some thought that the career structure needed overhauling for both men and women. Only one doctor thought that nothing should be done because women should stick to their role of wives and mothers, but perhaps his circumstances were a little special: 'I don't think a family is compatible with a career in hospital medicine. I know – I had parents who were consultants. They weren't good parents ...'

Recommendations for action to enhance women doctors' career prospects

We asked the doctors for practical recommendations and what they thought could be done by regional postgraduate deans, clinical tutors, college advisers in the regions, employing health authorities, the Royal Colleges, the BMA and the Department of Health. This was a rather longer list than we offered doctors last time, partly because of the increasing role played by clinical tutors and the interest shown by the BMA in the careers of women.

We had found in the last study that many doctors were rather hazy about the actual roles of some of the individuals or organisations who might be in a position to do something about enhancing the careers of women. We found that this situation had not changed a great deal.

Table 13.05 summarises the main suggestions made on possible action by key individuals or organisations concerned with doctors' careers. We should stress that these were all spontaneous suggestions made by the doctors. We did not present them with a list of options. One of the main problems, as we found last time, was that doctors had little idea of the role or function of some of the people concerned, so that they found it difficult to answer the question. We found again, for example, that one third of the respondents did not know what postgraduate deans did or could do to enhance the prospects for women doctors,

Table 13.05   What doctors think should be done to enhance career prospects for women doctors by key people or organisations

column percentages

	PG deans	Clinical tutors	Coll. advisers	HAs	Royal Colls	BMA	DOH
Encourage PT training/ advise on it	20	8	7	7	18	18	14
Better careers advice/ information	16	26	21	0	3	5	0
Encourage PT career posts	10	0	0	0	0	17	1
Encourage more flexible career structure/ organisation	7	2	0	12	0	0	8
Encourage job sharing	7	0	0	2	0	3	4
Be more accessible/ less remote	6	4	2	0	3	1	1
Expand staff grade/ assoc. spec.	6	0	0	0	0	0	0
Work to change attitudes/ more advocacy	6	6	6	6	10	36	5
Be more supportive/ encouraging	2	6	1	3	1	2	1
Listen to what doctors are saying	1	2	1	1	2	1	7
Increase number of PT posts	0	0	0	44	0	0	13
Increase number of job-share posts	0	0	0	15	0	0	4
Provide/fund creches/ childcare	2	0	0	18	0	0	6
Improve maternity leave	0	0	0	8	0	0	2
Develop refresher/ retraining course	4	3	2	1	2	0	0
More financial support/ more posts	1	0	0	18	0	0	10

Base: all thinking more should be done to enhance career prospects of women *(191)* *(191)* *(191)* *(191)* *(191)* *(191)* *(191)*

and the same proportion in this study were unaware of what clinical tutors and college advisers did or could do. The role of health authorities and the BMA was more clearly understood, but one fifth of the doctors did not know what the Royal Colleges did or could do and over a quarter were unclear of the role of the Department of Health. On the whole, men were more hazy about the possible contribution of any of these individuals or organisations than women were.

It can be seen from the table that some suggestions were made specifically about some people and organisations rather than others, with a clear recognition of their relative powers. In addition, there was a general call for all those concerned to ensure equal opportunities and liaise more with each other. In an attempt to keep the table under control we outline specific other recommendations in the text, and we draw attention to any particular group to whom specific recommendations were directed.

The main recommendations which were fairly general concerned better part-time training advice, encouragement and opportunities, better careers advice and information, more flexibility in the career structure, greater provision of jobs, especially part-time and job-sharing, easier accessibility to advice and more effort to change attitudes towards women doctors. The key role of regional postgraduate deans was rarely understood and doctors were very vague about who they were or where they could be found. They were mainly thought to be potentially instrumental in encouraging and advising on part-time working and a more flexible system of working, but few doctors had any specific comments, although some thought that they should be more accessible and less remote. SHOs who were not on GP vocational training schemes were more likely than any other group to consider that postgraduate deans should give better careers advice and information. Those in hospital medicine were more likely than those in general practice to say that they should encourage the development of part-time training.

The role and function of clinical tutors was also misunderstood and there were strong indications that many doctors had no idea of their existence. Even among those who had there was often caution about their role and remit, as a woman trainee GP noted: 'They exist but they don't do anything. Juniors should have the ability to criticise without loss of reference at the end of the job ...' This fear of loss of confidentiality and the desire for independent careers advice permeated many of the answers to this and other questions, and is discussed in detail in the next chapter. Clinical tutors were seen potentially as an important source of careers advice and counselling, but were rarely mentioned as having played this role. Some doctors specifically commented that clinical tutors should give more one-to-one individual advice and should tailor this to local circumstances and individual needs. This need was identified throughout the interviews, and clinical tutors were clearly in a position to fulfil this function.

College tutors in the regions were also thought to be in a good position to give better advice and information on careers, specialties and higher professional requirements. Apart from this, relatively few suggestions were made, and, again, there were many indications that doctors knew little or nothing about them. It was perhaps a matter of particular concern that nearly half the registrars and more than half the SHOs interviewed professed to know nothing about them.

The main role of health authorities in enhancing the career prospects of women doctors was seen as the provision of more part-time posts, and the advertising of such opportunities. 44 per cent of both men and women mentioned this. In addition it was thought that they could play a role in improving child care facilities and creches, create more posts in general, particularly job-share posts, and encourage a more flexible career structure. The purchaser:provider split has complicated the picture, and some of the potential responsibilities attributed to health authorities are now with the Trusts. Given the lack of knowledge of who did what displayed by many of the doctors interviewed, it is possible that the division of responsibilities has escaped their notice. It is, however, important that it is made clear to doctors who is, or might be, responsible for decisions which will affect the development of their careers.

A male registrar in general medicine thought that health authorities were responsible for the present distribution of duties among hospital staff: 'They should give funding for more staff. They should take the donkey-work away from junior doctors – mindless things like filing etc. Look at nurses who have clear definitions of what they're employed to do ...'

And a male GP principal was even more critical of health authorities: 'They have no concept of what doctors do anyway. They don't know what goes on in the jobs ...' A male GP principal could have enlightened them: 'If consultants will not come in at night, we shouldn't take those jobs – we mustn't take those jobs. But they dodge that one and rely on junior staff to carry the load ...' There is clearly a great deal of room for a full and frank exchange of information and views between doctors and their employers.

The role of the Royal Colleges in encouraging part-time training was thought to be crucial. Not only did doctors want them to encourage it and give advice about it, but there were a number of suggestions, particularly from women, on how the Colleges could encourage a more flexible attitude towards part-time training in general and towards examinations in particular. There were straightforward criticisms of the examination system and the lack of structured training programmes. A woman locum SHO was among several bitter doctors: 'Hundreds are leaving paediatric and general medicine because they cannot get the MRCP. We are all bright and prize-winners. Something is wrong with the club status of the College. MRCP is not a training exam – there is no structured training or course specified. I was not even allowed study leave because of the cost ...'

This woman singled out the Royal College of Physicians, but there were complaints about most other Royal Colleges and Faculties. The need to combine studying with full service commitments was found very exhausting by many of the doctors. Interviewers remarked on doctors who had apparently brilliant school and university careers who found it difficult to pass even Part 1 of their higher examinations. The trauma of failing an examination – 'I have never failed an exam in my life ...' – combined with the undoubted stress of being a junior doctor, was found overwhelming by some doctors.

It was also thought that the Royal Colleges could increase the number of women on their committees, provide more guidelines on the structure and content of part-time training, and should provide more advocacy and lobbying for women doctors in order to change attitudes among senior members of the profession.

The BMA's main role was thought to be to lobby on behalf of women to help change attitudes in the medical profession. Some thought they were doing well, like a woman registrar: 'The BMA are working hard at present on changes for junior doctors and women. They're doing a good job generally ...' But other doctors were more critical and thought that the BMA could do far more as far as part-time training and career post opportunities were concerned. It was interesting that the BMA was not thought of as a source of careers advice for women doctors by many respondents, although it could be argued that they are in a key position to develop this.

The main role to be played by the Department of Health was also related to part-time training opportunities and the creating of better part-time training schemes. However, it was also thought that the Department of Health should raise the profile of women doctors in general and could do more to initiate ideas to encourage or develop the careers of women doctors.

Some men were rather suspicious of too much action on the part of the Department of Health, like a GP principal: 'I think they pushed through a policy with regard to women GPs, because *I* didn't get jobs where women had to be appointed ...' But other men – and women – thought that too little interest was taken by the Department of Health in women doctors' problems. A male SHO in anaesthetics said: 'Their only interest is cost. Unless it can be shown that it would be cheaper to employ a female, they're not interested ...' And a woman on the retainer scheme said the Department of Health should alter the whole structure: '... right from house jobs, so that we're working less, earning more and being more on the ball because we're not so tired ...' And for many doctors, including a male SHO, the Department of Health was the key player: 'It's their responsibility all the way ...'

But for many of the doctors, all the people and organisations identified had a responsibility for ensuring that women doctors reached their full potential. A women registrar in obstetrics and gynaecology said: 'I think they will only take strenuous action when they are confronted by a shortage of skilled staff. They all want us to have career patterns on the lines of men, which is totally unrealistic these days. I heard (a leading woman obstetrician) saying that she did it all and had four children. How many decent nannies and housekeepers did it take to cover her long hours? I doubt it could be done today ...'

14 Opportunities for doctors in general

We recognised from the beginning of the last study that it was important to put our examination of the careers of women doctors firmly in the context of the career structure for all doctors. The medical career structure has not been without its critics over the years, and we suspected that many of the constraints and difficulties experienced by women were also felt to be constraints and difficulties by men. Essentially, we found in the last study that the problems encountered by women in medicine highlighted the problems experienced by men as well.

But it was not only the problems for potential high-flyers that we were investigating. Not everyone can fly high and a career structure in which there is restricted room at the top has dominated the discussion about doctors' careers for years. One of the most important factors has been the perceived rigidity of the career structure, with its assumption that 'sound' doctors reach certain grades at certain ages, and follow an assumed path to reach the top jobs – the career grades in medicine. Men and women in the last study criticised the lack of flexibility in the medical career structure more than any other aspect of their careers. They were particularly concerned about this in relation to what many saw as a tightening of career opportunities. We examined this in more detail in the present research, since there were indications in the last study that increased stress and regrets among doctors were related to feelings of insecurity, often caused by perceptions of lack of flexibility in the structure and organisation of medical careers.

We followed up our questions about women doctors by asking our respondents whether they thought that opportunities for doctors in general had changed since they had qualified. Again we compared their answers directly with those of the 1981 qualifiers interviewed last time at the same stage in their careers.

Table 14.01 shows a striking difference between the views of the 1981 and 1986 qualifiers five years after qualification. Whereas 84 per cent of the 1981 qualifiers thought that opportunities for doctors in general had changed since they qualified, only 43 per cent of the 1986 qualifiers shared this view. Among the 1981 qualifiers, men and women held this view in more or less equal proportions, but among the 1986 cohort, 51 per cent of men compared with only 36 per cent of women thought this.

What were the reasons for this? We found in the last study that around 50 per cent of the 1981 qualifiers who thought there had been a change in opportunities for doctors in general since they qualified considered that it was

Table 14.01   Views of doctors on whether opportunities for doctors in general had
changed since they qualified

column percentages

	Total 1981	Total 1986	Male 1981	Male 1986	Female 1981	Female 1986
Yes	84	43	86	51	81	36
No	16	54	14	49	19	58
Don't know	0	3	0	0	0	6
Base: all qualifiers	(204)	(229)	(101)	(105)	(103)	(124)

much harder to get to the top, and the same proportion thought that there were fewer jobs at all levels. Among the 1986 qualifiers noting a change in opportunities, only just over one third thought that it was harder to get to the top and only one in six thought there were fewer jobs at all levels. However, there was a clear difference in emphasis between the two cohorts, since one third of the 1986 women and nearly a fifth of the men thought there were more disappointed and disillusioned doctors around, whereas this view was held by only a handful of 1981 qualifiers. The possibility of unemployment was not mentioned at all by 1986 qualifiers (in spite of the fact that they were more likely to be unemployed than the 1981 cohort had been), whereas over a quarter of the 1981 men thinking there had been a change in opportunities since they qualified mentioned an increased likelihood of unemployment. One fifth of the 1986 women but fewer men thought that the career structure was more demanding of a straight career path, a view held less frequently by 1981 qualifiers.

It appeared that some of the differences could be accounted for by lower expectations on the part of 1986 qualifiers. The 1981 qualifiers often appeared to have noticed a change in opportunities because they had entered medicine at a time when hopes were still running high and opportunities appeared to be less restricted than five years later. The 1986 qualifiers were entering medicine at the time of the fieldwork for the last study, when the general perception was of tightening opportunities. Perhaps it was not surprising that fewer of them noticed a further decline.

The views on general practice were conflicting. Around one in ten of the 1986 qualifiers who had noticed a change in opportunities since they qualified thought that it was more difficult to get into general practice if they did not succeed in hospital medicine, but on the other hand a similar proportion thought there were more opportunities in general practice. It was interesting to see that a further 10 per cent of both sexes thought that there was an increased reluctance to enter general practice because of the new GP contract. Other changes for the worse included a perception that the bottleneck at senior registrar level was worse, that there was more emphasis on postgraduate qualifications and research, that there had been a reduction in research grants and that there had been a general reduction in money in the NHS.

On the other hand, some 1986 doctors thought that opportunities had improved since they qualified. For example, over one in ten who thought there had been changes said that different specialties were opening up, a further 10 per cent said that there had been an increase in senior posts, and one in ten of the women said that there were more opportunities because of the introduction of the staff grade.

Even if rather fewer 1986 qualifiers thought there had been a change in opportunities since they qualified, there were still many concerns expressed about the prospects for doctors. The perceived rigidity of the career structure and the dangers of deviating from a straight career path were illustrated by two men, the first a registrar in general surgery: 'It's to the total detriment of what you do. You need to see a wider picture. For example, I can't go off and do another specialty to increase my depth of knowledge. I'd like to do anaesthetics and intensive care, but I can't ...' The second man was a registrar in anaesthetics: 'I've decided to stay with anaesthetics through thick and thin rather than experiment with other specialties. Some of my older bosses drifted for years before *they* settled. They had a much wider knowledge of medicine ...'

The future of opportunities in general practice was quite clear to one male GP principal: 'It will happen in the next three or four years. There were twenty applicants in my local GP vocational training scheme last year. There were 250 when I thought of doing it ...' But on the other hand, at the time of the interviewing, we came across a rather high number of GP locums who were finding it difficult to get partnerships, as a male GP principal noted: 'I was lucky. I got a job, but many of my friends are still unemployed ...'

A woman registrar in radiology saw restricted opportunities in her specialty: 'I've got *my* job. Next year they won't appoint another registrar because the department can't afford it ...' And the emphasis on shortage of money was found frequently in relation to research. A male general medical registrar spoke for a number of his colleagues: 'The system for moving forward hasn't changed, but money for research has dried up. There's less MRC money and less university money. You need to do research to get on. The research I'm doing at the moment is totally supported by drug companies. There isn't the money or the time for me to do research. There's no locum cover for me. Morale in the NHS is related to the money available. It's sad that we spend so much time being concerned with costs. It makes it hard to innovate and move forward. Optimism is lacking in medicine at the moment ...'

Some doctors thought that there had been some improvements in the structure. A male GP locum said: 'The hospital career structure looks more rational. A lot more weeding out is done at the SHO level. It's more clear who's on the fast track and who's not. It's much clearer and better than throwing out registrars ...' A male registrar in cardiology agreed: '"Achieving a Balance" is working – up to a point. More people are failing but they're failing earlier, at the

SHO stage, which is better. But at (London teaching hospital) eleven consultants retired and they only appointed two in their place ...'

One of the effects of a perceived greater competition for jobs was thought to be a greater necessity for research, which was not always thought to be beneficial, either to the individual doctor or to medicine in general, as a surgical SHO explained: 'It's still tough. The training is over-long and still very dependent on who you know and not what you know. And there's a *disastrous* reliance on achieving research and higher degrees – taking you out of clinical medicine at crucial stages in your career. I've only been here for a year and they want to get me to go off for two years' research – disastrous!'

Another male SHO thought that opportunities for doctors had not changed but that the general atmosphere had: 'There's more internal cover, less study leave, more hassle. Conditions for all doctors have got worse, but not job opportunities ...'

What were the effects on those who had observed changes in opportunities since they had qualified? Over 40 per cent of doctors said there had been no effect on them personally. Over one in ten said that there was more job security and it was easier to get a job. On the other hand, a similar proportion said it was more difficult to get a job. The pressure on them to do research or to get higher qualifications was noted by a further 10 per cent. Other comments referred to pressure to make up their minds at an earlier stage than they would have liked, more pressure to keep up-to-date, to delay a family, to work longer hours and to change specialty. There were no mentions of any move towards part-time training. It appeared that such increased opportunities as there were in this area had completely passed our respondents by.

Shifts

Since the last study there had been a number of changes in the medical career structure, most notably the introduction of *Achieving a Balance* (Department of Health, 1987), as well as attempts to improve conditions of working and training for junior doctors. One of the main criticisms of conditions in the last study had been the long hours and on-call duties of doctors in training in particular. Since then there have been increasing moves towards introducing shift or partial shift systems in medicine, particularly in specialties such as Accident and Emergency. There are known to be conflicting views at a senior level about whether a shift system is a 'good thing'. We asked the 1986 qualifiers whether they had ever worked a shift or partial shift system in medicine, and whether they preferred such a system to the present rota arrangements for training posts in medicine.

Table 14.02 shows that 55 per cent of the 1986 qualifiers had worked a full shift system, 10 per cent had worked a partial shift system and 36 per cent had not worked a shift system. In each category there were almost identical proportions of men and women.

Almost 100 per cent of the doctors who had worked a shift or partial shift system had done so at SHO level and only 2 per cent had done so at registrar

Table 14.02   Whether doctors had ever worked a shift or partial shift system in medicine (1986 qualifiers only)

column percentages

	Total	Male	Female
Yes - full shift system	55	54	55
Yes - partial shift system	10	10	11
No	36	37	35
Base: all qualifiers	*(229)*	*(105)*	*(124)*

level. 52 per cent of them said they had worked a shift or partial shift system in Accident and Emergency, 2 per cent in surgery, 2 per cent in Obstetrics and Gynaecology and the rest did not specify the specialty, although it appeared to have been most common in A and E.

What did they think of the shift system? We asked all the doctors this question whether they had worked a shift system or not. Table 14.03 shows that 67 per cent of the total preferred a shift system to the present rota arrangements for training posts in medicine. There was an interesting difference between the sexes, with 73 per cent of the women but only 59 per cent of the men expressing a preference for shifts. 10 per cent of both men and women felt unable to express an opinion.

Table 14.03   Whether doctors preferred shift or partial shift system to present rota arrangements for training posts in medicine (1986 qualifiers only)

column percentages

	Total	Male	Female
Yes	67	59	73
No	23	30	17
Don't know	10	11	10
Base: all qualifiers	*(229)*	*(105)*	*(124)*

80 per cent of those who preferred the shift system said that they found it less tiring, gave them more time off and resulted in fewer working hours generally. A quarter of those who preferred the shift system said that it was better in professional terms, in that it was safer and ensured a good handover of responsibilities. Other comments were that anything was better than the present system and that it offered more flexibility in general. A small number of doctors preferred it in principle, but thought that it depended on the specialty.

The enthusiasts for shifts needed no convincing, like a male GP principal: 'Because when you're doing the rota system there's never a day when you get to bed without having the bleep on and it grinds you into the floor ...' A woman on the doctors' retainer scheme agreed: 'It was wonderful to be only in for a maximum of 12 hours at a time. I had time to be a human being. I could meet people – catch up on my sleep ...' And a woman GP trainee had found her life transformed: 'It changes your life. You get 10 or 12 hours off. You can do your job properly, learn on the job and eat ...'

It must be asked whether the life described by many of these young doctors was really suitable for anyone. It was not only the appalling quality of their own lives which was breathtaking, but also the constant reminder of the fatigue from which many were suffering. A woman registrar in general medicine summarised the views of many respondents about the rota system: 'In my renal job it was mad – up all night, all weekend, doing transplants. I was dangerous ...'

But some doctors said that, although they thought a shift system was preferable, their views were unlikely to be shared by senior doctors. A male anaesthetic registrar explained his preference for shifts: 'We can get our training in fewer hours. There's no need to do 100 hours per week. Surgeons are the worst. Consultants expect us to be there 9 to 5 every day and then do on-call. It could easily be changed to partial shift and reduce the hours to 50 or 60. They like to have juniors there so they can get out of their own duties. We are easily abused in the present system ...'

Some doctors were in favour of shifts but were concerned about possible cuts in pay for overtime. A registrar in general medicine noted that '... a doctor on-call is the cheapest form of labour. We're cheaper than cleaners and dinner ladies. It's the only job where you're paid less for overtime ...'

But nearly a third of the men, although less than one fifth of women, did not think that a shift or partial shift system was preferable. The main reason given was, interestingly, that shifts were disruptive of personal life. A quarter thought that they were disruptive in professional terms, in that it was difficult to ensure proper handover of responsibilities or continuity of care. Around one fifth thought that the present system worked quite well, while over one in ten said that they disliked night shifts and preferred on-call.

Some thought it depended on the specialty, like a male GP principal: 'If you're doing something such as casualty or emergency work, then shift work is OK, but in a job where you need continuity of care such as general medicine or general practice, geriatrics, then you need to work a normal week ...'

A male SHO in ophthalmology found the shift system personally disruptive: 'A shift system really puts you out of synch whereas a rota system is maybe more onerous but is easier to organise your life around ...' And his views were shared by a number of others, including a woman psychiatric registrar who had done shifts as an SHO in A and E: 'I found it more difficult to get into a routine and found it more disruptive to my sleep patterns and my personal life ...'

A male GP principal reluctantly felt that a rota system was better than a shift system: 'It's useful – it's not pleasant – but it's useful to be available on a 24-hour system. On a shift system you lose the following and subsequent investigations of the patients. You're not involved in the complete clinical case ...'

GP contract

At the time of the fieldwork in late summer and autumn of 1991, the new GP contract had been in operation for rather more than a year. It had been greeted with some criticism by GPs, and was thought by some to be potentially disadvantageous to women GPs, in spite of the fact that it had introduced contracts for half-time and three-quarters time principal posts.

Since the fieldwork was completed there has been increasing evidence of a dramatic decline in the numbers of doctors applying for GP vocational training schemes, and fears have been expressed that the GP contract has resulted in a big decrease in the numbers of doctors wishing to enter general practice. It has been said that women in particular are becoming increasingly reluctant to enter general practice because of the difficulty of getting part-time principal posts, a factor highlighted in the our report on general practice (Allen, 1992).

We asked the 1986 qualifiers what effect the GP contract had had on their careers to date, and whether they had any comments on the effects of the GP contract on the careers of women doctors in general. We asked all the doctors these questions, whether they were in general practice or not, since not only might they have been deterred from general practice by the new contract but they might also have been affected in some other ways. We recognised, of course, that some doctors would find the question inapplicable to them.

Table 14.04 shows that only 6 per cent of the 1986 qualifiers thought that the new GP contract had had a beneficial effect on their careers, 21 per cent thought it had had an adverse effect and 38 per cent thought it had had no effect. In just over a third of cases, the doctors found the question inapplicable. It was interesting to note that the proportions of men and women in each category were more or less the same.

We looked in more detail at the answers given to this question in relation to the jobs the doctors held at the time of the fieldwork. We found that all those saying that the new contract had had a beneficial effect were working in general practice. Just over 10 per cent of the GP principals, GP trainees and GP locums said that it had a beneficial effect on their careers. On the other hand, nearly 50 per cent of the GP principals said that it had had an adverse effect on their careers, a view shared by all but one of the GP assistants and women on the retainer scheme and one third of the GP locums. GP trainees and SHOs on GP vocational training schemes were more likely to say that it had had no effect on their careers, although a quarter of them said it had had an adverse effect. A scattering of other doctors said that it had an adverse effect on them, including half of those working in community health.

Table 14.04   Effects of new GP contract on career to date (1986 qualifiers only)

column percentages

	Total	Male	Female
Beneficial effect	6	6	6
Adverse effect	21	22	21
No effect	38	35	40
Not applicable	35	37	33
Base: all qualifiers	*(229)*	*(105)*	*(124)*

What had been the beneficial effects for the few doctors who mentioned them? They included a view that it had reduced competition for GP posts generally, that it had presented new challenges, that it had offered more jobs for women GPs and that it was geared to offering more health promotion. A woman GP trainee was quite clear about why she found it beneficial: 'At the moment I'm looking for GP jobs and there is less competition for jobs because the contract is unpopular ...' On the other hand, a woman on maternity leave at the end of her GP trainee year said: 'I've done my training year during the first year of the contract, so I've experienced working with it and have a good knowledge of its benefits. It's given me a good background and I'm in a good position now in applying for jobs ...'

What were the adverse effects of the new GP contract on doctors? The main effect was said to be that it had created more administrative work and less time for patients. This was a view held by nearly a quarter of the GP principals. The second most common adverse effect mentioned was the increased difficulty experienced in finding part-time jobs against an increased requirement for longer hours. Not surprisingly this was a view expressed mainly by women working in general practice. Other adverse effects included less job satisfaction, fears of a divided profession, discouragement from entering general practice, incentive to leave general practice, fewer financial incentives and a dislike of the commercial aspects of the new GP contract.

The effects of increased administrative duties on GPs have been well-documented in the medical press and similar complaints were found frequently among GP principals in this study. A male locum GP had decided against pursuing a career in general practice as a result of the new contract: 'The amount of bureaucracy and form-filling has increased drastically and the government are trying to increase budgetary controls and erode their status as self-employed practitioners. They are also dictating clinical practice ...' A woman SHO who had been considering general practice was concerned about increased business pressures reducing the amount of time for patients: 'It's made me aware that general practice is as much a business as being a clinician. You've got to be thinking more of the financial aspects. You've got to think how to use time as best you can. It's time that's precious. You've got to make work financially viable ...'

Some doctors outside general practice were also concerned about the effects of the new GP contract, like a male senior registrar, whose main concern appeared to relate to GP fundholders: 'Not yet, but it might do. I may not have the control and authority I have now. They may tell me what *they* want, whereas now *I* decide. It will restrict my clinical freedom – like in the United States. It's detrimental to one's job satisfaction and I may have to resign ...'

We were particularly interested in the perceived effects of the new GP contract on the careers of women doctors. Just over one third of male 1986 qualifiers and just under a quarter of the women felt unable to comment on this question, while a further quarter of both sexes said they did not know enough about it. However, among those who responded, three-quarters of the women and more than half the men thought that the new contract would make part-time working for women more difficult, particularly because of the more rigid requirements relating to the organisation of part-time hours. Over one in ten of those responding though that the new contract would make it harder for women GPs to get posts in general, while, on the other hand, a similar proportion thought that the new services required under the contract would bring about a need for increasing numbers of women doctors. A few doctors thought that the maternity leave arrangements were an improvement and a small number thought that it was now easier to work part-time. Some doctors thought that the new GP contract had made greater demands on women than on men, and there was a particular fear that women GPs might find themselves doing the 'women's' work rather than the full range of general practice – an anxiety expressed frequently in our study on *Part-time Working in General Practice* (Allen, 1992).

A woman SHO on a GP vocational training scheme said: 'I think in the short-term there are more jobs for women doctors who are prepared to work full-time. However part-time employment is much harder to get in general practice now, and, unfortunately, women GPs are frequently being asked to do smear clinics and well-women clinics and thus spend less time in general medicine ...' Her fears were confirmed by a male GP principal who was even less sanguine about the prospects for women: 'Women are less likely to be taken on as full-time principals and more likely to be used part-time to do women-type jobs ...'

There were indications that women GPs could not always expect sympathy, even from young men, as another male GP principal explained: 'Well, they have to come to terms with the real world. I knew a single female GP in a practice who complained because she got all the family planning and smear appointments, but that was what they had appointed her for. Otherwise they would have chosen a man. Here we don't intend to have a female partner at all. We share the work according to experience and qualifications. They've either got to be proper full-time or proper part-time. They've got to look for the deal that suits them ...'

A woman GP principal counted herself fortunate, but could see problems for some women: 'I think that the new arrangements for maternity are good. Some people will offer women part-time work as assistants where they don't have a say in the practice. I've been lucky in that I have partners who are positive and see women as a benefit, not a hindrance ...'

A woman GP locum thought that the GP contract was certainly not good news for women seeking part-time partnerships, particularly since the abolition of the full-time basic practice allowance for part-timers of 20 hours a week: 'There's less incentive to take on a partner because of the reduced basic practice allowance. Having a new partner means having a spread. The incentive now is to employ fewer people and use locums. But if you're a locum, you never get continuity ...'

Structured training programmes

The way in which postgraduate medical training has been traditionally conducted in this country has come in for criticism over the years. It has been criticised for lacking structure, not only in terms of having a structured programme ensuring that the training is planned and incremental and builds on previous experience, but also in terms of the actual content of the various training posts, with the assurance that doctors have a structured programme of work in which all aspects are properly covered.

Many of the criticisms have been addressed in the Calman Report (Department of Health, 1993), although it remains to be seen how the recommendations will be implemented in practice. There is surprisingly little concrete evidence on how doctors are actually trained in postgraduate medicine, and virtually no evidence on what they themselves have felt about it.

We were therefore interested in providing evidence on the extent to which doctors had had a structured training programme, with their posts linked in a pre-determined rotation, and what they felt about such structured training programmes. We then asked them whether they felt that there had been a structured training content in their posts, within a rotation or not, and what they felt about having a structured training content.

Structured training programmes – rotations

We asked the doctors about structured training programmes in posts at SHO level and at registrar level separately. It must be remembered that the vast majority of doctors had gone through SHO posts, but that less than 50 per cent had had registrar posts.

Table 14.05 shows that 52 per cent of all 1986 qualifiers (54 per cent of men and 49 per cent of women) said that they had had a structured training programme at SHO level, and that 25 per cent (31 per cent of men and 19 per cent of women) had had a structured training programme at registrar level. Looking only at the 84 doctors who had had registrar training (50 men and 34 women), we found that

Table 14.05   Whether doctors considered that they had had a structured training programme in that posts linked in pre-determined rotations (1986 qualifiers only)

column percentages

	Total	Male	Female
Yes: SHO level	52	54	49
No: SHO level	47	45	49
Not applicable: SHO level	1	1	2
Yes: registrar level	25	31	19
No: registrar level	12	16	8
Not applicable: registrar level	62	52	72
Base: all qualifiers	*(229)*	*(105)*	*(124)*

68 per cent overall had had a structured training programme (66 per cent of the men and 71 per cent of the women).

We should note that some doctors found this question very difficult to answer, and perhaps it is not surprising that data on training programmes has been difficult to come by in the past. The matter was complicated by the fact that some doctors had been on short rotations but had then done other jobs at SHO or registrar level. We had to impose a requirement that only those who had done all or most jobs at a grade in a rotation or vocational training scheme were eligible for inclusion in the 'yes' category, and sought the advice of Department of Health colleagues on the criteria to be applied in individual cases. Analysis of this type of data is not straightforward.

We asked doctors whether they thought that a structured training programme with a pre-determined rotation of posts was preferable to one without such rotations. Table 14.06 shows that the vast majority of doctors (79 per cent) thought it was, but that men (88 per cent) were much more in favour than women (73 per cent).

There were some interesting differences between doctors according to their grades in response to this question. Whereas over 80 per cent of GP principals and senior registrars, and over 90 per cent of registrars and research fellows, thought that a structured training programme was preferable, this view was shared by less than 60 per cent of the GP trainees and only three-quarters of the SHOs.

Why were doctors in favour of a structured training programme with rotations? The main reason was because it offered geographical stability and security. This view was expressed by over half of those who favoured a structured training programme and, perhaps surprisingly, rather more by men than women. Nearly 40 per cent were in favour because they felt a structured training

Table 14.06 Whether doctors considered that a structured training programme with pre-determined rotations preferable (1986 qualifiers only)

column percentages

	Total	Male	Female
Yes	79	88	73
No	14	10	16
Don't know	7	2	11
Base: all qualifiers	*(229)*	*(105)*	*(124)*

programme ensured that training was complete and covered all the necessary topics. A quarter of the doctors thought that it was a more efficient system in that it saved time and energy looking for jobs and going for interviews, and 10 per cent thought it offered greater continuity with colleagues and engendered good team-work. It was also thought to allow more time for other commitments, to allow doctors to plan ahead and to ensure maternity benefits. Others thought it depended on the individual or on the specialty. A small number were in favour, but noted that it was possible to get 'stuck' on a bad rotation.

The quest for geographical stability and security has been a marked feature of our research on doctors' careers. Some older doctors who have taken the need for geographical mobility for granted might think that younger doctors lack a sense of adventure, but perhaps they are only reacting like normal human beings. A male general surgical registrar said: 'We aren't gypsies. We want to live settled lives like anyone else ...' And a woman research fellow agreed: 'It enables you to have a wide variety of experience without having to keep looking for the next job. You can concentrate on the job in hand and not continually worry about the next job ...' The security was important to many, like a male GP locum: 'Because then you know where you are, you know where you're going to live and you have a goal ...'

There were definite concerns that without a proper structured training with pre-determined rotations doctors could get lost in the system, like a flock of flying Dutchmen. A woman paediatric SHO compared the training structure with that in other countries: 'In Britain you can wander round for years and there isn't a proper structure. It's easy to get stuck ... I never found anything I liked. I look at consultants and none provide a good role model. I'm sick of six months here and six months there. I've never had a home yet and I've failed MRCP twice ...' And another woman SHO appeared similarly at sea: 'You can do job after job and get nowhere. You've got to know where you're going. If you do bits and bobs you look around when you're 30, and people don't want to know you ...'

Rotations were not always thought to be particularly easy to find, as a male locum registrar noted: 'At SHO level there's fierce competition for rotational posts. On occasion you have 120 people applying for one post ...' And some doctors spoke of rotations being 'seeded': 'The top seed has a choice of rotations and the bottom has to take what's left. Therefore there's a lack of flexibility as you move down the ratings ...'

Others, like a male surgical registrar, although in favour of a structured training programme, agreed that there ought to be more flexibility in rotations: 'It's preferable at registrar level in surgery because all career numbered posts are in rotations, but not at SHO level. In a rotation of four jobs at SHO level, two might be OK but the other two not. They structure SHO rotations so that the good jobs are at the end, so you have to go through all the rubbish first ...'

And a perceived lack of flexibility was the main reason given by the few doctors who were not in favour of structured training programmes. Over one third of the men and half the women who preferred an unstructured training programme were concerned about the varying quality of the posts on rotations or GP vocational training schemes, like a woman GP principal: 'The advantages are that you will be guaranteed obs and gynae and paediatric experience. These are hard to get. But sometimes the posts they put in the schemes are terrible. You can end up in posts that are not specific to the specialty you have chosen ...'

Another woman trainee GP on maternity leave was also concerned about the lack of flexibility: 'It limits your choice of posts, and limits you if you need to move or your circumstances change. I left a vocational training scheme, which didn't go down very well ...' And other women felt that rotations forced them into posts they did not necessarily want. A woman had put together her own GP vocational training but was now finding it difficult to get a GP principal post: 'A predetermined course forces you to work in specialties you don't think are important and makes you miss specialties that you think are important ...'

One third of the doctors who preferred an unstructured training programme were concerned that a structured training programme could mean being 'stuck' in a bad rotation. One third of the men and a fifth of the women thought that it depended on the individual and one in ten thought it depended on the specialty. And five doctors preferred it because they actually liked moving around – a very small number out of the whole sample.

Structured training programmes – content

What about the actual content of their training? To what extent did the 1986 qualifiers feel that they had a structured training content in their posts?

Table 14.07 shows that exactly half the doctors thought that their training had been structured to cover the full educational content necessary, with rather more men (53 per cent) than women (47 per cent) saying this. A further 12 per cent said the content had been structured in some posts but not all, while 37 per cent said it had not been structured at all.

The fact that well over one third of doctors did not consider that their training had been structured to cover the necessary content was rather worrying, particularly in view of the fact that 92 per cent thought that a structured training

Table 14.07   Whether doctors considered that they had had a structured training content in their posts (whether in rotation or not) (1986 qualifiers only)

	Total	Male	Female
			column percentages
Yes	50	53	47
No	37	36	38
Some posts - not all	12	10	15
Not applicable	1	1	1
Base: all qualifiers	*(229)*	*(105)*	*(124)*

programme covering all necessary content was preferable to an unstructured programme, as Table 14.08 shows.

60 per cent of those who preferred a structured training content said that it ensured that doctors acquired all the relevant skills and knowledge. One third of them said that an unstructured programme was too hit and miss, and was not really training but was too service-orientated. One in ten of the doctors said that a proper structure set goals for the doctors in training. Other respondents mentioned that it provided continuity and allowed monitoring of progress, while some thought it depended on the individual or the specialty. The few doctors who were not in favour of a structured training content all agreed that it depended on the individual or specialty.

Some doctors were very concerned about the lack of structure in their training programmes. A male GP locum said: 'You're there to learn, as much as to provide a service. You *need* to learn and so often you don't learn. A structured weekly teaching system should be an integral part of any training scheme. It needs to be done with ability and enthusiasm – not necessarily by a consultant ...'

Table 14.08   Whether doctors think that a structured training content preferable (1986 qualifiers only)

	Total	Male	Female
			column percentages
Yes	92	92	92
No	3	6	0
Don't know	5	2	8
Base: all qualifiers	*(229)*	*(105)*	*(124)*

A woman SHO agreed: 'These are *training* posts. Junior doctors are learning all the time. It's essential that the training nature of the posts is recognised, rather than using junior doctors as dogs-bodies. I had *some* training, but in more than one job it was inadequate – lack of time, pressure of work. You spend your time in admin and looking for beds ...'

There was considerable emphasis in the answers to these questions on junior doctors being used as 'dogs-bodies' – a phrase used with surprising frequency. The service commitment of training posts was recognised by most, but many felt that it played far too large a part in many jobs. A male general medical registrar said: 'There's a lot of service demand. Jobs are designed to cover that, not to train doctors ...' Another man in the same grade and specialty agreed: 'You learn by osmosis. It's called a training programme, but you're just a work-horse ...' It was not thought to be much better in other specialties, as a woman GP principal noted: 'The problem with VTS training posts is that the consultants are not interested in the fact that you're going to be a GP. They're only interested in you providing a service ...'

Some of the doctors drew particular attention to difficulties in getting study leave, like a woman registrar in general medicine: 'At SHO level here I received no teaching at all. In this region, postgraduate teaching leaves a lot to be desired. There's no study leave. There wasn't much structure to my training. Although the posts were in rotation, there was no planning for exams or teaching ...' And a woman GP assistant agreed with her concerns: 'You should have an educational programme while you're doing the job. Getting study leave is always a fight. My husband is a registrar in radiology and is taking three weeks out of his five weeks' leave for study this year ...'

There were many indications that doctors thought that postgraduate medical training was better abroad. A male orthopaedic registrar gave a long and thoughtful answer to the question: 'You just pick things up as you go along at the moment. The Canadian system is much better, You should know what you should have done – certain procedures should be mastered at certain stages. It would be better to have guidelines about what level of skill people at different stages should have. Consultants don't seem to be able to tell me. Consultants should let their juniors get experience. The Trusts don't make allowances for training. You have to do so many operations in a certain length of time. If you give those to trainees, they take longer, so you don't fulfil your contract ...'

There was evidence of considerable isolation and lack of support expressed by many doctors in response to this question. The general feeling that they were not being trained properly, but just used as 'dogs-bodies', 'work-horses' and 'another pair of hands' permeated their answers. It was perhaps even more alarming that the criticisms did not only come from doctors who appeared to have lost their way, if only temporarily, but also from doctors in 'good' jobs in prestigious teaching hospitals. It was thought difficult enough if you had a good rotation in a teaching hospital and had a mentor or patron who gave you advice. Otherwise, the rather haphazard nature of postgraduate medical progression was highlighted time and again at this point in the interview, as a male surgical SHO noted: 'Our training methods are out-of-date. You only learn what you're exposed to and what you're taught. Some consultants teach – others don't give a damn ...'

Rating of structure and content of postgraduate training

So how did they rate the structure and content of their postgraduate training? Some doctors, of course, had completed their training, but those in hospital medicine usually had some way to go. It can be seen from Tables 14.09 and 14.10 that structure and content of training were usually closely allied in the minds of most doctors, although it was not unusual for doctors to say that the structure had

Table 14.09   Rating of structure of postgraduate training (to date) (1986 qualifiers only)

			column percentages
	Total	Male	Female
Very good	12	11	13
Good	40	43	37
Fair	27	25	29
Poor	12	10	13
Very poor	7	9	5
Some poor/some good	2	1	2
Had none (not in medicine)	1	1	1
Base: all qualifiers	*(229)*	*(105)*	*(124)*

Table 14.10   Rating of content of postgraduate training (to date) (1986 qualifiers only)

			column percentages
	Total	Male	Female
Very good	14	15	12
Good	40	37	43
Fair	27	26	27
Poor	10	12	9
Very poor	4	6	3
Some poor/some good	4	3	5
Had none (not in medicine)	1	1	1
Base: all qualifiers	*(229)*	*(105)*	*(124)*

been better than the content. There was not much difference between the views of the men and the women, although the men were rather more likely to be more critical of the content of the training programmes than the women were.

Overall, just over half the 1986 qualifiers rated the structure and content of their postgraduate training as good or very good, and just over a quarter rated it as fair. Nearly one fifth rated the structure as poor or very poor, while the content was given this rating by nearly one fifth of the men and 12 per cent of the women. Some 4 per cent rated some jobs good and some poor in terms of content.

There were some differences between doctors according to their present grades. For example, nearly three-quarters of the senior registrars rated the structure of their training programmes as good or very good, and nearly 90 per cent of them rated the content in the same way. On the other hand, these ratings on structure were given by only just over 40 per cent of the SHOs and on content by less than 50 per cent of the SHOs. It could be argued that the few senior registrars had made their grade because of the nature of their training programmes, as well as their ability.

The registrars presented a more mixed picture, with 50 per cent rating the structure and 60 per cent the content of their training programmes as good or very good. However, registrars were more likely than other grades to give their training programmes a poor or very poor rating. GP principals were more likely than other grades to rate their training programmes as good or very good, both in terms of structure and content, but GP trainees were not.

It is difficult to interpret the findings without looking at each individual case. It is possible that the doctors with 'good' training programmes have been helped by their training programmes, or it is possible that 'good' doctors rise to the top whether they have 'good' training programmes or not. There seems little doubt that many doctors felt that they had been inhibited by a lack of structure in their postgraduate training programmes, and their comments and criticisms of their experience need to be taken seriously.

As so often in this research, we found that much depended on luck and good fortune, and far too little was related to well-designed advice and planned career structures. For some doctors interviewed, this lack of structure was clearly disastrous and had already resulted in their losing their way in the competitive medical career structure. For others, the quality of the training left much to be desired. A male anaesthetic SHO said: 'The quality has been non-existent. I've had no formal training, I've learnt by experience – and self-motivation for the exams ...' Others rated their own experience as good, but felt the system needed a thorough overhaul, like a male psychiatric registrar: 'It depends entirely on good administration by consultants in each area setting up rotations rationally. Some do not have the ability or interest ...'

Hospital training was generally thought to be poorer than general practice vocational training, but none of the specialties was thought to offer a universally high standard. A great deal was left to individual doctors to find out for themselves, sometimes too late, whether a training programme was good or not.

There was little evidence that they were given much help, as a male GP locum noted: 'They're not interested in you as a person ...'

Careers advice, information and counselling

Surely someone was interested in these young doctors as people. Who was giving them the careers advice, information and counselling that would help them find their way in the jungle of postgraduate medical careers? The answer in the last report was that the system was extremely haphazard, with some doctors receiving excellent advice from patrons and mentors, while most found it very difficult to gain access to even the most elementary careers advice. There was also a strong undercurrent of accepted wisdom that 'real' doctors did not seek advice or counselling, even about their own careers. This reluctance to ask for careers advice until desperation set in was found again in our study on *Part-time Working in General Practice*, where women who wanted to work part-time only sought advice when they saw no alternative.

In the last study we did not ask specific questions about careers advice in the postgraduate years, but it was clear from the answers to other questions that this was a considerable cause for concern to many of our respondents. This time we asked the 1986 qualifiers about the nature and type of careers advice they had received in the postgraduate years, their rating of its helpfulness, accuracy and encouragement, rounded off by their recommendations for improving careers advice in the postgraduate years in medicine.

Given the limited amount of careers advice that even the 1986 qualifiers had received at school and medical school, it was reassuring to find that around two-thirds of both men and women had received some careers advice in the postgraduate years since they had qualified as a doctor, as Table 14.11 shows.

Table 14.11   **Whether doctors had had any careers advice in the postgraduate years since qualification as a doctor (1986 qualifiers only)**

			column percentages
	Total	Male	Female
Yes	66	68	65
No	34	32	35
Base: all qualifiers	*(229)*	*(105)*	*(124)*

Although there was little difference between men and women in general in terms of whether they had received postgraduate careers advice, and no difference between those working full-time and part-time, there were some differences according to present grade. For example, those in hospital medicine were more likely to have received careers advice than those in general practice. Only 50 per cent of the GP principals said that they had received careers advice compared with over 70 per cent of the senior registrars and nearly 80 per cent of the registrars. Even among the SHOs, who were the group most likely to complain about the present system, two-thirds said they had received some careers advice, although GP trainees in their trainee year were curiously less likely to have received advice than those in their SHO jobs.

One of the reasons for the difference between those in general practice and those in hospital jobs was perhaps related to the source of the careers advice. The main source of careers advice in medicine, mentioned by over two-thirds of those who had had any advice in the postgraduate years, was a consultant. But consultants were mentioned by over 80 per cent of hospital doctors compared with just over 40 per cent of GP principals.

It could be argued that GPs were less in need of careers advice than hospital doctors, although this was not the message which came through in the study on *Part-time Working in General Practice*, but the discrepancy was quite marked, and we would suggest that it needs attention. Nevertheless, GP trainers were mentioned as the second most frequent source of careers advice in the postgraduate years – by 23 per cent of those who had received any advice. Even so, less than half the GP principals had received postgraduate careers advice from a GP trainer, although all those on the retainer scheme and two-thirds of the GP locums had. It was perhaps surprising that only 40 per cent of the GP trainees and SHOs on a GP vocational training scheme said that they had received careers advice from a GP trainer.

Overall, of those who had received any postgraduate careers advice, one third of the women but only 11 per cent of men had received careers advice from a GP trainer. It looked as though many male GPs either did not seek or were not given careers advice from anyone, something which may possibly account for some of the stress noted in many of their accounts of their careers, both in this study and others.

Other sources of careers advice in the postgraduate years were mentioned far less frequently by the 1986 qualifiers. Professors were mentioned by 11 per cent of those who had been given careers advice, but most of these were registrars, and men rather than women. Regional postgraduate deans were mentioned by 9 per cent, but again, half of these were registrars, and again men outnumbered women. Clinical tutors were mentioned by 8 per cent of those who had been given postgraduate careers advice, again mostly registrars, with single mentions by SHOs, senior registrars, GP principals, GP locums and research fellows. Women were marginally more likely than men to have been given advice by clinical tutors, although the actual numbers of either sex were very small – 12 doctors out of the 229 respondents.

It was interesting, and perhaps depressing, that colleagues and other junior hospital doctors were more likely to be mentioned as sources of postgraduate careers advice than any group other than consultants and GP trainers. This was particularly true of men, and may well reflect a rather greater reluctance of men to seek careers advice, for fear of appearing to be less than secure in their career.

Other sources of advice were each mentioned by only a handful of doctors, including vocational training course organisers, college advisers in the region, medical officers or other officials at the regional health authority, lecturers or senior lecturers, and other representatives of professional organisations or colleges.

What kind of advice did these people give? Around half the doctors who had had any careers advice said that it was straightforward advice on career options or the direction their careers might take. A quarter said it was advice on which posts to apply for, and one fifth had been given advice on postgraduate qualifications and examinations. Some one in six had been given advice about different specialties they might pursue, while just over one in ten had been given specific advice about general practice. An important piece of advice, received by less than one in ten, had been encouragement to stay in a particular specialty.

Otherwise the advice had been received by very few doctors, less than ten in each category, and included advice on interviews and presentation, advice on posts for vocational training, advice on part-time training, and advice on how best to combine career and family. It was perhaps surprising that so little advice had been received on such important matters, particularly by women. Other advice, mentioned by a handful of doctors included advice to leave a specialty or advice to stay in medicine.

The advice was sometimes rather bizarre it appeared, but some doctors were fairly sanguine about it, like a woman SHO describing the advice she had from a consultant physician: 'He didn't think women should be doctors anyway – but that's just the way he was ...' Others were more critical, like a male locum GP describing his advice from a consultant geriatrician: 'He told me I was stupid, and that he thought that because I didn't like medicine I should see a psychiatrist ...'

Some of the reported careers advice was short and to the point, as a woman GP locum described: 'The consultant said, "Go into general practice, dear," and the GP principal said, "Don't get pregnant."' A woman senior registrar described her careers advice: 'They talked about opportunities in different subjects. No-one knew about palliative care. They hadn't even heard about it in Manchester ...'

Occasionally the doctors described encouraging advice, like that received from a consultant paediatrician by a clinical assistant in paediatrics who had wanted to change from general practice: 'He talked about the hardships and reality of working for postgraduate qualifications and the hardships of working in hospital specialties. He said I was mad, but I should do it ... I'd make a good consultant ...'

There was very little evidence of regular careers advice, and the experience of those who had had it was not necessarily encouraging, as a woman registrar observed: 'I have to see the senior lecturer every six months by appointment – no option. As an individual I wouldn't trust him an inch – backstabber. Not the right type of person to do that job at all ...'

Assessment of careers advice received
How helpful dd the 1986 qualifiers find the advice they had been given? The men found it more helpful than the women – 72 per cent said it had been helpful, compared with only 60 per cent of the women. Just under a quarter of the men and just over a quarter of the women said it had been fairly helpful, while 4 per cent of the men and one in ten of the women said it had been unhelpful. A further handful of women said some of it had been helpful and some not. The women with children were rather more likely than those without children to have found the advice helpful, but there was no difference between those working full-time or part-time in their assessment of the helpfulness of the careers advice they had received.

What about accuracy? It has been suggested that not all those giving careers advice are particularly well-informed about the full range of options available, and may even give misleading advice about requirements or opportunities in particular specialties. 65 per cent of the men and 69 per cent of the women found the advice accurate, but one fifth of the men and one in six of the women found it only fairly accurate while 5 per cent of the total found it inaccurate. Around 5 per cent found some accurate and some inaccurate. Part-timers were rather more likely to find the advice accurate than full-timers, but those who were not working at the time of the interview were more likely to report inaccurate advice than others.

Were they encouraged by the careers advice? There was much more doubt in the minds of the doctors about this, with 54 per cent of the men and 58 per cent of the women finding the advice encouraging, one third of the men and just over a quarter of the women finding it fairly encouraging and over 10 per cent of both sexes finding it discouraging, with a small number finding some encouraging and some discouraging. Again there was little or no difference between the part-timers and full-timers.

Whom did they find the most helpful source of careers advice? Only 22 per cent of the total (33 doctors – 14 men and 19 women) had actually received advice from more than one person about their postgraduate careers. Just over one third of them found a consultant the most helpful person, with men more likely to do so than women. One third of them – all men – found a professor the most helpful. Just over 40 per cent of the women – and no men – found a GP trainer the most helpful. Other sources, such as clinical tutors, college advisers in region, colleagues, relations, the regional postgraduate dean and other officers at the region each received single mentions as the most helpful person, while a handful of doctors did not think anyone was more helpful than others.

Why were these people particularly helpful? The main reason was that they had a good knowledge of the opportunities in a particular specialty. Men were more likely to say the person was helpful because they set them on the right career path, while women were more likely to say it was because they were friendly and sympathetic. Other factors found important by both sexes were that the person had a good knowledge of them as individuals or could take a broad view of the situation, presenting the situation from all sides.

Whom did the doctors find the least helpful? Over a third of the women but only a fifth of the men found a consultant the least helpful source of advice. A fifth of the men and one in ten of the women cited a professor as the least helpful, while regional postgraduate deans, clinical tutors, college advisers and relatives each received a couple of mentions. Nearly one fifth of the doctors found no one person less helpful than others.

The main reason for finding someone particularly unhelpful was their lack of knowledge or interest in the respondent's individual circumstances. Further problems were that the source had no knowledge outside his own specialty, gave unrealistic advice, too general advice, or were so busy and overwhelmed that the advice was found to be negative and unhelpful.

We asked the 34 per cent of 1986 qualifiers who had had no careers advice in the postgraduate years whether they would have liked any. As Table 14.12 indicates, most of them would have liked some. Nearly two-thirds of the total (59 per cent of the men and 68 per cent of the women) who had not had any postgraduate careers advice would have liked some. Among the women, three-quarters of those working part-time who had not had any postgraduate careers advice would have liked some

Table 14.12   Whether those who had had no postgraduate careers advice would have liked some (1986 qualifiers only)

			column percentages
	Total	Male	Female
Yes	64	59	68
No	36	41	32
Base: all those receiving no postgraduate careers advice	*(78)*	*(34)*	*(44)*

From whom would they have liked careers advice? The two main sources were consultants and people in the particular specialty or area that the qualifiers were interested in. In addition, some doctors would have liked careers advice from a GP trainer, someone with broad experience and an overview, a careers expert or a clinical tutor. One in ten would have liked careers advice from someone other than their consultant or 'boss' while a handful said that they would have liked careers advice from someone who was interested in them.

They mainly wanted advice about career options or the direction they should take. One in six wanted advice about the opportunities and requirements in different specialties. Others wanted advice on general practice, on postgraduate examinations, on posts to apply for, on organising a vocational training scheme, on combining a career and family, on part-time training and feedback on their personal progress and potential.

Many of the requests appeared perfectly normal and straightforward and it was difficult to see why the doctors had been unable to gain access to such advice. A woman psychiatric registrar said: 'I would have liked more feedback from the consultant on each individual firm. I was never shown any of the reports written about me so I had no idea how to gauge my competence ...' A male registrar in general medicine wanted the same: 'I would like to have known whether the jobs I did fulfilled their expectations ...'

Improvements to careers advice in the postgraduate years

There were clearly big problems in the delivery of careers advice in the postgraduate years in medicine. Some doctors had found the careers advice they had received helpful, accurate and encouraging, but a rather high proportion had not, and, more worryingly, over a third said that they had had no postgraduate careers advice at all. It was difficult to discern why some doctors had had some and others had had none. It often appeared to be simply a matter of the luck of the draw, with no evidence that the more articulate or more successful were more or less likely to seek or be offered careers advice. It did seem to be a matter of concern that two-thirds of those who had had no careers advice would have liked some. These doctors were not shy retiring violets on the whole. What was wrong with the system?

We asked the doctors how they themselves would improve careers advice in the postgraduate years in medicine. This question certainly brought forth long and detailed answers from many of our respondents. There were three main recommendations, each given by one fifth of the respondents: first that there should be generally increased availability of careers advice and easier access to it (one quarter of the women thought this); secondly that there should be compulsory meetings with seniors, feedback at every stage and formal interviews with the 'boss'; and thirdly that there should be one-to-one careers counselling.

What else did the doctors want? Ten per cent said that there should be easily accessible general advice on the opportunities in different specialties. The same proportion said that there should be meetings with *independent* advisers, stipulating that these should not be the consultant or boss. Independent confidential advice from experts about specific specialties was recommended by a similar proportion. Other recommendations included feedback and advice on personal potential and aptitude; study days or lecture days; general advice on progressing up the career ladder; that advice should be provided at undergraduate as well as postgraduate level; a national data information bank on posts available in various regions; meetings with postgraduate deans; advice on postgraduate training and courses; advice on examinations and higher qualifications; advice much earlier in postgraduate training; advice on research and funding; GP day release throughout the vocational training period; meetings with junior doctors and finally, a plea for training for all those giving careers advice.

It can be seen that the 1986 qualifiers drew up a blue-print for a careers advice handbook. Looking at the three main recommendations first, it can be seen that there was a general demand for more personal feedback on a one-to-one level with someone for whom one had worked. There seemed to be a surprisingly low level of feedback on performance. A woman registrar in radiology wanted: 'A compulsory interview, once a year, probably with a group of consultants in your current specialty, with an SR – someone you work with – to do a career review. It may be painful, but it would weed out a few unrealistic expectations ...'

The need for one person to take responsibility – or at least an interest – in the doctor's career was expressed in a number of different ways. A male GP principal said: 'Have one person responsible for tutoring or giving advice. It was completely ad hoc, if it happened at all. It would be nice if the consultant took you aside at the end of the job and had time to say, "What do you want to do now? Why?"'

But it appeared that few consultants saw this as their responsibility. There was concern by some doctors that people could easily lose their way without some feedback and advice. A male research fellow said: 'All SHOs and registrars ought to have appraisal once a year. They should discuss exams, and aims, and whether they are realistic. Some people fail MRCP three or four times ...' A male doctor who had had some difficulty in moving up the hospital ladder said: 'We need something more structured. It's totally haphazard at the moment. And people should be encouraged to find someone they can refer to as a mentor – someone we can really relate to ...'

The desire for independent advice, however, permeated many replies. Much as doctors wanted feedback from their consultants, they also wanted to be able to express their hopes and fears and anxieties. A woman senior registrar in psychiatry said there should be: 'Availability of friendly clinical tutors – people you can be honest with, without the fear of it jeopardising your future. People are frightened of saying what they really feel ...'

This fear that 'sound' doctors do not express doubts was certainly an inhibiting factor preventing doctors from seeking advice, as a male general medical registrar noted: 'It's very difficult really. I thought of running a careers service for disenchanted doctors, as an independent service. You can't go to the Royal Colleges – word gets around that you're uncertain ...'

Many doctors seemed to be totally unaware of the clinical tutor system. A male GP locum said: 'I think there should be a well-respected consultant in hospital who has a definite designated role, as well as having the enthusiasm to carry it out and refer one on to other specialties; plus the course organisers within VTS who should give advice to junior doctors on the schemes as and when they need it ...'

The relative lack of careers advice given to GPs was noted earlier in this chapter. A women GP locum who had completed her vocational training said: 'You'd have to cover it as a subject like any other – a block of teaching time in the SHO years ... I never wanted to work in a hospital – maybe that's why I didn't have any advice. If you go for a vocational training scheme, nobody gives you any advice. There are hundreds doing GP locums down here – I know ten in this district ...'

And those who had not been on organised vocational training schemes felt even more isolated, like a male GP locum: 'It would help to have access to an independent adviser to talk to and bounce ideas off, especially if you're not on a VT scheme. Currently there is no identity for GPs doing their own schemes – they're just seen as workhorses for consultants ...'

Another male GP locum said: 'The postgraduate tutors need to be more than just title posts – they need to be more effective and have training information at their disposal ... Perhaps careers advisers need to be independent and perhaps non-medical ...' A male doctor taking time out to study said: 'You need to know the name of a person you could approach – to know he had all the information and the knowledge to advise you in a constructive way. Ultimately it's your decision, but you need to have someone with a good overview of what's going to happen ... Perhaps a roaming careers adviser full-time, who could come to see you after hours at home ...'

There was thought to be a need for someone to take responsibility for doctors in the postgraduate years. A male GP trainee said: 'Every training post should have a formal elected tutor who should be responsible for career guidance. At (London teaching hospital) the postgraduate dean was supposed to do that, but he never saw me once. I didn't feel he knew I was there ...' Again there was a desire for a confidential adviser, as a woman clinical assistant recommended: 'I think you'd have to build in a structure where doctors were linked to advisers outside their own health authority where they could be given confidential advice. Or perhaps have some kind of careers advice for doctors where you could attend ...' And her views were shared by all kinds of rather unlikely doctors, like a male orthopaedic registrar: 'You need someone independent – someone who had no bearing on your CV or references – someone in confidence ...'

Some doctors, as we have seen, were concerned that more advice was needed in the early years after qualification. A woman senior registrar in public health said: 'It should be offered pre-registration and just after that. That year is the most important year. In that year they don't make informed choices and they should. With more advice they would go less distance in the wrong direction. It's soul-destroying to go too far in the wrong direction ...'

It sometimes seemed clear that doctors had been allowed to pursue careers or specialties which were totally unsuitable for them in terms of their own aptitudes and personalities. Although many felt that everyone should have the freedom to make mistakes, most recognised that the medical career structure was not geared to experiment, and there were many sad tales even among these young qualifiers of doctors losing their way for want of even a little help and counselling.

Accessibility was clearly a big problem for those who wanted advice. A male SHO in ophthalmology said: 'I'd make sure it was readily available for a start – also that people who are giving advice are people in the specialties. You do find that, for example, the regional postgraduate dean is giving advice about specialties in which he has never worked ...' But a woman in the same grade and specialty disagreed: 'I think an improved postgraduate department which has regular contact with doctors in training posts would help, particularly those in non-rotational posts. They are largely left to choose their own career pattern unless they actively seek advice ...'

There was surprisingly little comment in the answers to these questions on the need for careers advice for women doctors or for those who might wish to combine a family and career. As we have found so often in this research, both men and women expressed very similar views on the constraints of the medical career structure, on the deficiencies of the careers advice and counselling system, and, indeed, on most aspects of medical careers. There appeared to be a general underlying feeling that improvements in the structure and system of career advancement could only improve the lot of all doctors. Women doctors were not seeking special treatment or advice. They were certainly not getting it.

15 Doctors' assessment of their own careers

It might be thought that success in a medical career is easy to judge by certain objective criteria, for example, whether and when a doctor reaches career grade in medicine. This may have been true up to a point in the past, but it has become an increasingly crude measure of success. The definition of a successful career in medicine, when 50 per cent of those entering the profession are women, may need to be looked at more critically.

One of the most interesting aspects of the last study was the importance that most doctors attached to their CVs. It was a commonly held view that a 'good' CV could be seen at a glance, and the researchers and coders on this study quickly developed an eye for good, bad and indifferent CVs, although we perhaps lacked the refined skill brought to this task by senior members of the medical profession. There was little doubt in the minds of most of those interviewed that a 'straight' career path was the main route to success. It was thought a risk to deviate too much into interesting side-lines or spend too much time abroad or in remote parts of the British Isles, and 'good' and 'bad' jobs were clearly recognised as pluses and minuses on the CV. But it was also thought to be a risk to work part-time or take time out even to study.

Women were thought to find it more difficult than men to put together a good CV, and were certainly thought to find it more difficult to have a 'straight' career path. One of the results was that women were less likely than men to have reached career grade in medicine. Were they therefore less successful?

Success in careers

We asked the doctors in both studies whether they thought that they had had a successful career in medicine so far, and what criteria they were using for their answers. In the last study we found that 90 per cent of the 1966 men and 88 per cent of the 1976 and 1981 men thought that they had had a successful career in medicine, compared with only 75 per cent of the 1966 and 1976 women and 90 per cent of the 1981 women. As Table 15.01 shows, 91 per cent of the 1986 men thought they had had a successful career in medicine so far, compared with 82 per cent of the 1986 women.

The 1986 men were therefore similar to their 1981 counterparts, whereas the 1986 women were less likely than the 1981 women to rate their career successful, a feeling borne out by the objective data, as we have seen. Only 70 per cent of the 1986 women qualifiers with children thought that they had had a successful

Table 15.01   Whether doctors felt they had had a successful career in medicine so far

column percentages

| | Male | | | Female | | |
	1976	1981	1986	1976	1981	1986
Yes	88	88	91	75	90	82
No	12	8	6	20	10	14
Dont' know	0	4	3	5	0	4
Base: all qualifiers	*(105)*	*(101)*	*(105)*	*(105)*	*(103)*	*(124)*

career so far, compared with 85 per cent of the women without children. There was virtually no difference between women who were working full-time or part-time, but less than 70 per cent of the doctors who were not working thought that they had had a successful career.

There were certain differences among the grades of doctors, with all the GP principals, GP assistants, GP retainer scheme doctors, senior registrars, research fellows and medical officers thinking that they had had a successful career so far. Around 90 per cent of the GP trainees, GP locums and registrars shared this view. But less than three-quarters of the SHOs, only half the clinical assistants and only 70 per cent of those not working thought they had had a successful career so far.

But what criteria were the doctors using? In the last study we found that the main criterion used for rating a career successful was subjective – whether they enjoyed their jobs and were doing what they wanted to do. This was particularly marked among the older qualifiers, and more noticeable among men than women. We found that the 1981 qualifiers were more likely to rate their career successful if they had got to the right place at the right speed, while the 1966 qualifiers, especially men, were more likely to rate their careers successful because they had got to the top of their own specialty.

We can see in Table 15.02 that there were certain interesting differences between the 1986 qualifiers and those from 1976 and 1981. The 1986 men were much less likely than the men from the previous two cohorts to rate their career successful because they enjoyed it, but much more likely to rate it successful because they had got to the right place at the right time. The 1986 women were similar to the 1986 men in laying more stress than their predecessors on getting to the right place at the right time, but were similar to previous generations of women in giving enjoyment of their jobs as the most important ingredient of their success. This was a factor cited far more often by women working part-time than by those working full-time, and much more often by women with children than by women without children. It looked as though they were prepared to put up with not getting the top jobs as long as they were enjoyed their jobs, at least for a while.

Table 15.02   Reasons for doctors thinking own career successful

column percentages

	Male			Female		
	1976	1981	1986	1976	1981	1986
Doing job want to do/ enjoy it	78	64	51	71	62	68
Got to right place at right speed	33	51	67	30	40	52
Got to top of own specialty	22	2	2	30	6	5
Gained necessary qualifications	8	16	14	1	14	15
Have not been unemployed	4	10	4	3	10	2
Equal pace as men	0	0	0	0	0	7
Managed to combine career and family	1	0	2	4	3	2
Wide experience in training will help future career	0	0	9	0	0	9
Base: all qualifiers thinking own career successful	*(92)*	*(89)*	*(96)*	*(79)*	*(93)*	*(102)*

It was not surprising that few of the younger qualifiers, either from 1981 or 1986, cited getting to the top of their own specialty as proof of their success, since few had reached career grade. However, similar proportions of 1981 and 1986 qualifiers thought that gaining the necessary qualifications or passing their postgraduate examinations were reasons for rating their careers successful so far. An interesting difference between the 1981 and 1986 qualifiers was that 10 per cent of the 1981 qualifiers of both sexes had said their careers had been successful because they had not been unemployed, while this was rarely mentioned by the 1986 qualifiers. Nearly one in ten of the 1986 qualifiers rating their careers successful mentioned that they had had wide experience in training posts which would help their careers, a factor not mentioned at all by previous generations. A small number of women thought their careers had been successful because they had progressed at an equal pace to their male counterparts, and a handful of men and women thought they had been successful in that they had managed to combine a career and family.

Very few 1986 qualifiers said that they felt they had had a successful career because they were well-respected by their patients or colleagues, a factor mentioned mainly by the 1966 qualifiers in the last study, and only two doctors felt they had been successful because of their good lifestyle or income, another factor mentioned mainly by 1966 qualifiers.

Of the doctors who felt they had not had a successful career in medicine so far, one third of both men and women said that they had not got as far up the ladder as they would have hoped; two-thirds of the men and one fifth of the women said that it was because they had failed to get higher qualifications or had had difficulty passing the examinations; one fifth of the women said that they could not get a permanent post; one fifth of both sexes said that they had not found a specialty they were really interested in; and others said that they were in poorly paid jobs after years of training, in low status jobs because of the career structure, not working in their chosen specialty, not able to get a part-time post in their chosen specialty or simply not enjoying medicine.

A woman SHO summarised the feelings of many who did not rate their careers successful for a variety of reasons: 'It's disappointing. I always wanted to be a specialist and it's not turned out. I wanted it from the age of 11. Various things have disillusioned me. I'll be in general practice by a process of default. I wish I could say, hand on heart, that I wanted to do general practice – but it's by default ...'

There were few examples of the real frustration and even bitterness which we found among the older women in the last study when they talked about the success – or lack of success – of their careers, but it could be argued that these were still relatively early days in the careers of the 1986 qualifiers, and they were mostly similar to the 1981 qualifiers in the last study in still hoping that things would change. Nevertheless there were pointers in the lower rating given by the 1986 women qualifiers when assessing their success that hopes were not always running high.

Job satisfaction

We have seen that the 1986 male qualifiers thought their careers were as successful as the 1981 men so far, but that the 1986 women rated their success rather lower than the 1981 women had done at the same stage of their careers. But when it came to job satisfaction, the 1986 men and women were united in giving their jobs a much lower rating than that given by the 1981 qualifiers, as Table 15.03 shows.

In the last study we found that the 1976 qualifiers were the least likely to say that they were satisfied or very satisfied with their present jobs, but that the 1981 qualifiers were virtually as satisfied as the 1966 qualifiers. Looking at Table 15.03, we can see that there was a dramatic decline in job satisfaction, comparing the 1981 and 1986 qualifiers of both sexes.

55 per cent of the 1981 men and 43 per cent of the 1981 women had said that they were very satisfied with their present jobs, compared with only 27 per cent of both men and women in the 1986 cohort. Rather higher proportions of the 1986 cohort said that they were satisfied with their jobs, but nevertheless, the general level of satisfaction was noticeably lower among the 1986 qualifiers, with 15 per cent of both men and women saying that they were either not very

Table 15.03   Doctors' satisfaction with present job/status

column percentages

	Male			Female		
	1976	1981	1986	1976	1981	1986
Very satisfied	44	55	27	33	43	27
Satisfied	28	22	40	25	28	38
Fairly satisfied	11	14	17	27	16	16
Not very satisfied	12	5	12	8	8	12
Not at all satisfied	3	4	2	2	1	3
Not working	1	0	*	5	5	*
Outside medicine	1	0	*	1	0	*
Don't know	*	*	2	*	*	3
Base: all qualifiers	*(105)*	*(101)*	*(105)*	*(105)*	*(103)*	*(124)*

satisfied or not at all satisfied with their present jobs, compared with less than 10 per cent of the 1981 qualifiers.

There was little difference between women working full-time or part-time, or women with or without children. Men with children appeared more satisfied with their jobs than those without children. Doctors working in general practice were considerably more satisfied than others, and, indeed half the GP principals, GP assistants and GP trainees said they were very satisfied with their present jobs, compared with only a quarter of the registrars and only 6 per cent of the SHOs. On the other hand nearly 40 per cent of the GP locums said that they were dissatisfied with their jobs.

What were the main reasons for satisfaction? The main reason, given by more than half of those expressing general satisfaction, was that doctors were doing the job they wanted to do and were enjoying it. The second most frequent reason for job satisfaction was good professional support and back-up from seniors or colleagues, while the third most frequent reason was good teaching or good supervision. It was interesting, and perhaps not surprising, that personal interest and support from others played such an important part in job satisfaction.

Around one in ten finding their job satisfying said they had a good lifestyle generally, rather fewer said their jobs offered them good status, while other factors included finding their jobs worthwhile and rewarding, offering good research opportunities, a good salary, fitting in with domestic commitments and having little or no on-call work.

However, it should be emphasised that many who said that they were satisfied with their jobs, mainly because they enjoyed the work, had major criticisms of other aspects of their jobs, like a male registrar in gastroenterology who was very satisfied with the content of his job, but: 'Very little thought is paid to the conditions of work of junior doctors ... I feel exploited, not only by the hours but also the conditions. As a registrar I am on-call from home, but my SHO has to sleep in a room 8 feet by 3 feet, with no ventilation, when he's on-call. Until recently, on-call doctors could have a hot meal after midnight, free of charge, signed by the night sister. Now you can only get a juice. You're a temporary, abusable, disposable commodity ... When my wife and I were housemen, we shared a hospital flat. The hospital authorities expected my wife to clean the flat even though she was working the same hours as me ...'

A male GP principal was fairly satisfied with his job: 'I'm a professional person and I've worked hard, but GPs are slowly losing the respect they deserve. Doctors should be paid a lot more for what they do. I go out and save someone's life at 3 am and I get nothing, but a dentist extracts a tooth and gets £40. Accountants look after numbers and I look after lives. Who gets the financial reward?'

The fact that a number of doctors found their jobs satisfying because of the support they received from colleagues highlighted the lack of satisfaction engendered by lack of support. In the study on GPs, we found many examples of increasing isolation felt by doctors working in general practice, and this factor came up again in this study, as described by a male GP trainee who found his job fairly satisfying: 'It's not everything I dreamed of. I'm isolated as a GP. You work on your own, even if there are several partners. You're stuck in a room for hours on end. In hospital you meet at lunch – talk – discuss cases. General practice is lonely. I also miss the more practical and technological aspects of working in a hospital ...'

A woman psychiatric registrar underlined the effect of stability and support in enhancing job satisfaction: 'The current job is enjoyable and interesting and will stand me in good stead for the future. The on-call is not too arduous. I like being in an established rotation. It offers a good support network through having been with the same people for several years ...'

And it was the lack of stability and support which dominated many of the answers from doctors who were not satisfied with their present jobs. The main reason given for lack of satisfaction was the fact that the respondents were not in permanent posts, closely followed by comments that they were not getting the experience or training needed to achieve a move towards a permanent post. A male anaesthetic SHO was not very satisfied with his present job at a London teaching hospital: 'There's little consultant control, unsupervised training, lack of formal teaching, excessive hours – 104 per week, low pay, inadequate support services such as medical staffing and finance, and poor facilities for on-call ...'

Some doctors who were fairly satisfied also echoed much of the anxiety expressed by those who were not satisfied. A male surgical SHO was concerned about his future in his sub-specialty: 'I'm having to put in an enormous amount of commitment – enormous – with no security or guarantees – none whatsoever. The bottle-neck in (this sub-specialty) is from SHO to registrar. There are only 26 registrar posts in the whole country. There should be that many in the south of England ...' And his concern was shared by a male psychiatric registrar: 'I'd rather be a senior registrar. According to the Royal College of Psychiatrists I meet all the criteria for appointment but there are so few posts that one must do research and publish papers to get the posts ...'

There were rumblings of dissatisfaction from some 1986 male qualifiers reflecting the lack of satisfaction found among the male GPs in our recent study on general practice (Allen, 1992). A male GP locum said: 'I'm not at all satisfied, simply because I don't see myself doing the job I've trained for, for the next 40 years. I think that the quality of life that's offered by a career in medicine is poor, and although remuneration is generally quite good in full-time established career posts, the increasing demands of administration and the increase in controls on clinical work, allied with the lack of leisure time, make it unattractive ...'

Some of the women were particularly concerned about being in jobs that they felt were getting them nowhere, like a clinical assistant: 'I work so few hours that I don't have enough contact with what's going on in medicine. This job isn't actually leading to anything. I could go on doing it for ever and ever, but it wouldn't do me, or the patients, any good ...'

Assessment of future career

Where did the doctors see themselves in five years' time? To a large extent this was a measure of their optimism as well as their realism. It provided a useful benchmark by which to measure their achievement, and the parallel study to this, in which we followed up the ambitions and predictions of the 1976 and 1981 qualifiers, indicates clearly that many things can happen in five years of a doctor's life to affect career progress.

Both in this study and in the last study we recorded what doctors said they thought they would be doing in five years' time by grade and specialty in medicine, details of any jobs out of medicine, and whether doctors thought they would be working full-time, part-time or not working at all. We did the same in the study of GPs. We analysed the data slightly differently in the present study from the way we presented it in *Doctors and their Careers*, following the same pattern we used in *Part-time Working in General Practice*.

First, we looked at what they thought they would be doing in five years' time in terms of their employment status, for example whether they thought they would be working full-time, less than full-time and so on. We found, as Table 15.04 shows, that 93 per cent of the 1986 men qualifiers and 41 per cent of the women thought that they would be working full-time in clinical medicine, and that none of the men but 47 per cent of the women thought they would be working less than full-time in clinical medicine. In addition, 2 per cent of qualifiers thought that they would be working outside medicine but in a medically-related occupation, another 2 per cent thought they would be working outside medicine, 3 per cent of the women but no men thought they would not be working, and 3 per cent of the respondents did not know what they would be doing.

How did this relate to what they were doing at present? Over three-quarters of those who were now working full-time in clinical medicine thought they would

**Table 15.04   What doctors thought they would be doing in five years' time
(1986 qualifiers only)**

column percentages

	Total	Male	Female
Working FT in clinical medicine	65	93	41
Working less than FT in clinical medicine	25	0	47
Working outside clinical medicine but in medically-related occupation	2	3	2
Working outside medicine	2	2	2
Working both in and outside medicine	0	0	0
Not working	2	0	3
(Abroad)	(2)	(2)	(2)
Don't know	3	2	4
Base: all qualifiers	*(229)*	*(105)*	*(124)*

still be doing so, while 17 per cent of them (all women) thought they would be working less than full-time in clinical medicine. (36 per cent of the women at present working full-time thought that they would be working part-time in clinical medicine in five years' time).

Five doctors thought they would be working in medically-related occupation or outside medicine in five years' time. Of those currently working less than full-time in clinical medicine (27 doctors), all four of the men thought they would be working full-time (one outside medicine). Only two of the women currently working less than full-time thought they would be working full-time in clinical medicine, but most of the rest thought they would still be working less than full-time, although two thought they would not be working at all and one did not know what she would be doing.

Of the three doctors working outside clinical medicine in a medically-related occupation, one thought they would be full-time in clinical medicine, one less than full-time in clinical medicine and one thought they would still be in the same job. The doctors working outside medicine thought they would remain outside medicine. The five women on maternity leave thought that they would be working less than full-time in clinical medicine, while, of the 14 doctors who were not working, 6 thought they would be working full-time and 4 less than full-time in clinical medicine, 1 in a medically-related occupation, 1 thought she would not be working and 1 did not know.

The main message from this analysis was that the proportion of 1986 qualifiers working full-time in clinical medicine was destined to drop from 78 per cent at present to 65 per cent in five years' time. This reflected an increase in the proportion of men working full-time in clinical medicine, from 90 per cent

Table 15.05 **What job doctors thought they would be doing in five years' time (1986 qualifiers only)**

column percentages

	Total	Male	Female
FT GP principal	29	44	16
PT GP principal	18	0	34
PT GP assistant	1	0	2
GP (not specified)	1	0	2
Consultant	10	15	5
Senior registrar	29	34	25
Registrar	1	0	2
SHO	*	0	1
Associate specialist	0	0	0
Staff grade	1	0	3
Clinical assistant	0	0	0
SCMO/CMO	*	0	1
Medical officer (other)	1	1	1
Senior lecturer	*	1	0
Other academic/research	2	1	3
Outside medicine	3	3	3
Working abroad	*	1	0
Don't know	3	2	4
Same specialty in medicine	84	85	83
Different specialty in medicine	11	11	11
Base: all qualifiers who said they would be working	*(217)*	*(103)*	*(114)*

at present to 93 per cent in five years' time, but a decrease in the proportion of women, from 67 per cent at present to 41 per cent in five years' time. It is this prediction which must be examined closely by those involved in medical manpower planning. The women might not be able to achieve their aim, but this is what they thought they would be doing. Planning at a macro level must take account of what people are planning to do at a micro level. The reality is not that doctors are planning to leave medicine in large – or even small – numbers, but that a substantial proportion are planning to work less than full-time.

What exactly were they planning to do? Table 15.05 looks only at those who said they would be working in five years' time and shows that 44 per cent of the 1986 men and 54 per cent of the 1986 women qualifiers thought that they would be in general practice, but whereas all the men (44 per cent of the total) thought they would be full-time GP principals, only 16 per cent of the women thought they would, while 34 per cent thought they would be part-time GP principals, and a further 4 per cent thought they would be part-time GP assistants or in some post in general practice.

49 per cent of the 1986 men but only 33 per cent of the 1986 women qualifiers thought that they would be in hospital medicine. 15 per cent of the men but only 5 per cent of the women thought that they would be consultants; 34 per cent of the men and 25 per cent of the women thought they would be senior registrars; 2 per cent of the women and no men thought they would be registrars; and 1 per cent of the women and no men thought they would be SHOs.

Other branches of medicine attracted little interest. Only 1 per cent of women thought they would be in community health, and 1 per cent of both sexes thought they would be doing some other kind of medical officer work. 1 per cent of men thought they would be a senior lecturer and 1 per cent of men and 3 per cent of women thought they would be in some other branch of academic medicine or research.

3 per cent of both sexes thought they would be outside medicine, and 3 per cent of qualifiers did not know what they would be doing.

84 per cent, roughly equal proportions of men and women, thought that they would be in the same specialty in medicine as they were currently working in, while 11 per cent thought they would have changed specialty. Virtually all the men thought they would be working full-time, while 44 per cent of the women who thought they would be working said they would be working full-time and 54 per cent less than full-time, with a tiny proportion unable to predict which they would do. Three-quarters of the women who currently had children thought they would be working part-time, compared with half the women without children.

The vast majority of those who thought they would be working less than full-time thought they would be in general practice. Only one of the seven senior registrars, 10 per cent of the registrars and 14 per cent of the SHOs thought they would be working less than full-time in five years' time.

Looking at their present jobs, over 80 per cent of the GP principals but only 35 per cent of the present GP trainees thought that they would be working as full-time GP principals. It was interesting that one third of the SHOs on vocational training schemes but over one third of SHOs not on vocational training schemes also thought they would be working as full-time GP principals.

6 of the 7 senior registrars thought they would be consultants, as did nearly one fifth of the registrars and research fellows and 10 per cent of the SHOs. Over 70 per cent of the registrars, 50 per cent of the research fellows and 28 per cent of the SHOs thought that they would be senior registrars, while less than 10 per cent of the SHOs thought that they would be registrars. It was interesting that nearly half of those who were not working thought that they would be senior registrars (reflecting the fact that some were studying and others were between jobs), and over a quarter thought that they would be full-time or part-time GP

principals, confirming that for many doctors, a break from medicine was seen as a very temporary measure.

Two registrars and one non-working doctor thought that they would be staff grade doctors in five years' time. Those who thought that they would be outside medicine included a GP locum, a registrar, an SHO, one non-working doctor and the two doctors already outside medicine.

Nearly all the doctors working in general practice and all the senior registrars thought they would be in the same specialty, but only 83 per cent of registrars and two-thirds of SHOs thought they would.

We had found in the last study that nearly 30 per cent of the 1981 women who were currently working full-time thought that they would be working less than full-time in five years' time. In this study, the proportion was slightly greater at 36 per cent. This could probably be accounted for by the rather higher proportion of 1986 women who thought they would be working in general practice, where, although part-time partnerships were thought to be difficult to get, they were thought to be easier than part-time training or part-time career posts in hospital medicine. It was not insignificant that 26 per cent of women currently working full-time thought that they would be part-time GP principals in five years' time, while as we have seen, very few thought they would be part-time in any grade in hospital medicine.

The flight of women from hospital medicine was clearly marked in this study of 1986 qualifiers, and must leave many questions to be asked about the opportunities for part-time or less than full-time working in hospital medicine.

After the doctors had told us what they thought they would be doing we asked them whether this was what they would like to be doing in five years' time. 92 per cent of doctors said that it was, but 5 per cent (11 doctors – 6 women and 5 men) said it was not and 3 per cent were not sure.

Five of the 11 were registrars, 4 were SHOs (1 on a vocational training scheme), and the other two were a GP principal and GP trainee respectively. What would they like to have been doing? Two registrars and an SHO (all women) would like to have been part-time senior registrars, 1 registrar and 2 SHOs would like to have been part-time GP principals (2 men and 1 woman), 1 male registrar would like to have been a part-time consultant, and 1 male registrar and a male GP trainee would like to have been full-time consultants. One male GP principal and a female registrar would like to have been outside medicine and 1 female SHO was not sure. 7 of the 11 would like to have been working part-time.

The doctors thought they would not be able to realise their wishes mainly because they thought there were too few part-time training or career posts, or because they were in a very competitive field. Sometimes the two went together, and they felt it unwise or difficult to attempt to work less than full-time in such a competitive area.

Regrets about decision to become a doctor

In the last study our final question to the doctors was whether they had ever regretted their decision to become doctors. We had not originally intended to include this question, but we found as our preparatory work progressed that this information was being volunteered time and time again. We found that it was the question which evoked the longest answers even though it came at the end of a long interview, and in many cases it appeared to open up the floodgates, particularly among the younger doctors.

In our study on GPs we repeated this question, but followed it up with a question on whether the doctors still regretted their decision. It had been pointed out in response to our previous study that many doctors might have regretted their decision at some point in their careers but that this might well have been a transitory phase. We found among the GPs that although even higher proportions of respondents had regretted their decisions than we found among the cohorts of doctors in *Doctors and their Careers*, the proportion who currently regretted it was lower, but still disquietingly high at one fifth of all respondents, and nearly a quarter of the GP principals.

Perhaps the most striking aspect of the last study was the increase over the cohorts of qualifiers in the proportions of men and women who said that they had ever regretted their decision to become doctors. The trend was clearly marked, from 14 per cent of 1966 men to 26 per cent of 1976 men to 44 per cent of 1981 men. Among the women, the proportions were higher, but followed the same pattern, from 19 per cent of 1966 women to 30 per cent of 1976 women to as many as 49 per cent of 1981 women.

Table 15.06   Whether doctors had ever regretted their decision to become doctors

column percentages

| | Male | | | Female | | |
	1976	1981	1986	1976	1981	1986
Yes	26	44	58	30	49	76
No	74	56	42	70	51	24
Base: all qualifiers	*(105)*	*(101)*	*(105)*	*(105)*	*(103)*	*(124)*

This was not just a reflection of the age and stage of the doctors and their careers, since the question was whether they had *ever* regretted their decision to become doctors. Table 15.06 gives striking evidence that the trend over the years has continued with an alarming steepening of the curve, in that 58 per cent of 1986 men and 76 per cent of 1986 women said that they had regretted their decision to become doctors.

As in the last study we analysed the data by the present job of the doctors to see whether some grades or specialties attracted higher levels of regret than others. In the last study we found that over 50 per cent of SHOs and nearly half the registrars had regretted their decision, compared with less than one third of the senior registrars and under one fifth of consultants. We also found that only 24 per cent of GP principals had ever regretted their decision. It must be remembered that this must be seen in the context of the sample as a whole which covered three years of qualifiers.

In the present study we found not only a marked shift in the level of regret, even from the 1981 qualifiers of last time, but also a shift in the jobs of the doctors expressing this regret. For example, two-thirds of the GP principals said that they had regretted their decision to become doctors, as did all the GP assistants, three-quarters of the GP trainees and over 80 per cent of the GP locums. Equal proportions of men and women GP principals expressed regret, but the level of regret among women GP trainees was over 90 per cent and among male GP locums it was nearly 90 per cent. There was no doubt at all that the levels of regret among these 1986 qualifiers working in general practice were dramatically higher than we found among their predecessors in the last study.

In hospital medicine a different picture emerged, with less than 60 per cent of senior registrars and registrars saying that they had ever regretted their decision to become doctors. However, this was largely accounted for by a relatively low level of regret among the men, while among the women three-quarters of the senior registrars and 70 per cent of the registrars said that they had regretted their decision. The same was true of SHOs, among whom 65 per cent overall said that they had regretted it, representing just over half the men but over 70 per cent of the women. Among the SHOs on a GP vocational training scheme, the proportion was around 80 per cent for both men and women. Nearly two-thirds of the research fellows and three-quarters of the clinical assistants had regretted their decision.

It was perhaps not surprising that nearly 90 per cent of those who were not working had regretted their decision to become doctors, as had all those who were working outside medicine, in community health or working as medical officers.

Why had they regretted their decision? In the last study we looked at the three cohorts separately in that the reasons given were rather different according to the ages and grades of the doctors. We therefore compared the 1986 qualifiers in this study with the 1981 qualifiers from last time. We found that fatigue and exhaustion and dislike of the long hours and on-call responsibilities were mentioned by one third of the 1981 qualifiers expressing regrets. This proportion had risen to nearly 60 per cent of the 1986 qualifiers expressing regrets, with more women than men mentioning it. It was the single most important factor by far, and was found among all grades of doctors.

Although the hours were a source of great concern, comments about them were often merged into other complaints. A male GP locum said: 'You work 136 hours in a week. I wouldn't recommend it to anyone. I'd tell them what it involved. You go into medical school and no-one tells you that you'll work an

80-hour weekend. You qualify at medical school and wham! Students are not prepared ...' A woman GP trainee agreed: 'Usually following a period of 85 hours' work. I've still got vivid memories of how awful it is being a junior hospital doctor, and nobody gives a monkey's that you go through eleven shifts of nursing during a weekend on call. Nurses moan about missing their Friday night, and you think, "What's a Friday night?"'

The question elicited long answers, but a male research fellow said tersely: 'Being a junior doctor is at times absolutely loathsome. I will need an extra sheet if you want me to extend myself on that one ...' Some one in six doctors said that they had only sometimes regretted their decision, but their descriptions of their lives were often worse than those of other respondents, like a woman registrar in general medicine: 'In the middle of the night you think about it a lot. You compare it with other people's life-style – less intelligent but financially better rewarded. You are in a vocational job. If you do not accept that, you would never accept your pay. But you cannot help but compare it with salaries in the city. I regretted it more as an SHO – up all night and shouted at in the morning. And failing exams – you start to regret it ...'

Over one in ten of the men, but rather fewer women, compared their lives with those of their contemporaries, and did not like what they saw, like a male GP trainee: 'My standard of living is *not* what I was led to believe a doctor should have. I haven't had a holiday in three years ... I look at friends who didn't do as well at 'A' levels. They're better off than me – company cars – few financial worries ...'

The impact on doctors' personal and social lives was a source of great regret to some one in ten, with others commenting specifically on breakdown in relationships. A woman GP trainee spoke of getting overtired – '... and not having any time to do the things you want to do with friends and family. It has a disastrous effect on your personal life ...' And even male high achievers wondered whether it was all worth it, like an anaesthetic registrar: 'The novelty wore off very quickly. I felt undervalued for what I'd sacrificed – my social life, my youth ...' A woman registrar in general medicine agreed: 'I regretted it in my SHO years because of the stress and lack of sleep and the fact that you were working so hard and getting nothing back – no teaching. What was it all for? It took the toll on personal relationships and all that. Why should people go through two years of hell?'

There were surprisingly few references to children. Perhaps many 1986 women felt they had not reached that stage in their lives yet, like a women GP principal: 'I would like to have had children before now, and even now I cannot have children because it is too soon after having joined the practice. It is a stressful job and sometimes you think you are not equal to the demands. One of the posts I did I really disliked and I thought I would leave medicine ...'

There were many implications that doctors had not realised what they were letting themselves in for when they started. Both men and women were critical of medical school and even more critical of the lack of support offered at medical school and lack of preparation for the work to come. A woman GP locum said: 'At the end of medical school I was under the impression that there'd be a job and security and good pay. I'd no idea about the hours – and on-call – it's £1.75 an hour – less than the cleaners. A lot of my year dropped out straight after their first house jobs – 8 or 9 of them ...'

And a woman GP trainee was also critical of lack of support: 'I hated medical school. I hated having to learn by rote. You're trained to be a medical professional, not a doctor. There's no support. You're flapping in the breeze. You don't matter as a medical student. You don't feel you have a place ...'

As we have observed before, it often appeared that medical students and junior doctors were offered little or no support by anyone, while being expected to take enormous responsibility in very stressful situations. This, combined with feelings of job insecurity, was too much for some to bear. There were clearly some very depressed young doctors among those we interviewed, like a male surgical SHO: 'The only secure job is that of consultant. The hours worked can be appalling. And the remuneration for those hours is ridiculous. Career prospects for doctors in general are awful ...' Some were only counting the days until they could get out, like a male GP locum: 'I felt very trapped. I hated my job and didn't feel I was able to do anything else. Now I see medicine as a useful springboard to another career ...'

Table 15.07   Whether doctors currently regretted their decision to become doctors (1986 qualifiers only)

			column percentages
	Total	Male	Female
Yes	17	14	19
No	81	85	78
Don't know	2	1	3
Base: all qualifiers	*(229)*	*(105)*	*(124)*

What about present regrets? We had seen in the study on GPs that far fewer doctors said that they still regretted their decisions to become doctors, but that a substantial proportion did. Among the 1986 qualifiers, we found a corresponding drop in the proportion who currently regretted their decision to become doctors.

Table 15.07 shows that 17 per cent of the 1986 qualifiers (14 per cent of the men and 19 per cent of the women) said that they currently regretted their decision to become doctors. Among some of those who said they did not regret their decision a certain gallows humour emerged, as a male anaesthetic registrar observed: 'The only thing that keeps me going is not regretting anything. I'd shoot myself tomorrow if I regretted it ...'

We found that SHOs, GP trainees, clinical assistants and those not working were more likely than others to say that they currently regretted their decision to become doctors, although it was perhaps surprising that one of the women senior registrars said she still regretted her decision.

What was it that made doctors still have regrets? Some had clearly chosen the wrong job from the start, as a man who had moved into research from clinical medicine noted: 'There is never a good alternative to medicine when you're in medicine. It was my problem when I was 17 and it's remained my problem all the way through. There are lots of emotions about giving up medicine – guilt and anxiety – fear that I might have to be taken back into medicine. I might have to beg for a job if other things don't work out ...'

Some had left or knew that they would leave medicine, like a woman who had just finished her GP vocational training but was currently not working: 'I will always regret becoming a doctor. Ten years of my life would have been better doing something else ...' Another woman, currently working as a clinical assistant, said: 'It was the wrong decision at the time, but I do value the experience I've gained through doing it. I wish I had opted out sooner, but it wasn't really possible ...'

And yet another woman, currently on maternity leave, also regretted her decision: 'I would not have done it if I had known then what I know now. All my friends who are doctors are still moving on every six months to a year. What a social cost ...'

Some found the nature of the work overwhelming, like a woman medical officer: 'I find it very stressful. The stress is the unknown – that you can't put off things until tomorrow. It's not like pushing a bit of paperwork to the side of your desk. And if people die that you didn't expect to – that's distressing. Or a complaint – that would be terrible ...'

The reasons for continued regret were often complex. Another male qualifier working in research said: 'Medicine is becoming so unattractive as a career that I would discourage people from going into it. The pressure on junior doctors is always increasing, the salary does not compensate until later, the working conditions are deteriorating by each week and esteem is low too ...'

The prospects for some appeared bleak, as a male GP principal commented: 'I'm not brave enough to leave. I can't see myself doing anything else. Currently being a GP is 85 per cent boredom, 10 per cent tolerable and 5 per cent great fun. I just have to live for that 5 per cent and that doesn't seem right ...'

Perhaps the final word on regrets should go to a woman psychiatric registrar who summarised many of the careers of her contemporaries: 'I still regret it. It is a frightful price to pay for being good at science ...'

Thoughts of leaving medicine

In view of the high level of regret expressed by increasing numbers of doctors in the last study, and anecdotal evidence of doctors leaving medicine, the Department of Health asked us to include questions on whether doctors had ever

Table 15.08   Whether doctors had ever thought of leaving medicine (1986 qualifiers only)

column percentages

	Total	Male	Female
Yes	49	40	57
No	48	57	41
Has left medicine	2	3	2
Base: all qualifiers	*(229)*	*(105)*	*(124)*

thought of leaving medicine, their reasons, what they would do if they left, and how likely it was that they would leave. In terms of medical manpower planning, it was thought to be helpful to examine all the possible factors which might affect the future.

Nobody could feel sanguine about the results of these questions. Table 15.08 shows that nearly half the 1986 qualifiers had thought of leaving medicine, but that this represented 57 per cent of the women compared with 40 per cent of the men. 2 per cent of the qualifiers said that they had already left medicine.

It was perhaps more worrying that 70 per cent of the women working part-time had thought of leaving. There were certain differences between men and women in terms of grade and thoughts of leaving medicine. Women in general practice were more likely than men in general practice to have thought of leaving. This was particularly true of GP trainees and GP locums, with two-thirds of the women GP trainees and 80 per cent of the women GP locums having considered opting out. It was perhaps not surprising that three-quarters of the women clinical assistants and those not working at present had also thought of leaving medicine. Among the men, nearly half the SHOs and registrars had thought of leaving medicine.

It should be noted that, even though only one third of men GP principals had thought of leaving medicine, over 40 per cent of the women GP principals had done so. The proportions might have been lower than for those in other jobs, but it is perhaps depressing that so many of those who had reached career grade in their late twenties, and thus achieved the top jobs, had still thought of leaving medicine.

Why had the doctors thought of leaving? The two main reasons were those which had run through this research like a constant undercurrent of discontent: the hours, night duties and on-call responsibilities and the general lifestyle of medicine. These were each cited by one third of those who had thought of leaving. GPs in particular had thought of leaving for a better lifestyle, while the hours and on-call responsibilities were mentioned by doctors in most grades, but more often by women than men. Indeed, half the women who were working full-time said that they had thought of leaving medicine because of the hours and on-call commitments.

A further one in ten qualifiers said they had thought of leaving because of problems in passing postgraduate examinations, and a similar proportion had thought of leaving for more money or a better salary. One in ten of the women wanted more time for family commitments, and it was perhaps not surprising that this was mentioned by half the women with children who had thought of leaving medicine. In addition, rather less than one in ten said that they wanted more time for other interests. A woman senior registrar summarised the views of many of these: 'There's not a lot of room in medicine for people who are not 100 per cent committed. It's not a religion but they treat it like one ...'

There were a number of comments from doctors who had gone into general practice to escape from the hours and conditions of hospital medicine but had found it not what they expected, like a woman GP trainee: 'You get fed up with the conditions, the amount paid for what you do. It's a great shame because I'd like to work in hospitals. I find general practice very lonely. I'm just adjusting to that ...' And her views were echoed in different ways by others, like a male GP principal: 'The demands on us outweigh the satisfaction of the job. Patient demand and expectations far outweigh the satisfaction. There's a heavy load in this practice. I'd rather run a restaurant ...'

Some of the remarks appeared only half serious, but many doctors were very serious in answer to this question. There were many indications of acute disillusionment with medicine, and evidence of doctors in personal turmoil, like a woman GP trainee: 'It's the hours. They're too long. It's knocked every bit of enthusiasm right out of me. I'm at a massive crisis point – a great big crossroads. I feel I'd like to give up, but I don't know any other trade, so I'm a bit stuck really ...'

This general feeling of being unable to do anything else once they had embarked on a medical career at the age of 18 or 19 was very pervasive, both in this study and in the last study. A woman GP locum said: 'I feel trapped now because the options are so limited. All you've got is a degree. You've put so much of your life into it. You're nearly 30 and it seems a bit of a waste to change now ...'

And it was this general feeling of 'waste' if they had not reached the top jobs or were well on the way to them which was such a marked feature of these interviews. The bright young people who had set sail on their medical careers with such high hopes were difficult to reconcile with some of the bitter remarks made at the end of these interviews. A male general medical registrar spoke of his general disillusionment: 'I am fed up with the NHS. I'm not enjoying the job – no beds – sending people home – admitting them half-dead two days later. I'll never leave medicine but I might leave this country ...'

But what would they do if they did leave medicine? This question elicited an astonishing range of jobs, although one third of those who had thought of leaving said they did not know what they would do. A woman GP locum said:

Table 15.09   Likelihood of leaving medicine (1986 qualifiers only)

column percentages

	Total	Male	Female
Very likely	4	2	4
Fairly likely	4	0	7
Fairly unlikely	38	24	46
Very unlikely	52	71	41
Don't know	2	2	1
Base: all qualifiers saying had thought of leaving medicine	*(113)*	*(42)*	*(71)*

'Not a lot. There are not many things doctors can do. We're not trained to do anything else ...'

However, others knew perfectly well what they would do. Law, teaching, accountancy, pharmaceuticals, sports-related occupations, journalism, arts or design occupations and agriculture were each mentioned by 4 per cent or more of those who had thought of leaving medicine. Laboratory science or research, applied science and engineering were each mentioned by more than 5 per cent of the men, reflecting the fact that many had entered medicine because they were good at science. A small number of women spoke of psychotherapy or social work, while computing, NHS management, travel, the civil service, medical missionary work, building, catering and studying all attracted more than one mention each.

The most frequently mentioned alternative to medicine was, interestingly, running their own business, which attracted 10 per cent of those who had thought of leaving medicine. All those years of being at the beck and call of others had clearly taken their toll, and there were a few budding entrepreneurs among the 1986 qualifiers – if only they had the time to develop their skills.

How likely was it that they would actually leave medicine? As Table 15.09 shows, in spite of so much discontentment, the numbers of those who thought they would leave was very low. Of those who had thought of leaving medicine, who had not already done so, 4 per cent thought it very likely and 4 per cent thought it fairly likely, while 38 per cent thought it fairly unlikely and 52 per cent thought it very unlikely. However, 11 per cent of women said that it was very likely or fairly likely, compared with only 2 per cent of the men. And more men said it was very unlikely that they would leave medicine – 71 per cent compared with 41 per cent of the women who had considered leaving medicine. It was a matter of some concern perhaps that all but one of the doctors who said it was very or fairly likely that they would leave medicine were working in hospital medicine.

16 Discussion of findings

The point of departure for this study, as for the previous study of *Doctors and their Careers* (Allen, 1988), was the increasing number of women entering the medical profession. Women now account for some 50 per cent of those entering medical school, and indeed in some medical schools the proportion is now well over 50 per cent. The Department of Health has recognised for many years the importance for medical manpower planning of assessing the actual and potential contribution of women doctors. The profile of medical manpower has been changing fairly rapidly over the past ten years. Women accounted for 40 per cent of medical qualifiers in 1985, but the proportion is now nudging 50 per cent. It is clearly of crucial importance to examine what happens to these young women in career terms, not only in order to ensure that they can fulfil their own potential but also to make certain that the best possible use is made of the talents of all the medical workforce.

This report is one of two studies which followed up the findings of *Doctors and their Careers* five years after the first study examined the careers of men and women who qualified as doctors in 1966, 1976 and 1981. In this report we examined the careers and hopes and fears of a new cohort of doctors who qualified in 1986, while in the parallel study we looked at the experience of the 1976 and 1981 qualifiers whom we interviewed in the last study. We were interested to know what had happened to them in the intervening five years, but we also wanted to look closely at the views and experience of a new cohort of doctors five years after they had qualified. The 1986 qualifiers were at the same age and stage in their careers as the 1981 qualifiers had been five years earlier. What kind of changes had there been? How different were these younger qualifiers? What lessons could be learnt from their experience?

In the last report we observed how important it had been to examine the views of both men and women doctors in our research. It was clear from the start that many of the problems and constraints encountered by women doctors in developing their careers were exactly the same for men. One of the most striking findings of the research was the similarities between the men and women rather than the differences. There was little doubt in the minds of many of our respondents from all years of qualifiers that the medical career structure and the way careers were organised were major factors not only in preventing women from maximising their contribution to medicine but also in inhibiting the progress of those who were not able to follow a straight career path in a structure which many thought outdated and in conditions which many found unacceptable.

Since the last report was published, a number of changes have been introduced by the Department of Health with the aims of alleviating some of the undoubted workload pressure on all junior doctors, of introducing more opportunities for flexible or part-time postgraduate training in medicine, of encouraging women to enter specialties such as surgery where they are under-represented, of removing some of the discriminatory employment practices identified in the last report and, most recently, of drastically reducing the training period required for specialist medicine and clearly defining specialist training. In addition, the Opportunity 2000 initiative has introduced targets for increasing the proportion of women consultants and has turned its attention to the problems of women in general practice.

Many of these changes have been introduced in the last year or so, after the fieldwork for the present study took place. They have undoubtedly addressed many of the issues identified in this report, but nevertheless, as the evidence from this study and the parallel study shows, there is still a pressing need for change in many areas of medical careers if both men and women are to fulfil their potential in medicine and, at the same time, lead lives which are personally satisfying.

One of the main findings of the last study was that sheer weight of numbers is not enough. The argument that women will rise to the top simply because they account for 50 per cent of those entering the profession was not borne out by the facts. They might have accounted for increasing proportions of those entering the various grades of medicine, but they were still not represented in anything like the proportions expected if all other factors had been equal, as tables in *Health Trends* and the Report of the Joint Working Party on Women in Medicine have shown (Department of Health, 1991). There are clearly other factors at work, and one of the aims of the present study was to see how far these had been tackled in the five years since the last study and to examine what the effects had been. We also paid particular attention to looking at the future plans of the doctors and analysing the constraints they had encountered and those they perceived ahead. We drew extensively on the findings of the last study, making comparisons between the cohorts, and put our results in the context of other work we have carried out on the careers of young GPs (Allen, 1992) and staff grade doctors (Allen and Rolfe, 1994; SCOPME, 1994). The findings may not make comfortable reading for those who assume that slight adjustments to the present system are all that is needed for women to succeed in medicine. There are many indications in this report that change of a more fundamental nature is needed if the talents of all our doctors are to be maximised.

The changing profile of doctors
In the last report we drew attention to the differences between the three cohorts of doctors who qualified in 1966, 1976 and 1981 and were aged on average

around 43, 33 and 28 at the time that we interviewed them in 1986. The new cohort of doctors who qualified in 1986 were aged around 28 at the time of the follow-up study in 1991, and could be compared with the 1981 cohort in the last study.

We had observed in the last report that, although in many respects there were more differences between the cohorts than between the men and women within the cohorts, there was a marked difference between the men and women in the two older cohorts in terms of whether or not they had reached the career grades of consultant or GP principal. These were, and still are, the top jobs in medicine, and there was no doubt that the women who qualified in 1966 and 1976 were lagging far behind their male counterparts in terms of career achievement. The 1981 women were more or less level-pegging with the men at the time of the interviews in 1986, but there were ominous signs that this was not likely to continue, and the follow-up study of the 1976 and 1981 qualifiers carried out in parallel to the present study indicates that these signs were correct.

Perhaps the biggest difference between the men and women doctors in the last study was the extent to which the women were working, or had worked, less than full-time. Although nearly all the men in all three cohorts were working full-time, this was true of only just over half the 1966 women qualifiers, just over 40 per cent of the 1976 qualifiers and three-quarters of the 1981 qualifiers. The women had not dropped out of medicine – only 5 per cent of the women qualifiers from all three cohorts were not working at the time of the interviews – but a relatively high proportion were working less than full-time. In many cases, as we have observed so often in the course of our reports on doctors' careers, part-time working in medicine amounts to more than full-time working in most other occupations. Nevertheless, in terms of achievement, or of recognition as 'serious' doctors, part-time working in medicine is still regarded as a considerable handicap, and it is this issue more than any other which must be addressed if any real change in the contribution of women doctors is to be achieved.

Until the publication of the last report, it had largely been assumed that the main factors determining the contribution or participation rates of women doctors were domestic or family commitments, mainly characterised by marriage and children. We found last time that having children was indeed an important factor in determining whether women worked full-time or part-time, but that marriage alone was relatively unimportant. A much more important factor was the extent to which marriage interrelated with the need for geographical mobility which is such a dominating feature of medical careers. In the present study, we found that only one third of the women working part-time had children. There are many reasons for working part-time other than children, and the whole picture is not as simple as might have been thought when it was decided that part-time training opportunities should be restricted only to doctors with pressing domestic commitments.

In the present study we found that the proportion of 1986 qualifiers working full-time in clinical medicine was rather lower than that found among the 1981 qualifiers in the last study. The proportion of men working full-time in clinical medicine had dropped to 90 per cent from 99 per cent and the proportion of women from 73 per cent to 67 per cent. The proportion of men working part-time in clinical medicine had increased slightly while the proportion of women had remained the same at just under one fifth. However, the main increases were in the proportion of those on maternity leave and those not working at the time of the interview.

Some caution is necessary in interpreting the results, since the slight increase in the proportion on maternity leave could be related to the slightly later stage at which the 1986 cohort were interviewed compared with the 1981 qualifiers. Similarly, the increase in the proportion of those not working could be related to a slight increase in the numbers of those between jobs. Nevertheless, the fact that nearly 10 per cent of the women interviewed were not working at the time of the fieldwork should give some cause for concern. They were mainly intending to return to medicine, some within a matter of weeks, but there were indications that some had lost their way and were considering their prospects at an age when ambitious doctors knew that they had to keep both feet very firmly on the career ladder.

But it was clear that it was not only the women who were not working who had lost their way. Among both men and women in this study, as in the last study, there were examples of doctors who had not been able, or perhaps willing, to pursue a straight career path with no deviation. Some had been tempted into interesting sidelines, but others had been unable to succeed in particular specialties for a variety of reasons. There were many indications in the last study that doctors felt increasingly constrained in their careers by the need to follow a straight career path if they were to get anywhere, and that a straight career path was increasingly thought to entail the achievement of certain grades or stages by a certain age. We noted that this linking of age to grade in medical careers was a strong inhibiting factor to the careers of those whose progress might be slower than that of the high flyers, and that this was bound to include those who might reasonably take longer to achieve certain grades, if only because of part-time working, career breaks or late starts. Women doctors were likely to be disproportionately found among these doctors, and our evidence on the extent to which women were working or had worked part-time in medicine confirmed this.

One of the more disquieting findings of the present study was the extent to which the 1986 women qualifiers appeared to be falling behind the men five years after qualification to a rather greater extent than we found among the 1981 women, and, moreover, that they were less likely to be found in hospital medicine than the 1981 women at the same stage. We have advised caution in the interpretation of the figures, but nevertheless there were some indications that changes were afoot which might not augur well for increasing the representation of women in the top jobs in medicine.

Although we found that the proportion of women who were GP principals was much the same among the 1981 and 1986 cohorts at the time of the interviews (11 and 10 per cent respectively), the proportion of men GP principals had increased from 17 per cent of the 1981 qualifiers to 23 per cent of the 1986 qualifiers, meaning that the 1986 men were more than twice as likely as the women to have reached GP principal grade, although equal proportions of men and women were working in general practice at the time of the interviews. We did, however, also find that fewer 1986 qualifiers were working as SHOs as part of a GP vocational training scheme, so that the actual proportions of both men and women in the 1986 cohort who were currently either in general practice or on a GP vocational training scheme were lower than we found among the 1981 qualifiers in the last study.

We also found differences between the 1986 men and women qualifiers in hospital medicine, which, in some ways could be construed as of greater importance. Although in the last study we found that equal proportions of the 1981 men and women were working as senior registrars (2 per cent) and registrars (29 per cent), in the present study we found that 34 per cent of the 1986 men but only 17 per cent of the 1986 women were registrars, although the same proportions of both men and women had reached senior registrar level as we found among the 1981 qualifiers. We also found that the proportion of 1986 men working in hospital medicine (55 per cent) was similar to the proportion of 1981 men (59 per cent), whereas the proportion of 1986 women in hospital medicine (44 per cent) was well down on the 1981 figure for women, as well as being lower than that of the 1986 men.

What were the reasons for this apparent slowing of the achievement of women doctors in the 1986 cohort? Was it only a temporary phenomenon and would it change? The future plans of the doctors indicated that the vast majority intended to continue in medicine and wanted to achieve career grade, but there were many factors which were likely to affect these plans. Before we look in more detail at the constraints on the future careers of doctors of both sexes, it would be useful to look at some of the background to their present careers. How and why had they arrived where they were?

Home and school

In the last report we examined in some detail the family and school background of the different cohorts of doctors and their reasons for studying medicine. There had been marked changes in the profile of doctors, with far fewer qualifiers from the younger cohorts coming from independent boarding schools, fewer from medical families and increasing proportions with very good 'A' level results. There were also indications that women were more likely than men to have been strongly motivated towards studying medicine, particularly in the 1966 cohort, and to have made up their minds at an earlier stage that they wished to be doctors. However, there was clear evidence of a trend in the later cohorts, particularly among the men, of the qualifiers having decided to become doctors because they were good at science. We queried whether this was a particularly good basis for medical school entry, but concluded that it was probably no worse than being selected on the basis of excellence at sport or because of paternal influence.

There were many indications in the last report that the 1981 qualifiers were much more likely to be critical of the medical career system that they had entered, not only because they were at a stage in their careers when doctors have traditionally been overworked and dissatisfied, but also because many of them felt that they might be in the wrong jobs, felt 'trapped' in medicine and were unhappy about their present jobs and future prospects, particularly in comparison with their contemporaries outside medicine. The almost complete lack of careers advice on medicine at schools was compounded by misconceptions on the part of the students on the nature and implications of a medical career. Most doctors interviewed both for the last study and the present study had had little idea of what they were letting themselves in for when they started at medical school and the high level of regret found among the younger qualifiers was often a reflection of poor quality careers advice from home and school.

The trends noted in the last report continued among the 1986 qualifiers. They were almost as likely as the 1981 qualifiers to have studied medicine because they were good at science, but, more important, they were exceptionally good at science. The vast majority of the 1986 qualifiers had studied only science subjects at 'A' level, and their results were generally better than those of the 1981 qualifiers and considerably better than those of the 1976 qualifiers. But perhaps the most notable finding was the achievements at 'A' level of the women. 25 per cent of the 1986 women qualifiers had achieved three A grades or better in their 'A' levels, compared with 12 per cent of the 1986 men and 20 per cent of the 1981 men. The 1986 women were very high achievers in general, since over 40 per cent of them had achieved at least two As and a B at 'A' level. They were excellent mathematicians, with better results than the men. The mean scores of both men and women were higher among the 1986 qualifiers than among all their predecessors, and virtually none of them had achieved 10 points or less at 'A' level, compared with over a quarter of the 1976 men qualifiers.

There was an increase in the proportions of 1986 qualifiers attending state schools, and a particular increase in the proportions attending comprehensive schools, rising from 24 per cent of the 1981 men to 37 per cent of the 1986 men and from 22 per cent of the 1981 women to 36 per cent of the 1986 women. There was a marked decline over the years in the proportion of qualifiers attending independent boarding schools: from 29 per cent of the 1966 male qualifiers to only 8 per cent of the 1986 male qualifiers, and from 20 per cent of the 1966 women to 6 per cent of the 1986 women. There was no doubt at all that the schooling of the 1986 qualifiers more closely reflected that of their contemporaries in society at large than that of their older counterparts had done.

There was little difference between the qualifiers in their examination results related to their schooling. The 'A' level results of those attending state schools were very similar to those attending independent schools. In terms of academic achievement they were as likely to get into medical school. But this undoubtedly affected the profile of those entering the profession of medicine, and there can be little doubt that many of these more recent qualifiers were much less prepared, or able, to operate the traditional 'old boy' network referred to so often in the last report as being of enormous influence in career progression. It was quite apparent, in the course of our research, that we were beginning to see a certain clash of cultures, and it was by no means clear what kind of pattern would emerge in the future. There were, however, strong indications that being very clever and good at science at the age of 18 was no guarantee of continuing success in the competitive world of medicine.

The question arises of whether being good at science is necessarily a prerequisite for being a good doctor, or even whether good scientists make good – and happy – doctors. The 1986 qualifiers themselves were often not sure, but had usually felt there was little alternative. Most had not even considered the question at the time – 'Medical training was simply an extension of studying sciences ...' – but some had bitterly regretted it, and still did – 'It's a frightful price to pay for being good at science ...'

It may appear that there is a need to reconsider the selection of medical school students to ensure that people do not enter the medical profession just because they are good at science. Perhaps many of those who are good at science should become scientists and attributes other than academic excellence at 'A' level science should be taken more seriously by medical school selectors. It is possible that much of the regret and loss of confidence found among a substantial proportion of the 1986 women qualifiers was related to the fact that they had chosen the wrong career, and had found themselves unable to change direction.

There is also a pressing need to look at the careers advice given to young people considering a career in medicine. The advice from schools was generally agreed to be either non-existent or discouraging, and almost always ill-informed according to our respondents in both studies. It seems absurd that so many people enter medical school with so little real appreciation of what it entails. It costs nearly £200,000 to put a student through medical school, and such an investment should not be made on such little information.

Medical school

We have devoted some space to the background of the qualifiers since it had such far-reaching implications. But what about medical school? We found in the last report that careers advice at medical school was usually thought to be almost as limited as that at school, although there was evidence that the later qualifiers had access to rather more formal careers information in the form of careers fairs than the earlier cohorts. The situation had improved slightly among the 1986 qualifiers, but essentially they remained as critical as the earlier qualifiers about the careers advice received at medical school, if they had received any at all.

The main complaints about careers advice at medical school was that it was inadequate, inappropriate, not tailored to the personal requirements of the students, unrealistic about the demands of different specialties, and was particularly unsuitable for those who thought they might have made a mistake in studying medicine. There were widespread criticisms of a lack of a proper tutorial system, either to give personal support or for careers advice. But even if students knew that careers advice was available from tutors there was often a marked reluctance to take it up. There were disquieting comments from 1986 qualifiers from a range of medical schools that tutors were not seen as potential sources of advice on anything, let alone careers, and plentiful evidence that not all tutors were interested in their role. 'He was an anatomy demonstrator and didn't like contact with students, and it showed ...' was not an unusual observation and was not likely to lead to a full and frank exchange of views on future career prospects.

Many 1986 qualifiers, like their predecessors, got their careers advice informally, often on the job. This advice was mixed and patchy and rarely appeared related to the abilities and aptitudes of individual students. Respondents voiced their concern about the wisdom of admitting doubts or worries about future careers or courses of action to any member of staff, since it was generally perceived that this would be regarded as a sign of weakness. There was almost no discussion or advice on such important options as part-time training or part-time career posts in medicine, in spite of the fact that so many of the women were likely to work less than full-time at some point in their careers, and women accounted for around half the students in many of the medical schools at the time.

There were examples of encouraging role models at medical school, but, as we found in the last study, there were more examples of discouraging role models. These were to be found among surgeons in particular, and it must be a matter of concern that an even higher proportion of men and women in the present study than we found among the 1981 qualifiers said that they had been discouraged from surgery at medical school.

There was no evidence that the 1986 qualifiers were any less motivated and determined than any of their predecessors had been. However, what was clear was that they were perhaps more willing to express their discontent with a medical school system which apparently paid such little attention to the pastoral care of its students. The almost complete lack of evidence of a tutorial system which even approached the level found in most other university disciplines over the last fifty years was one of the marked features of these studies on doctors' careers. And yet medical students, particularly in their clinical years, were being exposed to stresses of a much greater magnitude and complexity than any likely to be encountered by students in other fields. We have observed before, like other commentators, that teaching by 'humiliation' appears to be relatively common in medical schools. This, combined with a lack of support from a well-developed tutorial system, is not conducive to reducing stress and enabling medical students to make well-informed and positive decisions about their future careers.

There were signs that women were more diffident than men at medical school about their future prospects, and the quotes from women in this report expressing concern that they were not clever enough to do hospital medicine, their feelings of insecurity in the face of their treatment by consultants, and their lack of confidence in their abilities can often only be construed as indictments of a system which does not recognise or develop the talents of such intelligent young women. It should be recognised that not everyone survives unscathed in a system where consultants are seen as people with 'killer ambitions', 'god-like creatures' and 'not very nice people', characterised by 'rigidity, lack of feeling and narrow-mindedness ...' Perhaps it was little wonder that so many career decisions made at medical school appeared to be taken negatively rather than positively, based on unpleasant encounters rather than a rational assessment of possible options.

There was a steady increase in the proportion of respondents over the years who thought that women were treated differently from men at medical school, and, although we heard fewer accounts of straightforward sexist remarks and blatant discrimination, it was still apparently commonplace for women medical students to be subjected to comments from staff which would have been regarded as totally unacceptable in other circumstances and which could only have been interpreted as discriminatory under the legislation. Many of the men found this type of behaviour intolerable, and there were signs that this younger generation of men were less prepared to take for granted a culture in which so many exceptionally well-qualified young women were left feeling undermined by their treatment at medical school.

The strong recommendation given in the last report by qualifiers from all cohorts that there was a need for a more sensitive, systematic and focused approach to the personal and career needs of medical students was reinforced by the 1986 qualifiers. The last report was published after these respondents had left medical school. It is to be hoped that many of the recommendations have now been implemented. There is compelling evidence from these studies that lack of support at medical school has far-reaching implications for the careers of both men and women doctors.

Life in the postgraduate years

The 1986 qualifiers had been more likely than their predecessors to have had some idea of what specialty they wished to pursue at entry to medical school. Many of these had changed their minds by the time they qualified, but again the 1986 qualifiers were more likely than their predecessors to have had a specific career intention at qualification. Again, a relatively high proportion changed their minds in the pre-registration year, but fewer of the 1986 qualifiers were opting for general practice at registration than we had found among the 1981 qualifiers at that stage.

The pre-registration year had not been a happy experience for many doctors, with special criticism reserved for house jobs in teaching hospitals, which, although recognised as being important for ambitious doctors, had had the effect of putting others off hospital medicine. The 1986 qualifiers were more articulate than any other cohort about their dislike at all stages of their careers of being undervalued. The descriptions of the experience of doctors in pre-registration jobs in teaching hospitals – 'treated like clerks' or 'little ants at the bottom of the heap' or 'underdogs', in an atmosphere characterised by 'back-stabbing' and 'boot-licking', were not unusual. They were echoed by descriptions of life in later posts, as we shall see, and such comments should be taken seriously by those who are concerned about morale in the medical profession. We have noted that it is probable that young doctors are less and less willing to accept a culture in which such a hierarchical structure is acceptable, and that there is an increasing desire among young doctors to be recognised as professionals rather than 'dogs-bodies'.

By the time we interviewed them four years after registration, only 60 per cent of the men and less than half the women were still in the same specialty they had chosen at registration. This highlights the danger of making assumptions about career intentions or changes from early statements of intent. Doctors' careers do not usually follow a neat pattern, and specialty intentions even at registration may not always be a real guide to what actually happens. Medical manpower planning has to take into account many other factors which may affect the careers of doctors. One of the most important factors in present-day terms is the extent to which women are likely to want to work less than full-time at some point in their careers. Since women now account for half those entering the medical profession, this is perhaps more important than statements about career or specialty intention at registration or any other time.

However, there is little doubt that early career decisions speed up career progression, and that those who had decided on a specialty at registration, and stuck to it, had made faster progress up the career ladder than those who had not. The perceived stress on progress linked to age and grade remains a formidable force in medicine, and, with the implementation of the Calman Report (Department of Health, 1993), it is possible that there may be even less room for manoeuvre.

All this underlines the importance of good careers advice, information and counselling which has been a recurrent theme in these reports. It is as important at the postgraduate stage as at medical school, and it remains important throughout postgraduate training. 1986 qualifiers who had found it difficult to settle on a specialty at an early stage of their careers appeared to be finding it more difficult than others to get satisfactory posts.

There were indications in this study, not found in the earlier study, of some doctors who were feeling rather lost, in that they were not pursuing a training programme which was leading anywhere. Although there have always been doctors who do not reach the heights in medicine, it must be questioned whether the investment made in doctors is always wisely husbanded. The strong demand made by an overwhelming majority of the 1986 qualifiers for more structured training programmes, both in terms of rotations and content, was indicative of a need for more closely supervised and supportive postgraduate training. It is to be hoped that this will be a result of the implementation of the Calman recommendations.

And yet, in spite of the undoubted discontent felt by many 1986 qualifiers, both at the time of the interview and in the immediate postgraduate years, less than a handful had left medicine. Of those who were not working at the time of the study, all but one definitely intended to return to medicine. As we found in the last study, it was impossible to discern a pattern in the reasons given by the doctors who were not working at the time of the research. Some were between jobs, some were deciding what to do, some were studying, but only a tiny number were taking time out to bring up children. As we remarked last time, there is no evidence that there is a pool of non-working UK-qualified doctors who can be called upon to fill any gaps. Doctors in this country are mostly working, or lost to medicine forever. But perhaps half the women are likely to be working less than full-time, particularly in their thirties. The most important point is to ensure that those who are working are satisfied and secure in their work so that their contribution can be maximised. This means that part-time or less than full-time working must be accorded the same status as full-time working.

Personal patronage and equality of opportunity

In the last report we had been surprised to find that personal patronage was still regarded as such an important factor in careers advancement in medicine. It was regarded as even more important by the 1981 qualifiers than by older generations, although there was evidence that many of them deplored a system which they regarded as secretive, unfair, related to the 'old-boy' network and liable to perpetuate systems which they regarded as archaic. It was thought to flourish in a structure where constant moves among junior doctors in the early stages of their careers were regarded as necessary and where structured training programmes were not usually the norm. More important, perhaps, the system was thought to favour 'conventional people with conventional careers', which many respondents thought was likely to disadvantage women who were less able than most men to lead conventional careers.

In the present study we found that patronage was still thought to be alive and well and an integral part of medical careers. It was still accorded importance by the 1986 qualifiers, although slightly less than we found among the 1981 qualifiers, and the 1986 qualifiers were a little more likely to approve of it as a system, although there was evidence that some were very much attracted by the idea that someone might be interested in them 'as people' and offer them encouragement and support, rather than approving of the idea of personal patronage in itself.

There were some indications in the present study that patronage was not only thought to be less widely extended to women, but that it was more likely to be confined to 'white middle-class men', a disturbing underlining of other remarks by 1986 qualifiers implying that the medical profession was not completely free from racism.

There were some interesting shifts in the practice of patronage, according to the 1986 respondents. The patronage of professors, which had been a feature of the careers of the 1966 qualifiers, had dwindled considerably, while that of male consultants was by far the most important. Women were rarely mentioned as patrons and seemed to have hardly emerged either as role models or as helpful contacts and mentors in the competitive world of medical careers.

We have noted before that the 1986 qualifiers, both men and women, appeared to express more acute needs for personal encouragement and support than earlier generations. This was apparent in many parts of the interviews, but was particularly evident in some of the discussions about positive and 'negative' patrons. There was general acceptance, however, that the system of patronage tended to reinforce a continuation of certain behaviour patterns among young doctors who felt that the best way to get on, particularly in hospital medicine, was to gain the support of certain powerful figures, who were easily identified and recognised as influential in their field. Women undoubtedly felt themselves to be at a disadvantage in this system, particularly if they were not able to guarantee that they would continue to work full-time with the same single-mindedness and dedication expected of ambitious young men.

We would query again the widespread acceptance of a system which perpetuates practices which could be interpreted as contrary to equal opportunities legislation, both in the spirit and in the letter of the law. There appears to be a need for vigilance on the part of those making appointments that fairness is seen to prevail and that unsolicited oral references are recognised as being out of order. It is to be hoped that the restructuring of specialist training helps to eradicate a system which is both inequitable and potentially discriminatory.

But the continuation of patronage was by no means the only matter for concern in the implementation of equal opportunities in medical careers. We had found in the last study evidence of employment and recruitment practices which were completely out of line with current legislation. Questions about personal circumstances and private lives were being asked at job interviews of women and not of men. Some of the questions were seen by both men and women as personally intrusive and bearing no relevance to their ability to do the jobs for which they were being interviewed. There were indications that medicine appeared to have been caught in a kind of time-warp, with attitudes allowed to be expressed at interviews which had long been controlled in other areas, particularly in public and statutory bodies, among which the National Health Service is one of the largest employers.

We found in the present study that, although there had been a fairly marked decline in the proportion of 1986 women reporting that they had been asked at job interviews whether they intended to have children, the question had still been asked of 40 per cent of the women compared with only 6 per cent of the men. We also found that women were more likely than men to be asked what arrangements they would make for the care of their children, whether they had any or not. In all these cases, the fact that the questions were asked of women but not of men was clearly discriminatory, but it must also be asked what kind of interpretation was put on the answers. This is almost as important as asking the questions of one sex and not the other.

In addition we found that both men and women had been asked a wide variety of questions about their personal lives and circumstances which might have been interpreted as potentially discriminatory. There were some interesting legal points here. For example, it appeared that when men were asked if they were married or likely to get married, an affirmative answer was regarded as desirable in general practice as indicative of a stable kind of person. On the other hand, an affirmative answer from a woman was thought to signal a danger that she might be contemplating having a baby, with all the problems surrounding maternity leave which were said to inhibit the appointment of women as partners in general practice.

The fact that questions at interview must be seen to be equitable and fair seemed to have passed by many of those interviewing the 1986 doctors for jobs in some areas of medicine, and it is undoubtedly too soon to be complacent about the extent to which equal opportunities legislation and recognised codes of practice have been fully adopted within the medical profession.

It was interesting that the proportion of 1986 women qualifiers who thought that they had failed to get a job because of their sex had actually doubled from that found among the 1981 women qualifiers. However, we asked the men the same question in the present study and were surprised to find that almost exactly the same proportion of men thought that they had failed to get a job because of their sex. These posts were mainly at GP principal level and the finding was thought to reflect the growing demand for women GPs among patients.

The proportion of 1986 qualifiers who did not consider themselves to be of white ethnic origin was higher than that found among previous cohorts, accounting for 10 per cent of the men and 7 per cent of the women. Only a tiny proportion of doctors thought they had failed to get a job because of their ethnic origin and, interestingly, included some doctors of white ethnic origin but with foreign-sounding names. It was impossible to generalise from the experience of so few doctors, but there were hints of racial discrimination in the medical profession which were deplored, as we have seen, in other comments by 1986 qualifiers.

Constraints on careers

We found in the last report that, although marriage and more often children were thought to be important constraints on the careers of women doctors, these domestic commitments were thought to be of less importance by younger doctors than the combination of factors which included the need for constant geographical mobility among young doctors. This was thought to be particularly difficult for married doctors, and the difficulties were not thought to be confined to women. The majority of wives of the young men doctors were working, often in professional occupations which did not lend themselves easily to constant uprooting. The constraints imposed both on medical careers and on family or personal lives by the demands of geographical mobility in medical careers cannot be underestimated, and this finding was forcibly underlined in our study on *Part-time Working in General Practice*. The problems were compounded when doctors were in marriages or relationships with other doctors. We have observed in all our studies the terrible strain which can be put on relationships when two young doctors are forced to live apart because of the demands of their careers.

There should be recognition that dual career families are now the norm rather than the exception and that if doctors of both sexes are to live reasonably satisfactory home lives, there must be increasing acceptance that the 'nomadic' style of life traditionally expected of junior doctors is not suited to the demands of young people today. This was reinforced in the present study by the emerging phenomenon of 'negative equity' and the great difficulty experienced by some doctors in moving home because they could not afford to do so. Perhaps it should be asked how necessary it is for so many doctors to move so often and so far.

We should not dismiss the constraints imposed on doctors' careers by having children. It was found to be a major constraint on the careers of the two older cohorts of women in the last study, although some found it difficult to disentangle whether it was having children or the consequent part-time working which had had the greater effect. However, for many women in the 1981 cohort last time and the 1986 cohort in the present study, the question of constraints imposed by children was somewhat academic, since only 14 per cent of the 1981 women and 18 per cent of the 1986 women qualifiers had children at the time of the interviews. It could be argued that the fact that over 80 per cent of these young women in their late twenties had no children could indicate some fear on their part that having children would act as a constraint on their careers, as indeed it did.

But, as we found in the last report, the biggest constraint on doctors' careers was thought to be the long hours and the on-call responsibilities. The proportion of 1986 qualifiers who reported this as a constraint on their careers had increased markedly over the proportion found among the 1981 qualifiers, who themselves had complained bitterly about fatigue and exploitation. It must be a cause for considerable concern that it was mentioned as a career constraint by over half the 1986 men and nearly three-quarters of the 1986 women qualifiers. Although the Department of Health has tackled the question of junior doctors' hours since the fieldwork for this study was completed and has introduced a reduction in hours, both of on-call and working responsibilities, there was clearly a pressing need for action.

Although previous generations of doctors have traditionally worked long hours, it is generally agreed that the demands on junior doctors have increased in the past few years. There is no reason to believe that the 1986 cohort of qualifiers were less tough and determined than their predecessors, but there were many examples of interviews with doctors who were quite literally at the end of their tether, as noted both by the author and by the interviewers who had worked on the last study. In reading the interviews there was absolutely no doubt that these were the outpourings of people under considerable stress, both men and women. These young doctors had gone into medicine with such bright hopes, and yet their comments on the question of hours and on-call working were peppered with remarks like 'it destroys you as a person' and 'it doesn't make you a balanced person' and 'it wrecks the best years of your life' and 'it's hard to maintain a relationship when you keep falling asleep all the time. It's considered boring ...' These were not odd one-off comments but represented the majority of 1986 qualifiers.

Perhaps it was not surprising that some doctors were determined to do anything other than work in hospital medicine, and perhaps it was not surprising that some were finding it difficult to pass their higher professional examinations. We found that among the other constraints mentioned by doctors, an increasing number were related to inability to study or pass examinations. We found doctors who had never failed an exam in their lives puzzled by their failure in examinations at this stage. Reading the accounts some gave of their working commitments and lack of study leave we sometimes wondered how any of them passed higher professional qualifications.

Again, we felt that many of the problems which were besetting so many of these doctors could have been ameliorated, if not removed, by the provision of counselling from independent sources in the postgraduate years. Much was needed in the form of careers advice and counselling, but we felt that in some cases, there was an urgent need for the provision of stress counselling, to help these young professionals to cope with the onerous and relentless responsibilities that many were having to bear, often with inadequate support from colleagues and under working conditions which some could only describe as primitive.

SHOs have recently been described as 'The Lost Tribes' (British Medical Journal, 1993), and the papers given at a conference of this title reinforced much of the evidence collected in the present report. There is clearly a need to monitor more closely what is happening to all junior doctors so that the country does not lose more of them.

Part-time working

The last report indicated that there was considerable support for an increase in the provision of part-time training posts in medicine. The support was overwhelming among women, rising to 88 per cent of the 1981 cohort, and two-thirds of the men from all three cohorts also supported it. Among the 1986 qualifiers, the support was almost universal, with 98 per cent of women and 87 per cent of men in favour of more part-time training opportunities.

But to what extent had the doctors taken advantage of the various schemes designed to facilitate part-time training in medicine? The answer was that only 5 per cent of the 1986 women had ever had part-time training posts and only 3 per cent were currently in part-time training posts. This was considerably lower than we found among the 1966 women qualifiers, and even though the 1986 qualifiers were at an earlier stage in their careers, there were indications that they were following the trend noted in the report of the working party on flexible training (NHSME, 1993) of decreasing take-up of part-time training posts. What were the reasons for this apparent decline in demand at a time when the interest in part-time training opportunities was at an all-time high?

The main message which emerged from the questions about various schemes designed to facilitate part-time training in medicine was how little doctors of both sexes knew about them, with two thirds of the 1986 women and a rather lower proportion of the men saying that they had never heard of the PM(79)3 scheme, the main scheme for part-time training opportunities for senior registrars, and even more saying they had never heard of the schemes for part-time training opportunities for registrars and SHOs. Even when doctors had heard of the schemes they stressed how difficult they found it to get information about them, and, once they had found out about them, how difficult they found it to go through the processes of getting a part-time training post. Most of those who had heard of the schemes had little idea of what they were, how they worked and how they could gain access to them.

This did not mean that the demand for part-time training opportunities was not there, but what it did mean was that a low take-up may have a great deal to do with factors other than lack of demand. The question of supply is clearly the most important factor, and there is general agreement that part-time training opportunities are relatively limited. In addition, they are usually supernumerary, the procedures for gaining access to them at senior registrar level are generally thought to be difficult and time-consuming, with no guarantee of a post or funding once central manpower approval has been granted, and criticisms have been voiced that the competition only takes place once a year. At registrar level, in which 5 per cent of career registrar manpower approvals are reserved for flexible training in each specialty group, there has been a relatively low take-up, particularly in some regions.

But in the eyes of the respondents to these studies on doctors' careers, including the present study, perhaps the two most important inhibiting factors were the lack of publicity or information about part-time or flexible training schemes and, most important, the perception that part-time, or less than full-time, or flexible training was in some way second-class and not to be indulged in by 'serious' or 'proper' doctors. It was thought to be a risk even to mention any idea of part-time training unless it was the only possible option, and consultants were thought to frown upon part-time training, with a few notable exceptions.

Respondents from all years agreed that little would change in the development of more part-time training opportunities unless attitudes among senior members of the profession changed. Young doctors considered it too much of a risk to seek part-time training unless they had no alternative. The implementation of the Calman Report recommendations, with the considerable shortening of the time to be spent in postgraduate training, will undoubtedly make things easier for many doctors, both male and female, but it would be unrealistic to assume that it will remove the need for the provision of more flexible or part-time training opportunities. It is perhaps surprising that there is no recommendation in *Training for Specialist Practice* (Annex C to the Calman Report) (Department of Health, 1993) on part-time training requirements. If women are not to be lost to hospital medicine, more such training posts should be made available. And, indeed, there are many arguments, heard not least from the 1986 men qualifiers, that such opportunities should be extended more readily to men and that the requirement to demonstrate overriding domestic commitments should be removed. The recommendation to this effect from the report of the Royal College of Physicians on *Part-time Work in Specialist Medicine* (1994) is to be welcomed.

The Joint Working Party on Flexible Training (NHSME, 1993) made a number of recommendations designed to facilitate an increase in part-time training opportunities, together with targets and requirements for the monitoring of the schemes. It remains to be seen how these recommendations are implemented. The Department of Health is now committed to the expansion of the numbers of part-time training posts to 5 per cent of the total, but it appears unlikely that this will satisfy demand.

The 1986 qualifiers were almost as keen on the provision of more part-time career posts as they were on an increase in part-time training opportunities. 97 per cent of the women and 79 per cent of the men supported an increase in part-time career posts, and again, there were many indications that such posts were not only being sought for domestic or family reasons. The Department of Health's provision of three-year funding for more part-time consultant posts (EL(93)39) was vastly over-subscribed, and it is likely that more applications would have been received if the funding period had been longer.

It is not surprising that so many women wanted more part-time career grade opportunities. Most of these young women wished to stay in medicine and most were very reluctant to abandon the idea of reaching career grade in medicine. They had assumed that they would have equal status with their male colleagues and they did not want to give up this idea. However, in analysing their future plans, a high proportion saw themselves as working less than full-time in clinical medicine in five years' time. To be able to fulfil this ambition there was clearly a need, not only for more part-time training opportunities, but also for more part-time career posts. Many of these women saw themselves in general practice in five years' time, and there was an overwhelming demand for more part-time GP principal posts, with easier access to them.

We noted that the problem was often circular. If more part-time opportunities were available and part-time working were more common, there might be fewer objections to it. But as long as it remains the exception to the norm, and as long as it is regarded as second-class and only adopted by doctors who are not able to give 100 per cent commitment, it will remain outside the mainstream of medicine, and women doctors who work less than full-time will continue to find it more difficult to realise their full potential.

We returned to the question we had explored in the last study of career grade posts in hospital medicine other than those of consultant grade. In this study we wanted to examine the views of the 1986 respondents on the staff grade, which had been introduced since the publication of our last report, and on the associate specialist grade, both of which were potentially useful to women – and men – who did not wish to take on the full responsibilities of the consultant grade.

We found that reaction to the staff grade was mixed, and that although just over half of both men and women 1986 qualifiers thought it a useful grade, one third did not, while others found it difficult to comment. Rather higher proportions of both men and women found the associate specialist grade a useful grade, although there was widespread evidence of a misunderstanding of the functions and status of both grades. It should be noted that the main criticisms of the staff grade were that it was a dead-end job and perceived to have second-class status. This confirms fears expressed by staff grade doctors in other studies we have conducted (Allen and Rolfe, 1994; SCOPME, 1994).

Although some 10 per cent of the 1986 men and 25 per cent of the 1986 women said that they themselves would like a career grade post without the full range of consultant responsibilities, there was by no means agreement that a staff grade post would fit their requirements. Both men and women were more likely to think that an associate specialist post would suit them, but, again, we found that many doctors appeared unaware of what an associate specialist was.

We concluded that, although there was a strong undercurrent of demand for career grade posts in hospital without the full range of consultant responsibilities, neither the staff grade nor the associate specialist grade appeared to represent the ideal grade for the relatively young UK qualifiers seeking hospital career grade posts other than consultant posts, indicating that some further refinement and thought about the nature and status of such posts might be desirable.

Specific issues in training
We asked specific questions in this study about shift working and about structured training programmes, in response to a request by the Department of Health. We found that some two-thirds of the respondents had worked a shift or partial shift system, usually in Accident and Emergency. Two-thirds of the doctors said that they preferred a shift system to the present rota arrangements for training posts in medicine, but it was interesting that nearly three-quarters of the women expressed this view compared with just under 60 per cent of the men. The women did seem to suffer more from the present rota arrangements than the men, although it was quite clear that neither men nor women found them acceptable and the preference for a shift system of some kind was held by the majority of 1986 qualifiers, many of whom had nothing but criticism of the conditions and potential dangers in the present rota arrangements.

We also found that the vast majority of 1986 qualifiers much preferred structured training programmes, with pre-determined rotations, to training programmes without such rotations. In this case, nearly 90 per cent of the men were in favour compared with three-quarters of the women. This was against a background in which only around half the qualifiers had had a structured training programme at SHO level, whereas over two-thirds of those who had had registrar training had had such a structured programme.

The main reasons for preferring structured training programmes were the geographical security and stability offered and the assurance that the training would be comprehensive and complete. We noted that the quest for geographical stability and security had been a marked feature of this research among doctors. There was undoubted evidence that constant moving around took its toll on the personal, emotional and working lives of many young doctors, and, in addition, contributed to a structure in which there were a number of able and talented doctors 'wandering' around the system adding to the 'lost tribes'.

There was certainly support among over 90 per cent of 1986 qualifiers for a structured training programme in terms of educational content, and again we found that only around half of those interviewed felt that their training had been structured to cover the full educational content necessary.

There was a considerable amount of evidence in the present study of the 1986 qualifiers being much more aware than their predecessors of their professional status and the fact that they were doctors in training. Concerns were frequently expressed about being used as 'dogs-bodies' and 'workhorses' and 'another pair of hands'. These doctors often referred to the fact that they were supposed to be training and voiced fears that their educational programmes were often treated as secondary to their service commitments, some of which they felt could be carried out by other staff.

Many criticisms were made of both the structure and content of the training programmes the 1986 qualifiers had experienced, and there was clear evidence that many of these doctors felt their training had been too haphazard. There was a recommendation that more supervision and monitoring was needed, both of the performance of doctors in training and of those who were teaching them.

Opportunities for women doctors

We have already seen that the 1986 qualifiers were much more likely than earlier cohorts to think that there should be an increase in part-time training and career grade opportunities. It could be argued that such increased opportunities could be useful to both men and women. What about increased opportunities specifically for women? We found a big increase among doctors in this study in the proportion of both men and women who thought that more should be done by the NHS or medical profession to help women doctors.

The increase was very marked, even over the two younger cohorts studied last time. For example, we found that as many as 92 per cent of the 1986 men and 98 per cent of the 1986 women thought that more should be done to help women doctors continue working while they had small children, compared with just over 70 per cent of the men and 85 per cent of the women from the 1976 and 1981 cohorts. We found that 82 per cent of the 1986 men and 91 per cent of the women thought that more should be done to help women who wanted to return to medicine after a break with opportunities for rising to senior positions, compared with around 70 per cent of the men and 80 per cent of the women in the 1976 and 1981 cohorts.

The near universal support for more help for women doctors to keep working was rather unexpected, but we noted that it did reinforce other evidence in the present report that the issue of equal opportunities for women doctors was seen increasingly as an issue in its own right rather than as an issue only for women. The main recommendation made by both men and women was the increased provision of creche facilities, which were thought to be woefully inadequate, followed by more part-time training posts, part-time career posts and job-sharing posts.

The question of creche facilities was not often well thought-out in practical terms, particularly in view of the long and anti-social hours worked by many doctors, but it was seen by most doctors as the only solution to what was seen as increasing difficulty in gaining access to suitable and affordable child care facilities. The fact was that the 1986 women with children were much less likely than their predecessors to have live-in help, and were more likely to report problems in child care, possibly reflecting a more general shortage of good child care facilities against an increasing demand as more women work outside the home. There were also a number of comments on the problems encountered in access to maternity leave by doctors, partly in view of their short contracts in so many training posts and partly because of the arrangements in general practice.

We found that increasing proportions of men and women doctors thought that more should be done to enhance the career prospects for women doctors in general – a rise from 70 per cent of the 1981 to three-quarters of the 1986 men and from 81 per cent of the 1981 women to 91 per cent of the 1986 women qualifiers. There was a general consensus among both men and women that it was a waste of resources to ignore the fact that women had special needs. Many respondents thought that it was unwise for the medical profession and the NHS to continue to organise the medical career structure with the assumption that most doctors would follow a traditional career path, and that anything other than full-time working was unusual and outside the norm.

We asked our respondents to make practical suggestions on what could be done by certain key individuals or organisations concerned with doctors' careers, and found again that many doctors were very hazy about the actual roles and responsibilities of many of these people who had enormous influence both over the future direction of the medical career structure and over the ways in which the talents of all doctors could be utilised. We were concerned at the lack of knowledge among these young doctors about important sources of information and advice both on their own careers and on the medical career structure in general. This was by no means confined to the question of women doctors' careers.

We found that better careers advice, information and counselling were advocated but these were often closely linked to recommendations for more part-time or job-sharing opportunities. It is becoming increasingly apparent that there is an inextricable link between good careers advice and counselling and an increase in good flexible working opportunities in medicine. This is becoming increasingly true for both men and women, and many doctors felt that a review of the whole medical career structure was the only way in which both men and women doctors could achieve their full potential while retaining their sanity.

There does seem to be an urgent need to make it explicit who is responsible for each aspect of postgraduate training, not only so that doctors can find it easier to gain access to proper advice and counselling on their careers but also to ensure that job opportunities are more closely matched to demand.

Careers advice, information and counselling

Throughout this report and throughout this discussion of findings we have reported the pressing need for better careers advice, information and counselling for doctors at all stages from school to medical school to postgraduate training and beyond. It could be argued that doctors should not really have to be spoon-fed and that they, like people in other occupations, should be able to find out for themselves what they want to do and determine the best ways of going about achieving their goals.

This may well be true of those doctors who decide at an early stage what they want to do, are not deterred by any subsequent experience and are helped in achieving their ambitions by a good training programme, helpful patrons and mentors, and, of course, shining abilities in their chosen specialty. It may well also be true of others who are not aiming to fly so high but settle for a particular career path in a specialty in which they are happy. But there do appear to be a number of important factors which inhibit the easy accessing of information, advice and counselling for many doctors, including those who are uncertain about which specialty they want to pursue, those who wish to work less than full-time at some point, and those who may wish to gain experience in more than one specialty before making up their minds.

It has been quite clear throughout these studies that doctors who do not pursue straight career paths, or even express doubts about which way to go, are in danger of being branded as 'unsound' in some way. This appears to be one of the major factors in preventing doctors from seeking careers advice unless they are desperate. At the same time, it appears that the present unstructured system of giving careers advice means that matching supply to demand continues to be haphazard.

We asked specific questions in the present study about the nature and type of careers advice received by the 1986 qualifiers in the postgraduate years and asked them for their recommendations for improving postgraduate careers advice. We found that one third of the 1986 qualifiers said that they had received no careers advice in the postgraduate years since they qualified as doctors. There was little difference between men and women, but doctors in general practice were less likely to have had advice than those in hospital medicine. By far the most frequently mentioned source of careers advice was a consultant, and, by definition, most of these consultants were men. Most doctors had only received careers advice from one source.

The men usually found the careers advice more helpful than the women, the advice was generally found to be at least fairly accurate, but only just over half the doctors had found it encouraging. Among the third of 1986 qualifiers who had not had careers advice, nearly two-thirds would have liked some.

There was thought to be a general need for improved careers advice in the postgraduate years, with special emphasis on increased availability and easier access to independent advice, to compulsory meetings with seniors, formal assessments and feedback on performance and prospects at every stage, and a general demand for more one-to-one personal careers counselling from someone who was well-informed. There was clearly some tension between the demands for better contact with a supervising consultant and the demands for independent counselling from someone who knew all the options but would not divulge any doubts and fears of the doctors to their 'bosses'.

Regrets and isolation

The evident isolation of so many doctors has been a recurrent theme in these studies. It was particularly marked in general practice (Allen, 1992), but it was found at all levels and in all specialties among both men and women, both in the present study and in the last study. The demand for better careers counselling often masked demands for more counselling and support in general. Being a doctor, whether in general practice or in hospital medicine, can often mean a lonely and isolated existence, particularly when there is no accepted culture of sharing doubts and fears, not only about careers but about personal relationships, the nature of the job and the stresses of dealing with death and illness.

We found it disquieting in the last study that the proportion of doctors who had regretted their decision to study medicine increased proportionately over the cohorts, with the trend clearly marked among both men and women, rising from 14 per cent of the 1966 men to 44 per cent of the 1981 men and from 19 per cent of the 1966 women to 49 per cent of the 1981 women. We found a dramatic steepening of the curve to 58 per cent of the 1986 men and 76 per cent of the 1986 women.

The malaise among the 1986 women qualifiers has been evident throughout the present study, but it should not disguise the discontent among the men as well. Although far fewer doctors said that they currently regretted their decision to study medicine, there were many indications that both men and women felt that the demands of medical careers were far too great. Even successful male high flyers spoke of the sacrifices they had made – 'my social life, my youth ...'

– while women frequently spoke of their fatigue and depression – 'It's knocked every bit of enthusiasm out of me. I feel I'd like to give up, but I don't know any other trade ...'

Perhaps, in view of the level of discontent expressed throughout these interviews, it was not surprising that nearly half the 1986 qualifiers had thought of leaving medicine, but it was of particular concern that this represented nearly 60 per cent of the women compared with 40 per cent of the men. Only 2 per cent of the qualifiers had already left medicine and under 10 per cent of those interviewed thought it was even fairly likely that they would leave medicine. Most doctors were going to stay with it. Some clearly loved their jobs, found them interesting and were happy and successful in their careers. Others were finding life easier once they had got through the first SHO years, while others were beginning to come to terms with the demands of medicine. But a substantial minority of others, including quite a number of doctors who had little to show in terms of achievement in grade or status, were unclear of what else they might do – 'There are not many things doctors can do. We're not trained to do anything else ...'

The future

The focus of this study was on the medical profession and the extent to which constraints are imposed on the careers of women doctors which may prevent them from maximising their contribution to medicine and from fulfilling their own potential. Like our previous study it has shown that many of the constraints suffered by women doctors are also reported by men doctors, but that the effects may be more significant in terms of career progress and achievement for the women.

It could be argued that some of the findings of this research which report low morale, threatened professionalism, feelings of isolation and uncertainty, and particular problems for women, would be replicated in studies of other occupations and professions. There are undoubtedly current similarities to be found. But, as we have pointed out throughout the report and in this discussion of findings, there are certain customs and practice which make medicine different from other professions and occupations. Some of these are structural, for example the unusually long period of postgraduate training, the excessively long hours, the conditions of service, the requirement for frequent geographical mobility and the type of work. But others are more subtle differences, often related to the tradition in medicine of learning the craft on the job and observing clearly recognised hierarchical conventions which may seem curiously out of place in the modern world but which young doctors challenge at their own risk.

Society is changing and the role and status of the medical profession within it is also changing. There were many indications in the present study that the 1986 qualifiers reflected the society in which they had been brought up more closely than their predecessors had done. And yet, at the same time, they were being subjected to more challenges than their predecessors in terms of perceived increased demands from both government and patients. They were extremely articulate in their comments about the drawbacks of the medical career structure and their working conditions, but often appeared unable to sort out how best to change their situation.

We found that the 1986 men on the whole were more likely than the women to think that they had had a successful career in medicine so far. But both men and women 1986 qualifiers were less satisfied with their present jobs than their 1981 counterparts had been, and even among those who were satisfied with their jobs there were many criticisms of various aspects of their working conditions, including lack of stability and support.

Looking to the future, we found that 93 per cent of the 1986 men but only 41 per cent of the 1986 women qualifiers thought that they would be working full-time in clinical medicine in five years' time. This meant that the proportion was destined to drop from 78 per cent of the 1986 qualifiers working full-time in clinical medicine in 1991 to 65 per cent in 1996. We have observed that it is this prediction which should be examined closely by those involved in medical manpower planning. It is possible that not everyone would be able to do what they planned to do, but it is clearly essential that planning at a macro level should take account of what people are planning to do at an individual level. The last study and the parallel study to this report shows that nearly half the women doctors ten years after qualification were working less than full-time.

We have seen that the 1986 women qualifiers were not planning to leave medicine in any numbers but they were planning to work less than full-time, and this has to be taken into account when looking at the future contribution of all doctors, not only women. There is obviously an imperative that the best possible use is made of the talents of the doctors who are not going to be working full-time. It is therefore increasingly important to ensure that part-time or less than full-time jobs have the same status and level of responsibility as full-time jobs. There is no longer room for complacency about the nature and content of these part-time jobs, since, if the plans of the women doctors in this study are to be fulfilled, they will account for an increasing proportion of medical jobs.

At the moment, the majority of those who thought they would be working less than full-time thought they would be in general practice. This not only reflects the supposition that it would be easier to find less than full-time jobs in general practice, but also underlines the difficulty these women thought they would have in working part-time in hospital medicine, both in training and in career grade posts. The fact that the 1986 women were much less likely than their 1981 counterparts to be working in registrar posts or in hospital medicine in general suggests that the flight of women from hospital medicine was already underway. This must be a matter for concern if women are to succeed in hospital medicine and if hospital medicine itself is not to lose the talents of women doctors. In *Part-time Working in General Practice*, we found that 25 per cent of the women GPs entering general practice in the 1980s would have stayed in hospital medicine if part-time training opportunities had been more readily available. The present study suggests that the same factors were determining the choices of the 1986 women qualifiers in the early 1990s, even though many were concerned about the effects of the GP contract on their careers.

Since we published the last study on *Doctors and their Careers*, there have been a number of key reports on different aspects of the medical career structure which have made important recommendations on the organisation of medical manpower and training which will bring about much-needed change. However, it should still be asked whether any one report has brought together and analysed some of the stark features identified in this report and others, many of which rest on simple arithmetic and the matching of supply and demand.

The profile of medical manpower has changed dramatically over the past ten years. 50 per cent of those entering the medical profession are women, and the proportion of women medical qualifiers has been over 40 per cent since the mid-1980s. All the available research indicates that around 50 per cent of women doctors will work less than full-time for some period of their careers, but that they will not drop out of medicine. The research also shows that women doctors in their late twenties are more likely than men to be working less than full-time in medicine, but that few of these are in part-time or flexible training posts. The take-up of part-time or flexible training posts at the moment is limited, both at senior registrar and registrar level, and hardly exists at SHO or GP trainee level. At the same time, the support for increased part-time training opportunities is almost universal among young men and women doctors, and it seems that the provision of such posts is being suppressed by factors other than demand. There is clearly a need for close monitoring of the present system of providing flexible training posts, so that a critical assessment can be made both of its effectiveness and whether it is meeting demand.

The evidence also shows that the hours or sessions worked by 'part-timers' in medicine, whether in training or career posts, are generally longer than those worked by 'full-timers' in other occupations or professions. In any other area of work the problem encountered by those wishing to work less than full-time in medicine would not exist, since they would be regarded as full-timers. The problem in medicine is to a large extent artificially created by the traditional demands of the medical career structure, particularly by the perceived necessity to work for excessively long hours to prove a full-time commitment.

There appears to be a need to conduct a close examination of what doctors actually do in their long hours of work. There were many indications in this report that young doctors in training were fulfilling functions which might better be carried out by other staff.

There are many reasons why young doctors, both men and women, find themselves unable or unwilling to put in the hours of work for years on end to reach career grade posts in hospital medicine. The Calman Report recommendations will go a long way to cutting the length of time required in training posts in hospital medicine, but there are still other factors which will affect the extent to which women will enter and stay in hospital medicine, many of which have been explored in this report.

At the moment, it appears that unless there is a readiness to consider more radical changes in the way that medical careers are organised, women will continue to be under-represented in consultant posts in hospital medicine, particularly in specialties such as surgery and general medicine, and will find it difficult to fulfil their full potential in general practice. At the same time, there is no guarantee that men doctors will be able or willing to provide the service to cover the gaps left by the women. The numbers speak for themselves. The question of how to balance supply and demand in medical manpower planning remains. It is beyond the remit of this report to provide the answer, but from the analysis of the evidence presented the challenge is clear.

17 Implications for policy makers of the main findings: conclusions and recommendations

This study is one of two parallel studies carried out to follow up the findings of *Doctors and their Careers* (Allen, 1988), a report which made a series of detailed recommendations in five main areas: (i) careers advice and counselling; (ii) the medical career structure; (iii) equal opportunities; (iv) less than full-time job opportunities; (v) special help for women doctors.

The present study, which compares the experience, views and characteristics of a sample of 1986 medical qualifiers with their counterparts from previous cohorts, was designed to examine the extent to which opportunities for women doctors had changed since 1986, to look at perceptions of constraints on the careers of women doctors, and to examine the question of part-time or less than full-time training and career posts in medicine. Like the previous study it examined these factors against the background of the medical career structure and its impact on the careers of both men and women doctors.

In pursuing the aims of the research, this study has highlighted the extent to which the medical career structure has been slow to adapt to the speed of change which has swept the health service since 1986 when the fieldwork for the original research took place. It has also failed to react to the stark reality of the changing profile of medical manpower, in which 50 per cent of those entering the profession are women, more than half of whom intend to work less than full-time for at least some period of their careers, usually during their thirties.

Doctors and their Careers demonstrated in 1988 that the medical career structure was perceived by many doctors to be out-of-date and rigid and was thought to have imposed constraints on the careers of both men and women. This follow-up study has demonstrated not only that many of the rigidities were still in place five years later, but that the lack of flexibility was showing every sign of imposing constraints not only on the careers of doctors themselves but also on the development of a medical workforce which was appropriately trained and staffed both to meet the health care needs of the nation and to adapt to the changing and flexible patterns of health care delivery increasingly demanded in hospitals and in the community.

The study has enormous implications not only for those designing the future training and careers of doctors from a professional standpoint. It is also of crucial importance for purchasers and commissioners of health care services, who are increasingly interested in the composition of the workforce needed to deliver health care services, for example in being able to give local women the choice of consulting a female obstetrician or gynaecologist. It also has far-reaching implications for the providers of health care services, the NHS Trusts, in whose interest it is to allow for a more flexible workforce as they seek to develop more flexible patient services.

There are clear signs that the role of the medical profession as the main force in determining the medical career structure will come under increasing pressure if senior members of the profession fail to recognise the need for fundamental changes in the system of training, supporting and maximising the talents of all its members.

The policy implications of the key findings of the research, together with recommendations for action, are outlined below.

I   Careers advice, information and counselling

1.   Careers advice received from home and school on medical careers was found to be as limited and misleading in this study as in the previous study. There was continuing evidence that young people decided on medicine as a career because they were very good at science at school and that much of the discontent and regret found among some young doctors was related to their having chosen the wrong career for the wrong reasons.

•   *Schools, medical schools and other careers advisers should ensure that clear, detailed information is made available to all prospective medical students on the realities of a medical career.*

•   *It is essential that a wide range of careers advice is made available for 'A' level science students considering a career in medicine.*

2.   Careers advice, information and counselling received at medical school was found to be almost as patchy and inappropriate as in the previous study and was infrequently related to the abilities and aptitudes of individual students. There was a marked inadequacy of personal tutorial systems at medical school through which advice and counselling could be given, not only on careers and achievement but also on the stresses encountered by many students in their medical school course. There was little evidence of women students receiving careers advice linked to their potential special needs.

•   *There is a need for a more sensitive, systematic and focused approach to the personal and career needs of medical students. An improved personal tutorial system appears to be of paramount importance.*

3   .Careers advice, information and counselling in the postgraduate years was found to be haphazard and in one third of cases non-existent. There were increasing indications in this study that some doctors were 'losing their way' in the absence of constructive careers advice. Those who made up their minds at an early stage and those with personal patrons or mentors

were usually at a distinct advantage, but those, like many women, who were unable to pursue a 'straight' career path, found it more difficult. Most careers advice was given by consultants, but many doctors stressed that this advice was often not as detailed and independent as they required and expressed the need for impartial, specialist and confidential advice. There was a perceived problem with the traditional role of consultant as boss, trainer, and careers adviser. Many doctors were concerned that seeking careers advice could be construed as a sign of weakness.

• *There is a need for a much more systematic and well-publicised approach to careers advice, information and counselling in the postgraduate years. This should be readily available from a variety of appropriate sources, including consultants, postgraduate deans, clinical tutors and college tutors.*

• *Strong consideration should be given to setting up a regional or national service offering independent, confidential advice and access to specialist information as well as counselling for doctors on careers and other issues.*

• *There is a need for the medical profession to look at good practice in structured career development. Much could be learnt from a close examination of successful approaches to management and professional development in other disciplines.*

II   Stress, isolation and regrets

The research uncovered high levels of stress and feelings of isolation among the doctors interviewed, with a marked increase in the levels of regret already observed among succeeding generations of doctors. This study also showed evidence that the present young generation of doctors resemble their counterparts outside medicine more closely than previous generations in terms of schooling and expectations and are less willing to accept the custom and practice of a medical careers system which they consider to be outmoded and punitive in the demands made upon them. There was clear evidence of a marked lack of personal support systems in a profession which is not only subject by definition to a considerable amount of stress in dealing with death and illness but has also recently felt itself under pressure from what it perceives as increasing demands from government and the public alike.

• *There is an urgent need for the development of a variety of systems and services for dealing with personal stress and crises of confidence among both doctors and medical students. Confidential, well-publicised, easily accessible services should be set up to help deal with problems at various levels. There is a strong need for counselling services to be offered to help people at an early stage before problems become acute. The keynote must be confidentiality.*

•   *However, support systems and counselling services alone are not enough to prevent stress, isolation and regrets. The causes of the problems are much more deep-rooted and the solutions are more likely to be found in changing the medical career structure and the culture of the medical hierarchy rather than in providing help after the event.*

III   The content and structure of postgraduate training

1.   The majority of doctors wanted more structured postgraduate training programmes, with pre-determined rotations and structured educational content. There were many criticisms by young doctors both of the quality and consistency of their training programmes and the extent to which the educational component of their training posts was regarded as secondary to the service commitment.

2.   In addition, there were continuing and increasing complaints from young doctors about the long hours, the on-call commitments, the physical conditions of service, the lack of recognition of their professional skills, the lack of time available to study for higher professional qualifications and the linking of age to grade which was thought to inhibit the development of the careers of those who did not adhere closely to expected patterns.

3.   Another major career constraint experienced by both men and women doctors was related to the need for geographical mobility which was thought to accompany an unstructured training programme. It was thought to impose considerable strain on personal relationships, particularly, but not only, where doctors were married or in relationships with other doctors.

•   *Although the recommendations of the Calman Report have offered solutions to some of these concerns, there are still six main issues which require attention:*

   (a)   *the actual content and appropriateness of the work-load of junior doctors in training;*

   (b)   *the responsibility for designing and supervising training posts and programmes;*

   (c)   *the optimum mix of training and service roles within training posts;*

   (d)   *the managerial and professional responsibility for ensuring that all junior doctors have proper and appropriate training;*

   (e)   *the recognition that dual career families are now the norm rather than the exception and an examination of the extent to which geographical movement is necessary in the postgraduate training period;*

(f)   *the development of more flexible patterns of training so that the traditionally accepted pattern linked closely to age and grade is discarded.*

IV   Equal opportunities

The present study indicated that there was no room for complacency about the extent to which equal opportunities legislation and recognised codes of practice had been fully adopted within the medical profession. Women doctors were still being asked questions which were not asked of men, and both sexes were being asked questions about their personal lives which would not have been admissible in other occupations. The interpretation of the answers to such questions was open to challenge on the grounds of discriminatory practices. There was also a general recognition that behind-the-scenes lobbying by personal patrons played a disproportionately important role in the medical appointments system.

- *It is essential that appointments procedures in the medical profession are strictly in line both with legal requirements and accepted good practice.*

- *Particular attention should be paid to eliminating unsolicited oral references or other methods of perpetuating a system of personal patronage which is both inequitable and potentially discriminatory.*

- *There appears to be a particular problem in appointments procedures in general practice and there is an urgent need to address this.*

V   Part-time and less than full-time job opportunities

1.   The report revealed further evidence of an increasing mismatch between the demand for and supply of part-time training opportunities, but this was complicated by low take-up in spite of almost universal support among both men and women for an increase in such opportunities. There was continuing evidence of lack of publicity, information, guidance or advice about flexible training opportunities, combined with a clear perception that less than full-time training was thought to be regarded as of lower status than full-time training and not to be contemplated unless it was the only possible option. There was also evidence that increasing numbers of men would have welcomed the opportunity to work less than full-time or more flexibly at some point in their postgraduate training period and that the requirements for demonstrating overriding domestic commitments for qualification for flexible training posts were regarded as irrelevant and potential discriminatory.

- *If doctors meet the required standard, posts should be designed more flexibly to meet their needs.*

- *There are three main courses of action which would help to increase opportunities for doctors wishing to train less than full-time in medicine for all or part of their training:*

  (a) *to increase the numbers of substantive less than full-time training posts offered by employers within the establishment and to discourage the practice of treating them as supernumerary posts. These posts could be half-time or split posts (see V.3 below);*

  (b) *to effect a change in attitudes by senior medical staff towards less than full-time training posts. This requires action on the part of the Royal Colleges, the BMA and individual consultants. Unless and until a clear indication is given by senior members of the profession that less than full-time training is regarded as having equal status to full-time training, little can be expected to change;*

  (c) *to allow men and women to apply for less than full-time training without restriction.*

- *There is a fourth course of action which would remove most of the demands for less than full-time training posts:*

  (d) *to reduce the number of hours expected in full-time training posts to 48 hours in line with the EC Directive on the organisation of working time. It remains unclear why the hours expected of junior doctors in training in this country are so far in excess of those expected of their counterparts in other countries, let alone those expected of their contemporaries in other professions in this country.*

- *In addition there is an urgent need for close monitoring of the present system of providing flexible training posts, so that a critical assessment can be made both of its effectiveness and whether it is meeting demand.*

2. There was also evidence of unmet demand for less than full-time career posts in medicine. Although most of the demand appeared to be in general practice, this only reflected the present perception that part-time training in hospital medicine was so difficult that only the most dedicated women stayed in hospital medicine with a view to reaching consultant status. It also reflected the fact that part-time GP principal posts are more readily available than part-time consultant posts, notwithstanding the problems encountered by women seeking part-time GP principal posts.

- *There is a need for an increased number of less than full-time career posts in hospital medicine and greater flexibility in meeting the needs of both men and women doctors who wish to work less than full-time in career posts at different stages in their careers.*

3. The concept of job-sharing or split jobs gained widespread support but, as we found in the last report, little recognition was given to the practical difficulties of making it work well.

• *There is a need for a detailed review of job-sharing, including actual examples of its successes and failures, and a critical examination of its potential, both in training and career posts.*

• *The setting up of substantive half-time training posts or split posts on a job-share basis could offer part-time training opportunities in regular posts with a constant stream of part-time trainees moving through. This would be part of a structured training programme and would have clearly identified funding.*

VI Managerial responsibilities and accountability for developing doctors' careers

One of the key findings of the research was the lack of clear lines of accountability for ensuring that the medical career structure can deliver the optimum level of health care to the public as well as maximising the use of the talents of all doctors. There was considerable confusion among doctors about the precise roles and responsibilities of key individuals or organisations concerned with the medical career structure. This was most clearly manifested in their response to questions about career development and advice, but, in fact pervaded the whole study. It has clear implications for the future, since the management of the medical workforce will be increasingly under scrutiny.

• *There is an urgent need to identify and to make explicit to all doctors and managers where the responsibility lies for each aspect of postgraduate medical training, including careers advice, information and counselling, structuring of training programmes, designing of posts, holding of budgets etc.*

• *The present trend is for more and more responsibilities to be placed with the postgraduate deans. There are, however, clear responsibilities for the management of the service and training interface which are properly in the domain of the clinical directorate. This directorate has a crucial role in managing the resource of junior doctors and is responsible to the medical director and general management.*

• *The potential tensions between the postgraduate deans and the Trust managements must be addressed.*

• *The role of the Royal Colleges should be clarified.*

VII Specific issues concerning women doctors

There was nearly universal support in this study for more help for women doctors. It was thought that the NHS and medical profession had failed to recognise that they would wish to work less than full-time for some part of their careers, that they wished to maximise their talents and that they represented 50 per cent of the potential workforce. The report showed disquieting evidence of increasing moves away from hospital medicine among the 1986 women qualifiers compared with their older counterparts. Many women were turning to general practice as an alternative to hospital medicine but were finding that general practice was no longer a satisfactory option. There were demands not only for more flexible training and career post opportunities but also for more child care facilities. Careers advice and counselling specifically geared to the needs of women doctors was not thought in itself to be sufficient.

- *There is a need to encourage more women doctors to stay in hospital medicine and to enter specialties such as surgery and general medicine which are still regarded as unwelcoming and hostile environments by a high proportion of women doctors.*

- *The problems associated with the conditions and hours of work in hospital medicine and the lack of less than full-time working opportunities outlined above must be tackled if women are to continue in the hospital specialties in which a significant proportion would remain if such conditions were different.*

- *There is a need to review the possibility of consultant posts without the full departmental and other responsibilities traditionally attached to such posts. These would be welcomed by many men and women doctors.*

- *There is a need to ensure that part-time or less than full-time principal posts in general practice are more readily available and accessible.*

VIII Leadership for cultural change in medicine

The study took place against a background of considerable changes both in the organisation of health care and in the composition of the medical workforce. There was clear evidence throughout the research that the extent of the cultural change among the younger members of the medical profession had not been recognised at more senior levels within NHS management or the profession itself. The disillusionment and disenchantment with medicine disclosed in this report among young doctors of both sexes gives serious cause for concern.

- *There is a need for a review of the methods by which society manages and nurtures young doctors and medical students. Responsibilities lie with the medical profession itself, with medical schools, with Government, with the NHS and with the Royal Colleges. The human and economic resources invested in training doctors are far too important to be wasted.*

Summary

Aims of the research

The main aims of the research carried out for this report and for the parallel study were (a) to examine what had happened in the previous five years to the 1976 and 1981 medical qualifiers interviewed for *Doctors and their Careers* (Allen, 1988), both in career and personal terms; (b) to compare the experience, views and characteristics of a sample of 1986 medical qualifiers with their counterparts from previous cohorts, especially the 1981 qualifiers interviewed for the last study who had been at the same stage in their careers five years earlier; (c) to examine the extent to which opportunities for women doctors were seen to have changed since 1986 and to look at perceptions of constraints on the careers of women doctors; and (d) to examine in detail the question of part-time or less than full-time training and career posts in medicine.

This part of the study was based on personal interviews with 229 doctors (105 men and 124 women) who had qualified at medical schools in Great Britain in 1986. The aim was to achieve interviews with 100 men and 100 women qualifiers and the sample was stratified by sex and medical school. The response rate was over 80 per cent and most non-response was due to the doctors concerned being abroad at the time of the fieldwork. Interviewing took place in the late summer and autumn of 1991 at which time the average age of the doctors interviewed was 28, the same as their counterparts from the 1981 cohort five years earlier.

Who were the doctors?

- 63 per cent of the men and 56 per cent of the women were married and 7 per cent of both sexes were living as married. 30 per cent of the men and 35 per cent of the women were single. Both men and women 1986 qualifiers were less likely than earlier cohorts to have got married as students or within two years of qualification.

- The pattern of dual career families among doctors was clearly established. 1986 women doctors were less likely than earlier cohorts of women to have been married to other doctors (43 per cent of 1986 married women qualifiers compared with 57 per cent of 1981 married women qualifiers). However, the husbands of 94 per cent of 1986 married women qualifiers were in occupations in social classes I and II. 80 per cent of the wives of 1986 married

271

men qualifiers were working, mainly in social classes I and II occupations. Just under a quarter of the wives were medically qualified. Over 60 per cent of wives with children were working either full-time or part-time.

- 22 per cent of the 1986 men qualifiers and 18 per cent of the women had at least one child at the time of interviewing. The vast majority of the women doctors with children had delayed the birth of their first child until at least three years after they had qualified. Only just over half the women doctors with children said that they had help with child care, most commonly from a childminder. Live-in child care was less usual than among earlier cohorts of women doctors.

- 91 per cent of the 1986 qualifiers (90 per cent of the men and 93 per cent of the women) were of white ethnic origin, 3 per cent were of Indian origin, 1 per cent of Pakistani origin, 2 per cent of Chinese origin, less than 1 per cent of Black-Caribbean origin and 2 per cent of mixed ethnic origin.

Present employment

- 78 per cent of the 1986 qualifiers were working full-time in clinical medicine (90 per cent of the men and 67 per cent of the women). (Comparable figures for the 1981 cohort had been 99 per cent of the men and 73 per cent of the women.)

- 12 per cent of the 1986 qualifiers were working less than full-time in clinical medicine (4 per cent of the men and 19 per cent of the women). (Comparable figures for the 1981 cohort had been 1 per cent of men and 19 per cent of women).

- 1 per cent of 1986 men and women qualifiers were working outside medicine, 1 per cent were working outside clinical medicine but in a medically related occupation.

- 4 per cent of the 1986 women qualifiers were on maternity leave (compared with 2 per cent of the 1981 women).

- 3 per cent of the 1986 men and 9 per cent of the 1986 women qualifiers were not working at the time of the survey – an increase on the 1981 figures. Most of these doctors said they were between jobs or studying, and only two doctors indicated that they definitely intended to leave medicine.

- Two-thirds of the women with children were working, with more than one-fifth of them working full-time.

- Comparing the 1981 and 1986 qualifiers at the time of interview, some five years after qualification as doctors, we found that roughly the same proportions were working in general practice (36 per cent of 1981 qualifiers and 35 per cent of 1986 qualifiers); there had been a drop in the proportions working in hospital medicine (56 per cent of 1981 qualifiers to 49 per cent of 1986 qualifiers); but there were similarly tiny proportions in academic medicine and public health. There had been an increase in the proportions on maternity leave, not working, unemployed or studying from 3 per cent of the 1981 cohort to 9 per cent of the 1986 cohort.

- The decrease in the proportion in hospital medicine was accounted for partly by a drop in the proportion of doctors in SHO posts as part of their GP vocational training and partly by a drop in the proportion of women working in hospital medicine, from 52 per cent of the 1981 women to 44 per cent of the 1986 women.

- Rather more disturbing trends in the progress of women doctors could be discerned when the actual posts of the doctors were examined. 23 per cent of the 1986 men but only 10 per cent of the 1986 women qualifiers were GP principals (compared with 17 per cent of 1981 men and 10 per cent of 1981 women). 34 per cent of the 1986 men but only 17 per cent of the 1986 women qualifiers were registrars (compared with 29 per cent of both men and women in the 1981 cohort).

- There was evidence of a decline in long-term plans to enter general practice among the 1986 qualifiers compared with the 1981 qualifiers (from 48 per cent of 1981 men to 38 per cent of 1986 men; and from 49 per cent of 1981 women to 40 per cent of 1986 women).

- Hours of work were very long for all doctors, with an average of 65 hours or 8 sessions a week for all those in work (including both full-time and part-time workers). Over one third of those in hospital medicine said that they were working 80 hours or more a week. Even those who regarded themselves as 'part-timers' were usually working more than 20 hours or six sessions a week.

What made them study medicine?
- Nearly a quarter of the 1986 men and over one fifth of the women said that they had decided to study medicine because they were good at science subjects at school.

- 18 per cent of the 1986 men and 14 per cent of the 1986 women had at least one medical parent, compared with over a quarter of men who had qualified in 1966 and 1976. Just over 70 per cent of the fathers of men qualifiers from both 1981 and 1986 were in social classes I and II occupations, compared with 81 per cent of the 1981 women and 74 per cent of the 1986 women.

- Only one third of the mothers of the 1986 qualifiers were not working. Most were in occupations in social classes I and II, and 14 per cent of the men and as many as 27 per cent of the women said their mothers were teachers or lecturers.

- The schooling of the 1986 qualifiers reflected much more closely that of their contemporaries in other occupations than had been the case among previous cohorts of doctors. There was evidence of a continuing shift away from independent school to state school education. Over 60 per cent of both men and women 1986 qualifiers had attended state schools, with 37 per cent of the men and 36 per cent of the women having attended comprehensive schools.

- The 'A' level grades attained by the 1986 qualifiers were higher than those attained by previous cohorts and were overwhelmingly in science subjects and mathematics. The 1986 women did particularly well, with 25 per cent of them achieving three A grades compared with 12 per cent of the 1986 men. 39 per cent of the 1986 men and 42 per cent of the women achieved AAB or better in their 'A' levels. There was little or no difference in the results achieved by those attending independent or state schools, and 30 per cent of the women attending comprehensive school gained three A grades.

- Careers advice on a medical career at school was generally considered poor or non-existent, with around 40 per cent of 1986 qualifiers saying that they had had none, a similar proportion to that found among 1981 qualifiers.

Medical school
- 1986 women were less likely than earlier cohorts of women to express strong motivation to study medicine. However, both men and women 1986 qualifiers were more likely than earlier cohorts to have some idea of what they wanted to do when they finished medical school, even if they were to change their career intentions later. Women were more likely to opt for general practice at this stage than men, often because hospital medicine was seen as very competitive and only for 'brilliant' doctors. This perception continued through medical school and was one of many indications found in the course of this research of the need for personal counselling, including confidence building, for medical students.

- Around one third of 1986 qualifiers had been encouraged to follow a particular specialty at medical school, an increase on the 1981 qualifiers, although this encouragement had often had no long-term effects in terms of present jobs.

- However, around a half had been discouraged or deterred at medical school from following particular specialties, with surgery being mentioned most frequently by both men and women, accounting for 35 per cent of all 1986 women and 30 per cent of all 1986 men qualifiers. (70 per cent of the men and nearly 60 per cent of the women who had been put off a specialty at medical school mentioned surgery.) The main reasons for this were attributed to the attitudes and teaching methods of those in the specialty, and there were many indications that women in particular were made to feel unwelcome and inferior by surgeons.

- 70 per cent of the 1986 respondents said they had received no careers advice at all at medical school, although only a quarter said that none was available. Over 80 per cent of 1986 qualifiers rated their careers advice at medical school as poor or non-existent. Particular criticism was levelled at the lack of careers advice from tutors, and there was generally agreed to be a strong need for a more systematic and sensitive approach to delivering more personal advice and counselling at medical school on a variety of subjects, including careers and personal aptitudes.

- Over 80 per cent of 1986 qualifiers thought there was a need for special careers advice for women students at medical school, mainly concerned with information and advice on specialties most compatible with domestic commitments and less than full-time training opportunities, preferably with increased access to women role models. Prejudice and discrimination against women in the medical profession were still thought to be problems, particularly by the men.

- There was evidence of a steady increase over the cohorts in the proportion of qualifiers who thought that women were treated differently from men at medical school, and 1986 women qualifiers reported practices which could only be described as humiliating and discriminatory. Both men and women suffered from what they described as unpleasant and intimidating teaching methods, and there was clear and continuing evidence that medical students at the time appeared to be treated in a manner which would have been unacceptable in any other discipline.

- At qualification, 51 per cent of the 1986 men and 34 per cent of the 1986 women wanted to work in hospital medicine, 30 per cent of the men and 42 per cent of the women in general practice, while 12 per cent of men and 16 per cent of women had no clear idea of what they wanted to do. (These proportions were similar to those found among the 1981 qualifiers.)

Pre-registration year
- There was a decline between the 1981 and 1986 cohorts in the proportion of doctors holding both pre-registration house officer posts in their own teaching hospital. There was no difference between the proportion of 1986 men and women qualifiers holding at least one of their posts in a teaching hospital.

- Around 60 per cent of 1986 qualifiers thought that the type of hospitals in which they held their pre-registration house posts had had an effect on their subsequent careers. Respondents were fairly equally divided on the impact of teaching hospital posts on their careers, with some thinking it had given them a boost in terms of career advancement, while others were very critical of what they described as the hierarchical atmosphere and rigid working conditions in teaching hospitals. It was nevertheless agreed that at least one job in a teaching hospital was essential for ambitious doctors.

- At registration, 57 per cent of the 1986 men and 41 per cent of the women had opted for hospital medicine, 35 per cent of the men and 42 per cent of the women for general practice, while 5 per cent of men and 13 per cent of women were still undecided. 26 per cent of the men and 15 per cent of the women who had expressed a career intention at qualification had changed their minds by the end of their pre-registration year.

Doctors' careers and their present job

- The doctors' curricula vitae were recorded in the same way as for previous cohorts, by recording the starting and finishing date of each job or other activity from the start of their careers post-registration to the time they were interviewed.

- We found little difference between the 1981 and 1986 qualifiers in the length of time spent since registration in medical jobs in Britain. The men from both cohorts had spent an average of 96 per cent of their careers in such jobs, compared with 89 per cent of the 1981 women and 91 per cent of the 1986 women qualifiers. These jobs were mainly full-time posts. Very few doctors of either sex in either cohort had spent much time in part-time medical jobs in Britain. This was by no means true of earlier cohorts of doctors, among whom women were much more likely than men to have worked less than full-time in medical jobs in Britain, often for long periods of their careers. It was too early for this pattern to be emerging among the 1986 cohort, although clear signs were given that less than full-time working was the intention for a substantial minority of the 1986 women.

Present job and changes since registration

- 60 per cent of the 1986 men and 49 per cent of the 1986 women were still in the same specialty chosen at registration, 30 per cent of the men and 25 per cent of the women were in a different specialty, and 5 per cent of men and 11 per cent of women had made up their minds since registration. 5 per cent of men and 15 per cent of women were not working, working outside medicine, on maternity leave or still had no clear idea of what to do. (Both men and women were less likely than their 1981 counterparts still to be in the same specialty chosen at registration.)

- Three-quarters of those who had chosen general practice at registration were still in the specialty, compared with 57 per cent of those who had chosen a hospital specialty. However, 67 per cent of men who had chosen a hospital specialty at registration were still in that specialty, compared with 46 per cent of the women who had chosen a hospital specialty.

The influence of 'patronage' on doctors' careers

- Patronage was thought to be important in furthering the careers of young doctors by 70 per cent of the 1986 qualifiers. 1986 qualifiers were rather less likely to disapprove of the system of patronage than 1981 qualifiers, but nevertheless one third of 1986 qualifiers disapproved while over one third were neutral on the subject.

- Unsolicited oral references were regarded as commonplace in medicine and 1986 qualifiers, like their predecessors, often criticised the system for its secrecy and behind-the-scenes activity. It was thought to be exacerbated by the constant movement expected by junior doctors in the early stages of their careers. This was said to encourage sycophantic behaviour and to continue to perpetuate an 'old-boy network' which excluded young women.

- Patronage appeared to be increasing rather than decreasing in medicine. The majority of patrons were said to be male consultants, and the proportion of doctors mentioning them had increased steadily over the years. Senior women doctors were seldom mentioned as patrons by either men or women qualifiers.

- There were clear indications that the 1986 qualifiers were seeking rather more personal help and advice than earlier cohorts. There was little doubt that this generation of doctors were experiencing greater stress, isolation and lack of confidence than earlier generations and this was reflected in the encouragement and support they sought from patrons.

- 12 per cent of both men and women 1986 qualifiers mentioned detrimental effects on their careers from 'negative patrons', who could be particularly damaging in medicine because of the system of behind-the-scenes references which was said to operate so freely.

- Women often felt vulnerable in a system which they considered favoured a view of 'successful' doctors fitting a particular conventional mould, which was summarised by one respondent as typified by 'outgoing conformists'. Compared with earlier cohorts, more 1986 men and women qualifiers thought that men were more likely to acquire patrons than women.

Constraints and difficulties in careers

- Traditional constraints on the careers of women doctors are thought to be marriage and children. Although marriage was seen as a constraint by around half of the 1986 women who were married, and children as a constraint by the overwhelming majority of women with children, it appeared that other factors, integral to the medical career structure, were of increasing importance in constraining the careers of both men and women.

- The main career constraints mentioned by 1986 qualifiers were the long hours and on-call commitments expected of them. This was mentioned as a constraint by over 70 per cent of the 1986 women and over 50 per cent of the men. It was often related to the intensity of the work commitment during the long hours, combined with poor working conditions. It was said to be inimical to the development or sustaining of personal relationships or any kind of social life. When combined with the perceived constraint imposed by continual geographical mobility in the early years of doctors' careers, it was said to impose considerable strain on relationships as well as careers, particularly when the careers of partners had to be taken into account.

- We noted in the report that some of the interviews carried out with 1986 medical qualifiers could only be described as heart-breaking in their descriptions of fatigue, stress and depression, and we concluded that this requires close monitoring if British medicine is not to lose some of these glittering young people who had started out on medical school with such high hopes.

Interviews, jobs and equal opportunities
- Directly discriminatory questions at job interviews appeared to have decreased since the last study, but questions were still asked of women which were not asked of men. 40 per cent of the 1986 women qualifiers had been asked at least once at job interviews whether they intended to have children, compared with only 6 per cent of 1986 men qualifiers. 12 per cent of the 1986 women were asked what arrangements they would make for the care of their children, even if they had none, compared with only 3 per cent of the men.

- Nearly 60 per cent of the 1986 qualifiers reported other questions of a personal nature at job interviews, many of which related to marriage plans and were open to different interpretations according to the sex of the respondent. Many of the personal questions were indirectly, if not directly, discriminatory under the legislation, and bore no relation to recognised good practice in selection and recruitment procedures. Personal questions of this nature were said to be commonly asked of both men and women in job interviews for partnerships in general practice.

- 14 per cent of 1986 women thought they had failed to get a job because of their sex (double the proportion found among 1981 women), but so did 13 per cent of the 1986 men. The majority of men citing discrimination on the grounds of sex thought they had failed to get a GP principal post because the practice wanted a woman partner.

- 5 per cent of 1986 men and 2 per cent of women thought they had failed to get a job because of their ethnic origin. Of these doctors, three were of white ethnic origin but of non-British origin.

Part-time or less than full-time training posts

- Only 3 per cent of the 1986 women and none of the men were in part-time training posts. (This represented 6 per cent of the 1986 women actually in training grades.) This was a marked decrease over the proportions found in earlier cohorts. However, 9 per cent of women had considered part-time training, and one third of the women said they might consider it in future, mainly at registrar or senior registrar level and only for a relatively short period of time, usually about two years.

- 44 per cent of the 1986 men but only 27 per cent of the women thought that there were specialties which were unsuitable for part-time training – a big drop on the proportions taking this view in the last study.

- The main criticisms of the current schemes for facilitating part-time training were lack of knowledge of their existence and lack of information on how they worked or how access could be gained to them. Among those who knew about the schemes, there were familiar criticisms of complicated administrative systems, and the length of time needed to get manpower approval, set up posts and find the necessary funding.

- There was a definite imbalance between supply and potential demand for part-time training, since 98 per cent of 1986 women and 87 per cent of 1986 men said that there should be greater availability of part-time training posts. One of the main reasons given for not seeking part-time training posts was the perception that such posts were regarded as having second-class status and that doctors taking such posts were not regarded as 'proper' doctors. There was clear evidence that doctors were worried about even mentioning the possibility that they might be considering less than full-time training unless they had no other option. It was generally regarded very much as a 'last resort'.

- It was thought that lack of proper organisation and unwillingness on the part of senior members of the medical profession were the main factors that stood in the way of increasing the feasibility of part-time or less than full-time training in all specialties.

Part-time working and other career posts

- 97 per cent of the 1986 women and 79 per cent of the men thought there should be greater availability of part-time career posts. Of the 229 1986 qualifiers interviewed, only 4 were in part-time career posts – all of whom were women part-time GP principals.

279

- The main recommendation for organising more part-time career posts was the development of more job-sharing or split posts. Both men and women expressed an interest in such posts.

- 25 per cent of the 1986 women and 10 per cent of the men said that they would like a career grade post without the full range of consultant responsibilities. Few of them thought that staff grade or associate specialist grade posts would fit their requirements in this respect.

- Most 1986 qualifiers knew little about staff grade posts and, although over 50 per cent of the respondents thought that it was a useful grade – mainly for other people – it was thought to have 'second-class' connotations and to be a dead-end job in which no career progress or return to training was possible.

- Nearly 60 per cent of 1986 qualifiers thought that the associate specialist grade was useful, but again few knew much about it, and it appeared to be confused with staff grade among many respondents.

Women doctors

- 98 per cent of 1986 women and 92 per cent of the men thought that the medical profession and NHS should do more than at present to help women doctors continue working while they have small children. This was a big increase on the proportions found among the 1981 qualifiers.

- 91 per cent of the 1986 women and 82 per cent of the men thought that the medical profession and NHS should do more than at present to help women doctors return to medicine with opportunities for rising to senior positions, which was also a big increase on the proportions found among 1981 qualifiers.

- The main suggestion was for increased and improved creche facilities, reflecting the difficulties reported in finding suitable and affordable child care for young doctors, particularly those working unsocial hours in training posts.

- The main suggestion for women returners was the provision of more refresher or retraining courses, more part-time training opportunities and more flexibility of careers in general, with particular reference to the need to get away from the traditional linking of age to grade so prevalent in medicine.

- 91 per cent of the 1986 women and 74 per cent of the men thought that more should be done to enhance the future career prospects for women doctors in general. The main recommendations were for better advice, encouragement and opportunities in part-time training, better careers advice and information in general, more flexibility in the career structure, greater provision of part-time and job-share jobs in general, easier accessibility to advice, and more effort to change attitudes towards women doctors.

- The roles of the key individuals and organisations which held the power to enhance the future career prospects for women doctors were rarely understood. Doctors found it very difficult to identify who could do what for women doctors, or, indeed, to assess who could be responsible for changing custom and practice within the medical career structure in general.

Opportunities for doctors in general

- 55 per cent of 1986 qualifiers of both sexes had worked a full shift system, 10 per cent a partial shift system and 36 per cent had not worked a shift system.

- 73 per cent of all the 1986 women and 59 per cent of the men (whether they had worked a shift system or not) preferred a shift system to the present rota arrangements in training posts, mainly because it was less tiring, gave them more time off and generally resulted in shorter working hours. Some of the accounts given by doctors of the present rota arrangements described practices and working conditions which they considered endangered patients' lives as well as resulting in very poor quality for their own lives.

- The 1986 qualifiers were overwhelmingly in favour of structured post-graduate training programmes, both in terms of pre-determined rotations and in terms of content. Only 52 per cent of all 1986 qualifiers had had a structured training programme at SHO level, although of those who had reached registrar status, 68 per cent had had structured training programmes.

- 88 per cent of 1986 men and 79 per cent of women were in favour of structured training programmes with pre-determined rotations, mainly because they offered geographical stability and security and because a structured programme was thought to ensure that the training would be comprehensive and complete. It was also thought to be more efficient, offered greater continuity, allowed doctors to plan ahead and ensured maternity benefits. The desire for greater geographical stability was a marked feature of these interviews, and there was increasing evidence of 'lost' doctors wandering around the system.

- Only 50 per cent of 1986 qualifiers considered that they had had a structured training programme in terms of content, but 92 per cent of them were in favour of such a structured programme.

- There was considerable evidence of 1986 qualifiers feeling that they were being used as 'work-horses' and 'dogs-bodies' and resentment that their training needs were being subjugated to the service requirements of their posts.

- The 1986 qualifiers showed concern throughout these interviews that their professional and intellectual capabilities were underrated and under-utilised. They were often critical of their postgraduate training, and only just over half of them rated the structure and content of their postgraduate training as good.

- Only 66 per cent of 1986 qualifiers had had any careers advice in the postgraduate years since qualification. Two thirds of those who had had no careers advice would have liked some.

- The quality and quantity of the careers advice and counselling received by those who had had any was very patchy, and access to it appeared as haphazard as had been found among earlier cohorts. Those working in hospital medicine were more likely to have received careers advice than those in general practice.

- The main source of careers advice were male consultants. GP trainers were the second most frequently mentioned source of careers advice, but less than half the GP principals and 40 per cent of those on GP vocational training schemes had received any careers advice from a GP trainer.

- Other likely sources of careers advice, such as postgraduate deans, clinical tutors, college tutors or advisers and other senior doctors, were mentioned by few respondents, and colleagues and other junior hospital doctors were mentioned more frequently as careers advisers than any of these sources.

- Although the careers advice received was generally considered to have been helpful by the men, women were less convinced. Only two-thirds of the doctors receiving advice found it accurate, and only just over half of them found it encouraging.

- There was a strong desire for more accessible, more personally focused, more independent and better-informed careers advice and counselling among 1986 qualifiers, whether they had had any or not. It was also thought that careers advice and counselling on personal progress should be a compulsory part of ongoing assessment and support from consultants or supervisors.

- In addition, there were many calls for impartial, confidential advice and counselling from experts with specialist knowledge in the field, with access to a system in which doubts and fears could be frankly discussed without jeopardising chances of career advancement. There was thought to be a pressing need for more advice and help concerning flexible or less than full-time training opportunities.

Doctors' assessment of their own careers

- 91 per cent of the 1986 men and 82 per cent of the women thought that they had had a successful career in medicine so far, a slight decline on the proportion of 1981 women.

- There was a considerable decline in job satisfaction among the 1986 qualifiers compared with earlier generations. Only 27 per cent of the 1986 men and women said that they were very satisfied with their present jobs or status, compared with 55 per cent of the 1981 men and 43 per cent of the 1981 women at a similar period in their careers. The main reason for satisfaction was that the doctors were doing the job they wanted to do and enjoying it. Even so, many of these had major criticisms of other aspects of their jobs, particularly the hours and conditions of work.

Future prospects
- 93 per cent of the 1986 men but only 41 per cent of the 1986 women thought that they would be working full-time in clinical medicine in five years' time; none of the men but 47 per cent of the women thought that they would be working less than full-time in clinical medicine. In addition, 2 per cent of all qualifiers thought they would be working outside medicine but in a medically-related occupation, 2 per cent thought they would be working outside medicine, 3 per cent of women but no men thought they would not be working, and 3 per cent of all qualifiers did not know what they would be doing.

- The main message from this was that the proportion of 1986 qualifiers working full-time in clinical medicine was destined to drop from 78 per cent at present to 65 per cent in five years' time.

- 44 per cent of the 1986 men and 54 per cent of the women thought that they would be in general practice; 49 per cent of the men but only 33 per cent of the women thought that they would be in hospital medicine. Other branches of medicine attracted little interest. The flight from hospital medicine was marked among the 1986 women qualifiers, and was clearly related to the perceived lack of opportunities for less than full-time training and career posts.

- 58 per cent of the 1986 men and 76 per cent of the 1986 women said that they had regretted their decision to become doctors, a sharp increase on the proportion of 1981 qualifiers among whom the proportions were 44 per cent of the men and 49 per cent of the women. There had been a steadily increasing upward trend in the proportion of those expressing regrets among the four cohorts of qualifiers studied in this research.

- The main reasons for regret given by the 1986 qualifiers were fatigue and exhaustion and dislike of the long hours and on-call responsibilities. It was the single most important reason among all grades and both sexes.

- 14 per cent of the men and 19 per cent of the women said that they still regretted their decision to become doctors. Many of these had clearly chosen the wrong profession but had found it difficult to change course. The prospects for some appeared very bleak. Even among those who had succeeded in career terms there were still high levels of regret, and were summarised by a young women registrar: 'I still regret it. It is a frightful price to pay for being good at science...'

- Nearly half the 1986 qualifiers had thought of leaving medicine (57 per cent of the women and 40 per cent of the men) but only 2 per cent had actually left medicine and only 8 per cent thought it was likely that they would leave. Nevertheless there was a strong impression of many doctors, particularly women, feeling trapped in a profession with few career options outside and limited options inside.

- There were clear indications that there was a need for a radical reassessment of the medical career structure and the way it is organised. Although recent recommendations on restructuring postgraduate training should go a long way to shortening the time spent in training posts in this country, there are still many factors which affect the extent to which women, who represent 50 per cent of those entering the medical profession, can achieve their full potential. The numbers speak for themselves. The question of how to balance supply and demand in medical manpower planning remains. There are compelling arguments for a strong lead to be given by senior members of the medical profession, which should recognise the extent of the culture change which has overtaken it.

References

Allen, I. (1988a) *Doctors and their Careers*. Policy Studies Institute

Allen, I. (1988b) *Any Room at the Top?* Policy Studies Institute

Allen, I. (ed) (1989) *Discussing Doctors' Careers*. Policy Studies Institute

Allen, I. (1992) *Part-time Working in General Practice*. Policy Studies Institute

Allen, I. and Rolfe, H. (1994) *Staff Grade Doctors: a Structured Enquiry into their Educational Needs*. Policy Studies Institute

British Medical Association (1989) *Report of the Council Working Party on Career Progress of Women Doctors*. BMA

British Medical Association (1992) *Stress and the Medical Profession*. BMA

British Medical Association (1993) *Childcare for Doctors in the NHS*. BMA

British Medical Association (1993) *Patronage in the Medical Profession: Report from the Career Progress of Doctors Working Party*. BMA

Department of Health and Social Security (1979) *Opportunities for Part-time Training in the NHS for Doctors and Dentists with Domestic Commitments, Disability or Ill-health*. PM(79)3

Department of Health and Social Security (1986) *Hospital Medical Staffing: Achieving a Balance*. DHSS

Department of Health and Social Security (1987) *Hospital Medical Staffing: Achieving a Balance: Plan for Action*. DHSS

Department of Health (1988) *The New Hospital Staff Grade*. HC(88)90

Department of Health (1991) *Women Doctors and their Careers: Report of the Joint Working Party*. Department of Health

Department of Health (1991) *Part-time Training Scheme for Career Registrars*. Executive Letters EL(91)5 and EL(91)135

Department of Health (1991) *Hours of Work of Doctors in Training: the New Deal*. Executive Letter EL(91)82

Department of Health (1991) *Junior Doctors: the New Deal.* Department of Health

Department of Health (1992) *Planning the Medical Workforce. Medical Manpower Standing Advisory Committee: First Report* (MMSAC) (The Campbell Report). Department of Health

Department of Health, Medical Manpower and Education Division (1993) 'Medical and dental staffing prospects in the NHS in England and Wales 1991' *Health Trends* Vol. 25 No.1, 4-12

Department of Health (1993) *Hospital Doctors: Training for the Future: The Report of the Working Group on Specialist Medical Training* (The Calman Report). Department of Health

Department of Health (1993) *Training for Specialist Practice: a Report to the Chief Medical Officer's Working Group to advise on Specialist Training in the United Kingdom* (Annex C to the Calman Report). Department of Health

Department of Health (1993) *Part-time Consultant Posts* Executive Letter EL(93)39

Department of Health (1993) *Flexible Training for Senior Registrars* Executive Letter EL(93)49

Department of Health (1994) *Medical and Dental Staffing: Centrally Funded Part-time Consultants Scheme* Executive Letter EL (94) 42

Department of Health (1994) *Statistical Bulletin 1994/4: Statistics for General Medical Practitioners in England and Wales, 1983-1993*

Department of Health (1994) *Statistical Bulletin 1994/10: Hospital, Public Health Medicine and Community Health Service Medical and Dental Staff in England 1983 to 1993*

Dillner, L. (1993) 'Why are there not more women consultants?' in *British Medical Journal* Vol. 307: 949-50

Dillner, L. (1993) 'Senior house officers: the lost tribes', in *British Medical Journal* Vol. 307: 1549-51

Electoral Reform Ballot Services (1992) *Your Choices for the Future. A Survey of GP Opinion. UK Report.* Electoral Reform Ballot Services

Esmail, A. and Everington, S. (1993) 'Race discrimination against doctors from ethnic minorities', in *British Medical Journal* Vol. 306: 691-92

European Community Directive 75/636

Firth-Cozens, J. (1987) 'Emotional distress in junior house officers', in *British Medical Journal* Vol 295: 533-36

Fogarty, M. Allen, I. Walters, P. (1981) *Women in Top Jobs 1968-79*. Policy Studies Institute, Heinemann

General Medical Services Committee (1994) *Women in General Practice* (ed. Dr Judy Gilley). British Medical Association

Hale, R. and Hudson, L. (1992) 'The Tavistock Study of Young Doctors: Report of the Pilot Phase', in *British Journal of Hospital Medicine* Vol.47,No.6

Joint Committee on Postgraduate Training for General Practice (1982) *Training for General Practice*. JCPTGP

NHS Management Executive (1991) *Equal Opportunities in Recruitment and Selection Procedures for Doctors and Dentists in the Hospital and Community Health Service*. Department of Health

NHS Management Executive (1992) *Women in the NHS: An Implementation Guide to Opportunity 2000*. Department of Health

NHS Management Executive (1992) *Women in the NHS : An Employee's Guide to Opportunity 2000*. Department of Health

NHS Management Executive (1993) *Flexible Training: Report of the Joint Working Party*. Department of Health

NHS Management Executive (1993) *Flexible Opportunities for Doctors and Dentists in Training*. Department of Health

NHS Women's Unit (1994) *Opportunity 2000: the Challenge in General Practice*. Department of Health

Richards, P. (1990) *Learning Medicine*. British Medical Association

Royal College of Physicians (1993) *Staff Grade Doctors: Towards a Better Future*. Royal College of Physicians

Royal College of Physicians (1994) *Part-time Work in Specialist Medicine*. Royal College of Physicians

Smith, D.J. (1980) *Overseas Doctors in the National Health Service*. Policy Studies Institute, Heinemann Educational Books

Social Services Committee, Fourth Report, Session 1980-81 (1981) *Medical Education with special reference to the number of doctors and the career structure in hospitals*. 4 volumes, HMSO

Standing Committee on Postgraduate Medical Education (1994) *Meeting the Educational Needs of Staff Grade Doctors and Dentists*. SCOPME

Appendix

Methodology

The sampling of doctors

1. The study was designed to achieve interviews with 100 men and 100 women from medical qualifiers in the year 1986.

2. In preparing for the last study (Allen, 1988) agreement was reached between the DHSS and the General Medical Council (GMC) that PSI should be allowed access to the graduation lists of all students qualifying from medical schools in Great Britain during the years 1966, 1976 and 1981. The lists of Conjoint and Scottish Triple graduates were also included. (We did not include Northern Ireland.)

3. In the present study the GMC again gave us permission to sample from the lists they held of all students graduating from medical schools in Great Britain in 1986. In addition we scrutinised the names of students of medical schools in Great Britain who obtained a Conjoint qualification in 1986. In this way we compiled a sampling frame of all those obtaining a first registrable qualification in the year 1986.

   (* Conjoint is a first registrable qualification. Doctors were classified as 1986 Conjoint qualifiers if this was their *only* medical qualification or if they passed Conjoint in 1986 but obtained a medical degree *after* 1986. If a doctor obtained Conjoint plus a British degree in 1986, they were classified under the medical school where they obtained the degree and not as Conjoint qualifiers: only one example of this came up in the 1986 sample.)

4. Separate lists of male and female qualifiers were compiled (queries concerning sex were checked in the 1987 Medical Register). Lists were arranged in alphabetical order of medical school, with Conjoint qualifiers at the end. Within each medical school, names were arranged alphabetically for each date of graduation, and dates of graduation were arranged chronologically.

(* Medical schools varied as to how they reported students graduating with Honours: some did not specify, some provided a separate, alphabetically ordered list preceding the other graduate names, and others included Honours graduates in the main list. Students graduating 'in absentia' were also listed in a variety of ways. The researchers did not reorder these lists but used them in the form in which they were sent to the GMC by the universities.)

5. As in the last study it was decided to select the sample in two stages, since we did not know what proportion of doctors were overseas, dead or otherwise untraceable. We therefore generated a random sample of 200 men and 200 women from the total population of 2005 men and 1522 women. The lists of 200 male and 200 female doctors were then sent back to the GMC. The GMC compiled a computer printout of details of all these doctors, including last known address, which was sent back to the investigators. Details of doctors no longer on the medical register were also provided (2 men and 2 women).

6. The investigators then removed all doctors from the list who were on the Overseas Doctors List (8 men and 2 women) or who had died (2 men). Therefore, of the original sample of 400 doctors, 388 (190 men and 198 women) were eligible for inclusion in the next stage of the sampling.

7. A sampling fraction was then generated to give a sample of 143 doctors of each sex from the total eligible sample, on the expectation of a 70 per cent response rate, following the procedure adopted in the last study. This final list was sent back to the GMC, who provided address labels from the file of these names. Each of the 4 doctors no longer on the register happened to be included in the final sample of 143 male and 143 female doctors, which included 4 doctors (3 men and 1 woman) who had overseas addresses despite being on the Principal List.

Interviewing

8. From the list of names and addresses supplied by the GMC, we traced as many telephone numbers as possible centrally. A letter inviting the doctors to participate in the survey, together with a reply-paid envelope, information about PSI and a sheet for doctors to complete with details of up-to-date address and telephone number, was sent out at the end of June 1991. A reminder letter with the above 'pack' was sent at the end of July to all non-responders for whom we could not find a telephone number. The GMC provided an update on some addresses of non-respondents whom we could not trace, and new letters were sent to these doctors in mid-September 1991. A final reminder and 'pack' were sent to all doctors of whom we could still find no trace (n=27) at the end of September 1991. (In addition, further attempts were made to contact individual doctors who had returned

an address and/or telephone number but did not respond to our efforts to find them. We assumed that most of these had moved on.)

1986 sample response

9. Of the total 286 doctors in the sample, 21 (7 per cent) were found to be overseas and therefore unavailable for interview at the time of the study. (These included the 4 doctors on the Principal GMC list who had overseas addresses at the start of the study).

Of the remaining 265 doctors who constituted the available sample, 229 were interviewed (86 per cent of the available sample; 80 per cent of the total sample), 12 refused (4 per cent of available sample, 4 per cent of the total sample), and 24 could not be traced (9 per cent of available sample, 8 per cent of total sample). (It is probable that some of these were overseas.) 2 of the doctors no longer on the register were interviewed (one man and one woman) while the remaining 2 could not be traced (one man and one woman).

Of the 143 men doctors, 15 were known to be overseas, leaving 128 men doctors available for interview. 105 men doctors were interviewed, representing 73 per cent of the total male sample and 82 per cent of the available male sample.

Of the 143 women doctors, 6 were known to be overseas, leaving 137 women doctors available for interview. 124 women doctors were interviewed, representing 87 per cent of the total female sample and 91 per cent of the available female sample.

Summary of 1986 response

	Total	Male	Female
Total sample	286	143	143
Total overseas	21	15	6
(% of total sample)	(7%)	(10%)	(4%)
Total available sample	265	128	137
Completed interviews	229	105	124
(% of available sample)	(86%)	(82%)	(91%)
(% of total sample)	(80%)	(73%)	(87%)
Refusals	12	8	4
No contact/no trace	24	15	9

Questionnaires and interviewers

10. The questionnaires were fully structured, in that questions were asked in predetermined sequence and using identical wording for each interview. A fairly high proportion of questions were open-ended, requiring the interviewer to record verbatim responses. Most of the questions were identical to those used in the questionnaire administered in the last study of *Doctors and their Careers* (Allen, 1988). Some additional questions were added at the request of the Department of Health and were developed in close collaboration with staff from the Department. A very small number of questions which were no longer relevant were dropped from the new questionnaire.

11. The interviews were carried out in the doctor's place of work or home by a team of experienced interviewers, most of whom had worked on the previous study. The interviewers had been trained and given extensive oral and written briefing on the questionnaires and the background to the research.

Analysis

12. The questionnaires were coded using their predetermined codes, as well as coding frames developed from detailed textual analysis of the open-ended questions. Verbatim quotes were extracted from the questionnaires and selected for inclusion in a rigorous manner in proportion to the numbers making such comments.